Student Solutions Manual to accompany
COLLEGE MATHEMATICS I
Third Custom Edition

DANIEL S. MILLER

Taken From:
Student Solutions Manual to accompany *Algebra & Trigonometry*,
Third Edition, by Robert Blitzer
by Daniel S. Miller

PEARSON
Custom
Publishing

PEARSON
Prentice
Hall

Taken from:

Student Solutions Manual to accompany *Algebra & Trigonometry, Third Edition, by Robert Blitzer*
by Daniel S. Miller
Copyright © 2007 by Pearson Education, Inc.
Published by Pearson Prentice Hall.
Upper Saddle River, New Jersey 07458

This special edition is published in cooperation with Pearson Custom Publishing.

Printed in the United States of America

10 9 8 7 6 5 4 3 2 1

ISBN 0-536-26076-1

2006360687

EM

Please visit our web site at *www.pearsoncustom.com*

PEARSON CUSTOM PUBLISHING
75 Arlington Street, Suite 300, Boston, MA 02116
A Pearson Education Company

Acknowledgement

Many thanks to Dr. Earl Mark and Dr. Xuan Ma of the Indianapolis, Indiana campus, ITT Technical Institute, for their editorial review and selection of this textbook.

The following chapters have been chosen specifically for this course by your Curriculum Manager. Sections have been selected from various sources and the publisher makes every attempt to ensure consistency throughout this custom textbook. We apologize for any internal references that do not match.

Contents

Chapter P

Section P.1

Check Point Exercises

1. $8+6(x-3)^2 = 8+6(13-3)^2$
$$= 8+6(10)^2$$
$$= 8+6(100)$$
$$= 8+600$$
$$= 608$$

2. The year 2000 is 40 years after 1960.
$P = 0.72x^2 + 9.4x + 783$
$$= 0.72(40)^2 + 9.4(40) + 783$$
$$= 0.72(1600) + 376 + 783$$
$$= 1152 + 376 + 783$$
$$= 2311$$
The equation's value of 2311 models the data in the bar graph quite well.

3. The elements common to $\{3, 4, 5, 6, 7\}$ and $\{3, 7, 8, 9\}$ are 3 and 7.
$\{3,4,5,6,7\} \cap \{3,7,8,9\} = \{3,7\}$

4. The union is the set containing all the elements of either set.
$\{3,4,5,6,7\} \cup \{3,7,8,9\} = \{3,4,5,6,7,8,9\}$

5. $\left\{-9,\ -1.3,\ 0,\ 0.\overline{3},\ \dfrac{\pi}{2},\ \sqrt{9},\ \sqrt{10}\right\}$

   a. Natural numbers: $\sqrt{9}$ because $\sqrt{9} = 3$

   b. Whole numbers: $0,\ \sqrt{9}$

   c. Integers: $-9,\ 0,\ \sqrt{9}$

   d. Rational numbers: $-9,\ -1.3,\ 0,\ 0.\overline{3},\ \sqrt{9}$

   e. Irrational numbers: $\dfrac{\pi}{2},\ \sqrt{10}$

   f. Real numbers:
$$\left\{-9,\ -1.3,\ 0,\ 0.\overline{3},\ \frac{\pi}{2},\ \sqrt{9},\ \sqrt{10}\right\}$$

6.   **a.** $\left|1-\sqrt{2}\right|$

   Because $\sqrt{2} \approx 1.4$, the number inside the absolute value bars is negative. The absolute value of x when $x < 0$ is $-x$. Thus,
$$\left|1-\sqrt{2}\right| = -\left(1-\sqrt{2}\right) = \sqrt{2}-1$$

   b. $\left|\pi-3\right|$

   Because $\pi \approx 3.14$, the number inside the absolute value bars is positive. The absolute value of a positive number is the number itself. Thus,
$$\left|\pi-3\right| = \pi-3.$$

   c. $\dfrac{|x|}{x}$

   Because $x > 0,\ \ |x| = x.$

   Thus, $\dfrac{|x|}{x} = \dfrac{x}{x} = 1$

7. $|-4-(5)| = |-9| = 9$
The distance between -4 and 5 is 9.

8. $7(4x^2 + 3x) + 2(5x^2 + x)$
$$= 7(4x^2 + 3x) + 2(5x^2 + x)$$
$$= 28x^2 + 21x + 10x^2 + 2x$$
$$= 38x^2 + 23x$$

9. $6 + 4[7 - (x-2)]$
$$= 6 + 4[7 - x + 2)]$$
$$= 6 + 4[9 - x]$$
$$= 6 + 36 - 4x$$
$$= 42 - 4x$$

Exercise Set P.1

1. $7 + 5(10) = 7 + 50 = 57$

3. $6(3) - 8 = 18 - 8 = 10$

5. $8^2 + 3(8) = 64 + 24 = 88$

7. $7^2 - 6(7) + 3 = 49 - 42 + 3 = 7 + 3 = 10$

9. $4 + 5(9-7)^3 = 4 + 5(2)^3$
$$= 4 + 5(8) = 4 + 40 = 44$$

11. $8^2 - 3(8-2) = 64 - 3(6)$
$$= 64 - 18 = 46$$

13. $\dfrac{5(x+2)}{2x-14} = \dfrac{5(10+2)}{2(10)-14}$
$$= \dfrac{5(12)}{6}$$
$$= 5 \cdot 2$$
$$= 10$$

15. $\dfrac{2x+3y}{x+1}; x = -2, y = 4$
$$= \dfrac{2(-2)+3(4)}{-2+1} = \dfrac{-4+12}{-1} = \dfrac{8}{-1} = -8$$

17. $C = \dfrac{5}{9}(50-32) = \dfrac{5}{9}(18) = 10$
10°C is equivalent to 50°F.

19. $h = 4 + 60t - 16t^2 = 4 + 60(2) - 16(2)^2$
$$= 4 + 120 - 16(4) = 4 + 120 - 64$$
$$= 124 - 64 = 60$$
Two seconds after it is kicked, the ball's height is 60 feet.

21. $\{1,2,3,4\} \cap \{2,4,5\} = \{2,4\}$

23. $\{s,e,t\} \cap \{t,e,s\} = \{s,e,t\}$

25. $\{1,3,5,7\} \cap \{2,4,6,8,10\} = \{\ \ \}$
The empty set is also denoted by $\varnothing$.

27. $\{a,b,c,d\} \cap \varnothing = \varnothing$

29. $\{1,2,3,4\} \cup \{2,4,5\} = \{1,2,3,4,5\}$

31. $\{1,3,5,7\} \cup \{2,4,6,8,10\}$
$$= \{1,2,3,4,5,6,7,8,10\}$$

33. $\{a,e,i,o,u\} \cup \varnothing = \{a,e,i,o,u\}$

35. **a.** $\sqrt{100}$

b. $0, \sqrt{100}$

c. $-9, 0, \sqrt{100}$

d. $-9, -\dfrac{4}{5}, 0, 0.25, 9.2, \sqrt{100}$

e. $\sqrt{3}$

f. $-9, -\dfrac{4}{5}, 0, 0.25, \sqrt{3}, 9.2, \sqrt{100}$

37. **a.** $\sqrt{64}$

b. $0, \sqrt{64}$

c. $-11, 0, \sqrt{64}$

d. $-11, -\dfrac{5}{6}, 0, 0.75, \sqrt{64}$

e. $\sqrt{5}, \pi$

f. $-11, -\dfrac{5}{6}, 0, 0.75, \sqrt{5}, \pi, \sqrt{64}$

39. 0

41. Answers may vary.

43. True; −13 is to the left of −2 on the number line.

45. True; 4 is to the right of −7 on the number line.

47. True; $-\pi = -\pi$

49. True; 0 is to the right of −6 on the number line.

51. $|300| = 300$

53. $|12 - \pi| = 12 - \pi$

55. $|\sqrt{2} - 5| = 5 - \sqrt{2}$

57. $\dfrac{-3}{|-3|} = \dfrac{-3}{3} = -1$

59. $||-3|-|-7|| = |3-7| = |-4| = 4$

61. $|x+y| = |2+(-5)| = |-3| = 3$

63. $|x| + |y| = |2| + |-5| = 2 + 5 = 7$

65. $\dfrac{y}{|y|} = \dfrac{-5}{|-5|} = \dfrac{-5}{5} = -1$

67. The distance is $|2 - 17| = |-15| = 15$.

69. The distance is $|-2 - 5| = |-7| = 7$.

71. The distance is
$|-19 - (-4)| = |-19 + 4| = |-15| = 15$.

73. The distance is
$|-3.6 - (-1.4)| = |-3.6 + 1.4| = |-2.2| = 2.2$.

75. $6 + (-4) = (-4) + 6$; commutative property of addition

77. $6 + (2 + 7) = (6 + 2) + 7$; associative property of addition

79. $(2 + 3) + (4 + 5) = (4 + 5) + (2 + 3)$; commutative property of addition

81. $2(-8 + 6) = -16 + 12$; distributive property of multiplication over addition

83. $\dfrac{1}{x+3}(x+3) = 1; x \neq -3$, inverse property of multiplication

85. $5(3x + 4) - 4 = 5 \cdot 3x + 5 \cdot 4 - 4$
$\qquad\qquad\qquad = 15x + 20 - 4$
$\qquad\qquad\qquad = 15x + 16$

87. $5(3x - 2) + 12x = 5 \cdot 3x - 5 \cdot 2 + 12x$
$\qquad\qquad\qquad = 15x - 10 + 12x$
$\qquad\qquad\qquad = 27x - 10$

89. $7(3y - 5) + 2(4y + 3)$
$\quad = 7 \cdot 3y - 7 \cdot 5 + 2 \cdot 4y + 2 \cdot 3$
$\quad = 21y - 35 + 8y + 6$
$\quad = 29y - 29$

91. $5(3y - 2) - (7y + 2) = 15y - 10 - 7y - 2$
$\qquad\qquad\qquad\qquad = 8y - 12$

93. $7 - 4[3 - (4y - 5)] = 7 - 4[3 - 4y + 5]$
$\qquad\qquad\qquad\qquad = 7 - 4[8 - 4y]$
$\qquad\qquad\qquad\qquad = 7 - 32 + 16y$
$\qquad\qquad\qquad\qquad = 16y - 25$

95. $18x^2 + 4 - [6(x^2 - 2) + 5]$
$\quad = 18x^2 + 4 - [6x^2 - 12 + 5]$
$\quad = 18x^2 + 4 - [6x^2 - 7]$
$\quad = 18x^2 + 4 - 6x^2 + 7$
$\quad = 18x^2 - 6x^2 + 4 + 7$
$\quad = (18 - 6)x^2 + 11 = 12x^2 + 11$

97. $-(-14x) = 14x$

99. $-(2x - 3y - 6) = -2x + 3y + 6$

101. $\dfrac{1}{3}(3x) + [(4y) + (-4y)] = x + 0$
$\qquad\qquad\qquad\qquad\qquad = x$

103. $|-6| \; \square \; |-3|$
$\qquad 6 \; \square \; 3$
$\qquad 6 > 3$
Since $6 > 3$, $|-6| > |-3|$.

105. $\left|\dfrac{3}{5}\right| \; \square \; |-0.6|$
$|0.6| \; \square \; |-0.6|$
$0.6 \; \square \; 0.6$
$0.6 \; = \; 0.6$
Since $0.6 = 0.6$, $\left|\dfrac{3}{5}\right| = |-0.6|$.

107. $\dfrac{30}{40} - \dfrac{3}{4} \; \square \; \dfrac{14}{15} \cdot \dfrac{15}{14}$
$\dfrac{30}{40} - \dfrac{30}{40} \; \square \; \dfrac{\cancel{14}}{\cancel{15}} \cdot \dfrac{\cancel{15}}{\cancel{14}}$
$\qquad 0 \; \square \; 1$
$\qquad 0 < 1$
Since $0 < 1$, $\dfrac{30}{40} - \dfrac{3}{4} < \dfrac{14}{15} \cdot \dfrac{15}{14}$.

109. $\dfrac{8}{13} \div \dfrac{8}{13} \;\square\; |-1|$

$\dfrac{8}{13} \cdot \dfrac{13}{8} \;\square\; 1$

$1 \;\square\; 1$

$1 = 1$

Since $1 = 1$, $\dfrac{8}{13} \div \dfrac{8}{13} = |-1|$.

111. $x - (x+4) = x - x - 4 = -4$

113. $6(-5x) = -30x$

115. $5x - 2x = 3x$

117. $8x - (3x+6) = 8x - 3x - 6 = 5x - 6$

119. $N = 17x^2 - 65.4x + 302.2$

$= 17(4)^2 - 65.4(4) + 302.2$

$= 17(16) - 261.6 + 302.2$

$= 272 - 261.6 + 302.2$

≈ 313

The formula models the graph's data very well.

121. $N = 17x^2 - 65.4x + 302.2$

$= 17(6)^2 - 65.4(6) + 302.2$

$= 17(36) - 392.4 + 302.2$

$= 612 - 392.4 + 302.2$

≈ 522

The formula predicts that there will be 522 U.S. billionaires in 2006.

123.   Model 1: $N = -2.04x + 10.24$

$= -2.04(0) + 10.24$

$= 10.24$

Model 2: $N = 0.04x^2 - 3.6x + 11$

$= 0.04(0)^2 - 3.6(0) + 11$

$= 11$

Model 3: $N = 0.76x^3 - 4x^2 + 1.8x + 10.5$

$= 0.76(0)^3 - 4(0)^2 + 1.8(0) + 10.5$

$= 10.5$

Model 3 was the best model for 1999.

125.   Model 1: $N = -2.04x + 10.24$

$= -2.04(4) + 10.24$

$= 2.08$

Model 2: $N = 0.04x^2 - 3.6x + 11$

$= 0.04(4)^2 - 3.6(4) + 11$

$= -2.76$

Model 3: $N = 0.76x^3 - 4x^2 + 1.8x + 10.5$

$= 0.76(4)^3 - 4(4)^2 + 1.8(4) + 10.5$

$= 2.34$

Model 3 was the best model for 2003.

126.   Model 1: $N = -2.04x + 10.24$

$= -2.04(4) + 10.24$

$= 2.08$

Model 2: $N = 0.04x^2 - 3.6x + 11$

$= 0.04(4)^2 - 3.6(4) + 11$

$= -2.76$

Model 3: $N = 0.76x^3 - 4x^2 + 1.8x + 10.5$

$= 0.76(4)^3 - 4(4)^2 + 1.8(4) + 10.5$

$= 2.34$

Model breakdown occurs for model 2 in 2003 as shown by the negative result.

127.   **a.** $0.05x + 0.12(10,000 - x)$

$= 0.05x + 1200 - 0.12x$

$= 1200 - 0.07x$

   b. $1200 - 0.07x = 1200 - 0.07(6000)$

$= \$780$

141.   **a.**   False; x has a coefficient of 1.

   b.   False; $5 + 3(x-4) = 5 + 3x - 12 = 3x - 7$

   c.   False; $-x - x = -2x$.

   d.   True; $x - 0.02(x + 200)$

$= x - 0.02x - 4$

$= x - 0.02x - 0.02(200)$

$= 0.98x - 4$

(d) is true.

4

143. $-\pi > -3.5$

145. a. $x = 100$

$$\frac{0.5x + 5000}{100}$$

$$= \frac{5050}{100}$$

$$= \$50.50$$

$x = 1000$

$$\frac{0.5(1000) + 5000}{1000}$$

$$= \frac{5500}{1000}$$

$$= \$5.50$$

$x = 10,000$

$$\frac{0.5(10,000) + 5000}{10,000}$$

$$= \frac{10000}{10000}$$

$$= \$1$$

b. No, they would need make 10,000 clocks for the cost to be $1 so they can add $.50.

Section P.2

Check Point Exercises

1. a. $3^3 3^2 = 3^{3+2} = 3^5$ or 243

b. $(4x^3 y^4)(10x^2 y^6) = 4 \cdot 10 \cdot x^3 \cdot x^2 \cdot y^4 \cdot y^6$

$$= 40x^{3+2} \cdot y^{4+6}$$

$$= 40x^5 \cdot y^{10}$$

2. a. $\dfrac{(-3)^6}{(-3)^3} = (-3)^3 = -27$

b. $\dfrac{27x^{14}y^8}{3x^3 y^5} = \dfrac{27}{3} \cdot \dfrac{x^{14}}{x^3} \cdot \dfrac{y^8}{y^5} = 9x^{14-3} y^{8-5} = 9x^{11} y^3$

3. a. $5^{-2} = \dfrac{1}{5^2} = \dfrac{1}{25}$

b. $(-3)^{-3} = \dfrac{1}{(-3)^3} = \dfrac{1}{-27} = -\dfrac{1}{27}$

c. $\dfrac{1}{4^{-2}} = \dfrac{1}{\frac{1}{4^2}} = 1 \cdot \dfrac{4^2}{1} = 4^2 = 16$

d. $3x^{-6}y^4 = 3 \cdot \dfrac{1}{x^6} \cdot y^4 = \dfrac{3y^4}{x^6}$

4. a. $(3^3)^2 = 3^{3 \cdot 2} = 3^6$ or 729

b. $(y^7)^{-2} = y^{7(-2)} = y^{-14} = \dfrac{1}{y^{14}}$

c. $(b^{-3})^{-4} = b^{-3(-4)} = b^{12}$

5. $(-4x)^3 = (-4)^3 (x)^3 = -64x^3$

6. a. $\left(-\dfrac{2}{y}\right)^5 = \dfrac{(-2)^5}{y^5} = \dfrac{-32}{y^5}$

b. $\left(\dfrac{x^5}{3}\right)^3 = \dfrac{(x^5)^3}{3^3} = \dfrac{x^{15}}{27}$

7. a. $(2x^3 y^6)^4 = (2)^4 (x^3)^4 (y^6)^4 = 16x^{12} y^{24}$

b. $(-6x^2 y^5)(3xy^3)$

$$= (-6) \cdot 3 \cdot x^2 \cdot x \cdot y^5 \cdot y^3$$

$$= -18x^3 y^8$$

c. $\dfrac{100x^{12} y^2}{20x^{16} y^{-4}} = \left(\dfrac{100}{20}\right)\left(\dfrac{x^{12}}{x^{16}}\right)\left(\dfrac{y^2}{y^{-4}}\right)$

$$= 5x^{12-16} y^{2-(-4)}$$

$$= 5x^{-4} y^6$$

$$= \dfrac{5y^6}{x^4}$$

  d. $\left(\dfrac{5x}{y^4}\right)^{-2} = \dfrac{(5)^{-2}(x)^{-2}}{(y^4)^{-2}}$

$$= \dfrac{(5)^{-2}(x)^{-2}}{(y^4)^{-2}}$$

$$= \dfrac{5^{-2}x^{-2}}{y^{-8}}$$

$$= \dfrac{y^8}{5^2 x^2}$$

$$= \dfrac{y^8}{25x^2}$$

8. **a.** $-2.6 \times 10^9 = -2,600,000,000$

    b. $3.017 \times 10^{-6} = 0.000003017$

9. **a.** $5,210,000,000 = 5.21 \times 10^9$

    b. $-0.00000006893 = -6.893 \times 10^{-8}$

10. $410 \times 10^7 = \left(4.1 \times 10^2\right) \times 10^7$

$$= 4.1 \times \left(10^2 \times 10^7\right)$$

$$= 4.1 \times 10^9$$

11. **a.** $\left(7.1 \times 10^5\right)\left(5 \times 10^{-7}\right)$

$$= 7.1 \cdot 5 \times 10^5 \cdot 10^{-7}$$

$$= 35.5 \times 10^{-2}$$

$$= \left(3.55 \times 10^1\right) \times 10^{-2}$$

$$= 3.55 \times \left(10^1 \times 10^{-2}\right)$$

$$= 3.55 \times 10^{-1}$$

    b. $\dfrac{1.2 \times 10^6}{3 \times 10^{-3}} = \dfrac{1.2}{3} \cdot \dfrac{10^6}{10^{-3}}$

$$= 0.4 \times 10^{6-(-3)}$$

$$= 0.4 \times 10^9$$

$$= 4 \times 10^8$$

12. $\dfrac{2.02 \times 10^{12}}{2.88 \times 10^8} = \dfrac{2.02}{2.88} \cdot \dfrac{10^{12}}{10^8}$

$$\approx 0.7014 \times 10^4$$

$$\approx 7014$$

The per capita tax was \$7014 in 2002.

Exercise Set P.2

1. $5^2 \cdot 2 = (5 \cdot 5) \cdot 2 = 25 \cdot 2 = 50$

3. $(-2)^6 = (-2)(-2)(-2)(-2)(-2)(-2) = 64$

5. $-2^6 = -2 \cdot 2 \cdot 2 \cdot 2 \cdot 2 \cdot 2 = -64$

7. $(-3)^0 = 1$

9. $-3^0 = -1$

11. $4^{-3} = \dfrac{1}{4^3} = \dfrac{1}{4 \cdot 4 \cdot 4} = \dfrac{1}{64}$

13. $2^2 \cdot 2^3 = 2^{2+3} = 2^5 = 2 \cdot 2 \cdot 2 \cdot 2 \cdot 2 = 32$

15. $\left(2^2\right)^3 = 2^{2 \cdot 3} = 2^6 = 2 \cdot 2 \cdot 2 \cdot 2 \cdot 2 \cdot 2 = 64$

17. $\dfrac{2^8}{2^4} = 2^{8-4} = 2^4 = 2 \cdot 2 \cdot 2 \cdot 2 = 16$

19. $3^{-3} \cdot 3 = 3^{-3+1} = 3^{-2} = \dfrac{1}{3^2} = \dfrac{1}{3 \cdot 3} = \dfrac{1}{9}$

21. $\dfrac{2^3}{2^7} = 2^{3-7} = 2^{-4} = \dfrac{1}{2^4} = \dfrac{1}{2 \cdot 2 \cdot 2 \cdot 2} = \dfrac{1}{16}$

23. $x^{-2}y = \dfrac{1}{x^2} \cdot y = \dfrac{y}{x^2}$

25. $x^0 y^5 = 1 \cdot y^5 = y^5$

27. $x^3 \cdot x^7 = x^{3+7} = x^{10}$

29. $x^{-5} \cdot x^{10} = x^{-5+10} = x^5$

31. $\left(x^3\right)^7 = x^{3 \cdot 7} = x^{21}$

33. $\left(x^{-5}\right)^3 = x^{-5 \cdot 3} = x^{-15} = \dfrac{1}{x^{15}}$

35. $\dfrac{x^{14}}{x^7} = x^{14-7} = x^7$

37. $\dfrac{x^{14}}{x^{-7}} = x^{14-(-7)} = x^{14+7} = x^{21}$

39. $\left(8x^3\right)^2 = 8^2(x^3)^2 = 8^2 x^{3 \cdot 2} = 64x^6$

41. $\left(-\dfrac{4}{x}\right)^3 = \dfrac{(-4)^3}{x^3} = -\dfrac{64}{x^3}$

43. $(-3x^2 y^5)^2 = (-3)^2 (x^2)^2 \cdot (y^5)^2$
$\qquad = 9x^{2\cdot2} y^{5\cdot2}$
$\qquad = 9x^4 y^{10}$

45. $(3x^4)(2x^7) = 3 \cdot 2 x^4 \cdot x^7 = 6x^{4+7} = 6x^{11}$

47. $(-9x^3 y)(-2x^6 y^4) = (-9)(-2)x^3 x^6 y y^4$
$\qquad = 18x^{3+6} y^{1+4}$
$\qquad = 18x^9 y^5$

49. $\dfrac{8x^{20}}{2x^4} = \left(\dfrac{8}{2}\right)\left(\dfrac{x^{20}}{x^4}\right) = 4x^{20-4} = 4x^{16}$

51. $\dfrac{25a^{13} \cdot b^4}{-5a^2 \cdot b^3} = \left(\dfrac{25}{-5}\right)\left(\dfrac{a^{13}}{a^2}\right)\left(\dfrac{b^4}{b^3}\right)$
$\qquad = -5a^{13-2} b^{4-3}$
$\qquad = -5a^{11} b$

53. $\dfrac{14b^7}{7b^{14}} = \left(\dfrac{14}{7}\right)\left(\dfrac{b^7}{b^{14}}\right) = 2 \cdot b^{7-14} = 2b^{-7} = \dfrac{2}{b^7}$

55. $(4x^3)^{-2} = (4^{-2})(x^3)^{-2}$
$\qquad = 4^{-2} x^{-6}$
$\qquad = \dfrac{1}{4^2 x^6}$
$\qquad = \dfrac{1}{16x^6}$

57. $\dfrac{24x^3 \cdot y^5}{32x^7 y^{-9}} = \dfrac{3}{4} x^{3-7} y^{5-(-9)}$
$\qquad = \dfrac{3}{4} x^{-4} y^{14}$
$\qquad = \dfrac{3y^{14}}{4x^4}$

59. $\left(\dfrac{5x^3}{y}\right)^{-2} = \dfrac{5^{-2} x^{-6}}{y^{-2}} = \dfrac{y^2}{25x^6}$

61. $\left(\dfrac{-15a^4 b^2}{5a^{10} b^{-3}}\right)^3$
$\qquad = \left(\dfrac{-3b^{2-(-3)}}{a^{10-4}}\right)^3$
$\qquad = \left(\dfrac{-3b^5}{a^6}\right)^3$
$\qquad = \dfrac{-27b^{15}}{a^{18}}$

63. $\left(\dfrac{3a^{-5} b^2}{12a^3 b^{-4}}\right)^0 = 1$

64. $\left(\dfrac{4a^{-5} b^3}{12a^3 b^{-5}}\right)^0 = 1$

65. $3.8 \times 10^2 = 380$

67. $6 \times 10^{-4} = 0.0006$

69. $-7.16 \times 10^6 = -7,160,000$

71. $7.9 \times 10^{-1} = 0.79$

73. $-4.15 \times 10^{-3} = -0.00415$

75. $-6.00001 \times 10^{10} = -60,000,100,000$

77. $32,000 = 3.2 \times 10^4$

79. $638,000,000,000,000,000$
$\qquad = 6.38 \times 10^{17}$

81. $-5716 = -5.716 \times 10^3$

83. $0.0027 = 2.7 \times 10^{-3}$

85. $-0.00000000504 = -5.04 \times 10^{-9}$

87. $(3 \times 10^4)(2.1 \times 10^3)$
$\qquad = (3 \times 2.1)(10^4 \times 10^3)$
$\qquad = 6.3 \times 10^{4+3} = 6.3 \times 10^7$

89. $(1.6 \times 10^{15})(4 \times 10^{-11})$
$\qquad = (1.6 \times 4)(10^{15} \times 10^{-11})$
$\qquad = 6.4 \times 10^{15+(-11)} = 6.4 \times 10^4$

91. $\left(6.1\times10^{-8}\right)\left(2\times10^{-4}\right)$

$=\left(6.1\times2\right)\left(10^{-8}\times10^{-4}\right)$

$=12.2\times10^{-8+(-4)}$

$=12.2\times10^{-12}=1.22\times10^{-11}$

93. $\left(4.3\times10^{8}\right)\left(6.2\times10^{4}\right)$

$=\left(4.3\times6.2\right)\left(10^{8}\times10^{4}\right)$

$=26.66\times10^{8+4}$

$=26.66\times10^{12}$

$=2.666\times10^{13}\approx2.67\times10^{13}$

95. $\dfrac{8.4\times10^{8}}{4\times10^{5}}=\dfrac{8.4}{4}\times\dfrac{10^{8}}{10^{5}}$

$=2.1\times10^{8-5}=2.1\times10^{3}$

97. $\dfrac{3.6\times10^{4}}{9\times10^{-2}}=\dfrac{3.6}{9}\times\dfrac{10^{4}}{10^{-2}}$

$=0.4\times10^{4-(-2)}$

$=0.4\times10^{6}=4\times10^{5}$

99. $\dfrac{4.8\times10^{-2}}{2.4\times10^{6}}=\dfrac{4.8}{2.4}\times\dfrac{10^{-2}}{10^{6}}$

$=2\times10^{-2-6}=2\times10^{-8}$

101. $\dfrac{2.4\times10^{-2}}{4.8\times10^{-6}}=\dfrac{2.4}{4.8}\times\dfrac{10^{-2}}{10^{-6}}$

$=0.5\times10^{-2-(-6)}$

$=0.5\times10^{4}=5\times10^{3}$

103. $\dfrac{480,000,000,000}{0.00012}=\dfrac{4.8\times10^{11}}{1.2\times10^{-4}}$

$=\dfrac{4.8}{1.2}\times\dfrac{10^{11}}{10^{-4}}$

$=4\times10^{11-(-4)}$

$=4\times10^{15}$

105. $\dfrac{0.00072\times0.003}{0.00024}$

$=\dfrac{\left(7.2\times10^{-4}\right)\left(3\times10^{-3}\right)}{2.4\times10^{-4}}$

$=\dfrac{7.2\times3}{2.4}\times\dfrac{10^{-4}\cdot10^{-3}}{10^{-4}}=9\times10^{-3}$

107. $\dfrac{\left(x^{-2}y\right)^{-3}}{\left(x^{2}y^{-1}\right)^{3}}=\dfrac{x^{6}y^{-3}}{x^{6}y^{-3}}$

$=x^{6-6}y^{-3-(-3)}=x^{0}y^{0}=1$

109. $\left(2x^{-3}yz^{-6}\right)\left(2x\right)^{-5}=2x^{-3}yz^{-6}\cdot2^{-5}x^{-5}$

$=2^{-4}x^{-8}yz^{-6}=\dfrac{y}{2^{4}x^{8}z^{6}}=\dfrac{y}{16x^{8}z^{6}}$

111. $\left(\dfrac{x^{3}y^{4}z^{5}}{x^{-3}y^{-4}z^{-5}}\right)^{-2}=\left(x^{6}y^{8}z^{10}\right)^{-2}$

$=x^{-12}y^{-16}z^{-20}=\dfrac{1}{x^{12}y^{16}z^{20}}$

113. $\dfrac{\left(2^{-1}x^{-2}y^{-1}\right)^{-2}\left(2x^{-4}y^{3}\right)^{-2}\left(16x^{-3}y^{3}\right)^{0}}{\left(2x^{-3}y^{-5}\right)^{2}}$

$=\dfrac{\left(2^{2}x^{2}y^{2}\right)\left(2^{-2}x^{8}y^{-6}\right)\left(1\right)}{\left(2^{2}x^{-6}y^{-10}\right)}$

$=\dfrac{x^{18}y^{6}}{4}$

115. 62.6 million $=62.6\times10^{6}=6.26\times10^{7}$

So, 6.26×10^{7} people will be 65 and over in 2025.

117. $131.2-34.9=96.3$

96.3 million $=96.3\times10^{6}=9.63\times10^{7}$ There will be 9.63×10^{7} more people 65 and over in the year 2100 than in 2000.

119. 20 billion $=2\times10^{10}$

$\dfrac{2\times10^{10}}{2.92\times10^{8}}=\dfrac{2}{2.92}\times\dfrac{10^{10}}{10^{8}}$

$\approx0.6849\times10^{10-8}$

$=0.6849\times10^{2}$

$=6.849\times10^{1}\approx68$

The average American consumes about 68 hotdogs each year.

121. 8 billion $=8\times10^{9}$

$\dfrac{8\times10^{9}}{3.2\times10^{7}}=\dfrac{8}{3.2}\times\dfrac{10^{9}}{10^{7}}$

$=2.5\times10^{9-7}$

$=2.5\times10^{2}=250$

$2.5\times10^{2}=250$ chickens are raised for food each second in the U.S.

123. $\dfrac{6.8 \times 10^{12}}{2.9 \times 10^8} = \dfrac{6.8}{2.9} \cdot \dfrac{10^{12}}{10^8}$

$\approx 2.3448 \times 10^4$

$\approx 23,448$

If the national debt was divided evenly among every individual in the U.S., each citizen would have to pay $23,448.

133. **a.** False, $4^{-2} = \dfrac{1}{16} > 4^{-3} = \dfrac{1}{64}$

b. True, $5^{-2} = \dfrac{1}{25} > 2^{-5} = \dfrac{1}{32}$

c. False, $16 = (-2)^4 \ne 2^{-4} = \dfrac{1}{16}$

d. False. $\begin{aligned}5^2 \cdot 5^{-2} &= 5^{2-2} = 5^0 = 1 \\ 2^5 \cdot 2^{-5} &= 2^{5-5} = 2^0 = 1\end{aligned}$

1 is not greater than 1

135. $b^A = MN, b^C = M, b^D = N$

$b^A = b^C b^D$

$A = C + D$

Section P.3

Check Point Exercises

1. **a.** $\sqrt{81} = 9$

b. $-\sqrt{9} = -3$

c. $\sqrt{\dfrac{1}{25}} = \dfrac{1}{5}$

d. $\sqrt{36 + 64} = \sqrt{100} = 10$

e. $\sqrt{36} + \sqrt{64} = 6 + 8 = 14$

2. **a.** $\sqrt{75} = \sqrt{25 \cdot 3} = \sqrt{25}\sqrt{3} = 5\sqrt{3}$

b. $\sqrt{5x} \cdot \sqrt{10x} = \sqrt{5x \cdot 10x}$

$= \sqrt{50x^2}$

$= \sqrt{25 \cdot 2x^2}$

$= \sqrt{25x^2} \cdot \sqrt{2}$

$= 5x\sqrt{2}$

3. **a.** $\sqrt{\dfrac{25}{16}} = \dfrac{\sqrt{25}}{\sqrt{16}} = \dfrac{5}{4}$

b. $\dfrac{\sqrt{150x^3}}{\sqrt{2x}} = \sqrt{\dfrac{150x^3}{2x}}$

$= \sqrt{75x^2}$

$= \sqrt{25x^2} \cdot \sqrt{3}$

$= 5x\sqrt{3}$

4. **a.** $8\sqrt{13} + 9\sqrt{13} = (8 + 9)\sqrt{3}$

$= 17\sqrt{13}$

b. $\sqrt{17x} - 20\sqrt{17x}$

$= 1\sqrt{17x} - 20\sqrt{17x}$

$= (1 - 20)\sqrt{17x}$

$= -19\sqrt{17x}$

5. **a.** $5\sqrt{27} + \sqrt{12}$

$= 5\sqrt{9 \cdot 3} + \sqrt{4 \cdot 3}$

$= 5 \cdot 3\sqrt{3} + 2\sqrt{3}$

$= 15\sqrt{3} + 2\sqrt{3}$

$= (15 + 2)\sqrt{3}$

$= 17\sqrt{3}$

b. $6\sqrt{18x} - 4\sqrt{8x}$

$= 6\sqrt{9 \cdot 2x} - 4\sqrt{4 \cdot 2x}$

$= 6 \cdot 3\sqrt{2x} - 4 \cdot 2\sqrt{2x}$

$= 18\sqrt{2x} - 8\sqrt{2x}$

$= (18 - 8)\sqrt{2x}$

$= 10\sqrt{2x}$

6. **a.** If we multiply numerator and denominator by $\sqrt{3}$, the denominator becomes $\sqrt{3} \cdot \sqrt{3} = \sqrt{9} = 3$. Therefore, multiply by 1, choosing $\dfrac{\sqrt{3}}{\sqrt{3}}$ for 1.

$\dfrac{5}{\sqrt{3}} = \dfrac{5}{\sqrt{3}} \cdot \dfrac{\sqrt{3}}{\sqrt{3}} = \dfrac{5\sqrt{3}}{\sqrt{9}} = \dfrac{5\sqrt{3}}{3}$

b. The *smallest* number that will produce a perfect square in the denominator of $\dfrac{6}{\sqrt{12}}$ is $\sqrt{3}$ because $\sqrt{12}\cdot\sqrt{3}=\sqrt{36}=6$. So multiply by 1, choosing $\dfrac{\sqrt{3}}{\sqrt{3}}$ for 1.

$$\frac{6}{\sqrt{12}}=\frac{6}{\sqrt{12}}\cdot\frac{\sqrt{3}}{\sqrt{3}}=\frac{6\sqrt{3}}{\sqrt{36}}=\frac{6\sqrt{3}}{6}=\sqrt{3}$$

7. Multiply by $\dfrac{4-\sqrt{5}}{4-\sqrt{5}}$.

$$\frac{8}{4+\sqrt{5}}=\frac{8}{4+\sqrt{5}}\cdot\frac{4-\sqrt{5}}{4-\sqrt{5}}$$
$$=\frac{8(4-\sqrt{5})}{4^2-(\sqrt{5})^2}$$
$$=\frac{8(4-\sqrt{5})}{16-5}$$
$$=\frac{8(4-\sqrt{5})}{11}\ \text{ or }\ \frac{32-8\sqrt{5}}{11}$$

8. **a.** $\sqrt[3]{40}=\sqrt[3]{8\cdot5}=\sqrt[3]{8}\cdot\sqrt[3]{5}=2\sqrt[3]{5}$

b. $\sqrt[5]{8}\cdot\sqrt[5]{8}=\sqrt[5]{64}=\sqrt[5]{32}\cdot\sqrt[5]{2}=2\sqrt[5]{2}$

c. $\sqrt[3]{\dfrac{125}{27}}=\dfrac{\sqrt[3]{125}}{\sqrt[3]{27}}=\dfrac{5}{3}$

9. $3\sqrt[3]{81}-4\sqrt[3]{3}$
$=3\sqrt[3]{27\cdot3}-4\sqrt[3]{3}$
$=3\cdot3\sqrt[3]{3}-4\sqrt[3]{3}$
$=9\sqrt[3]{3}-4\sqrt[3]{3}$
$=(9-4)\sqrt[3]{3}$
$=5\sqrt[3]{3}$

10. **a.** $25^{\frac{1}{2}}=\sqrt{25}=5$

b. $8^{\frac{1}{3}}=\sqrt[3]{8}=2$

c. $-81^{\frac{1}{4}}=-\sqrt[4]{81}=-3$

d. $(-8)^{\frac{1}{3}}=\sqrt[3]{-8}=-2$

e. $27^{-\frac{1}{3}}=\dfrac{1}{27^{\frac{1}{3}}}=\dfrac{1}{\sqrt[3]{27}}=\dfrac{1}{3}$

11. **a.** $27^{\frac{4}{3}}=\left(\sqrt[3]{27}\right)^4=(3)^4=81$

b. $4^{\frac{3}{2}}=\left(\sqrt[2]{4}\right)^3=(2)^3=8$

c. $32^{-\frac{2}{5}}=\dfrac{1}{32^{\frac{2}{5}}}=\dfrac{1}{\left(\sqrt[5]{32}\right)^2}=\dfrac{1}{2^2}=\dfrac{1}{4}$

12. **a.** $\left(2x^{4/3}\right)\left(5x^{8/3}\right)$
$=2\cdot5x^{4/3}\cdot x^{8/3}$
$=10x^{(4/3)+(8/3)}$
$=10x^{12/3}$
$=10x^4$

b. $\dfrac{20x^4}{5x^{3/2}}=\left(\dfrac{20}{5}\right)\left(\dfrac{x^4}{x^{3/2}}\right)$
$=4x^{4-(3/2)}$
$=4x^{(8/2)-(3/2)}$
$=4x^{5/2}$

13. $\sqrt[6]{x^3}=x^{3/6}=x^{1/2}=\sqrt{x}$

Exercise Set P.3

1. $\sqrt{36}=\sqrt{6^2}=6$

3. $-\sqrt{36}=-\sqrt{6^2}=-6$

5. $\sqrt{-36}$, The square root of a negative number is not real.

7. $\sqrt{25-16}=\sqrt{9}=3$

9. $\sqrt{25}-\sqrt{16}=5-4=1$

11. $\sqrt{(-13)^2}=\sqrt{169}=13$

13. $\sqrt{50}=\sqrt{25\cdot2}=\sqrt{25}\sqrt{2}=5\sqrt{2}$

15. $\sqrt{45x^2} = \sqrt{9x^2 \cdot 5}$

$\qquad = \sqrt{9x^2}\sqrt{5}$

$\qquad = \sqrt{9}\sqrt{x^2}\sqrt{5}$

$\qquad = 3|x|\sqrt{5}$

17. $\sqrt{2x} \cdot \sqrt{6x} = \sqrt{2x \cdot 6x}$

$\qquad = \sqrt{12x^2}$

$\qquad = \sqrt{4x^2} \cdot \sqrt{3}$

$\qquad = 2x\sqrt{3}$

19. $\sqrt{x^3} = \sqrt{x^2} \cdot \sqrt{x} = x\sqrt{x}$

21. $\sqrt{2x^2} \cdot \sqrt{6x} = \sqrt{2x^2 \cdot 6x}$

$\qquad = \sqrt{12x^3}$

$\qquad = \sqrt{4x^2} \cdot \sqrt{3x}$

$\qquad = 2x\sqrt{3x}$

23. $\sqrt{\dfrac{1}{81}} = \dfrac{\sqrt{1}}{\sqrt{81}} = \dfrac{1}{9}$

25. $\sqrt{\dfrac{49}{16}} = \dfrac{\sqrt{49}}{\sqrt{16}} = \dfrac{7}{4}$

27. $\dfrac{\sqrt{48x^3}}{\sqrt{3x}} = \sqrt{\dfrac{48x^3}{3x}} = \sqrt{16x^2} = 4x$

29. $\dfrac{\sqrt{150x^4}}{\sqrt{3x}} = \sqrt{\dfrac{150x^4}{3x}}$

$\qquad = \sqrt{50x^3}$

$\qquad = \sqrt{25x^2} \cdot \sqrt{2x}$

$\qquad = 5x\sqrt{2x}$

31. $\dfrac{\sqrt{200x^3}}{\sqrt{10x^{-1}}}$

$\qquad = \sqrt{\dfrac{200x^3}{10x^{-1}}}$

$\qquad = \sqrt{20x^{3-(-1)}}$

$\qquad = \sqrt{20x^4}$

$\qquad = \sqrt{4 \cdot 5x^4}$

$\qquad = 2x^2\sqrt{5}$

33. $7\sqrt{3} + 6\sqrt{3} = (7+6)\sqrt{3} = 13\sqrt{3}$

35. $6\sqrt{17x} - 8\sqrt{17x} = (6-8)\sqrt{17x} = -2\sqrt{17x}$

37. $\sqrt{8} + 3\sqrt{2} = \sqrt{4 \cdot 2} + 3\sqrt{2}$

$\qquad = 2\sqrt{2} + 3\sqrt{2}$

$\qquad = (2+3)\sqrt{2}$

$\qquad = 5\sqrt{2}$

39. $\sqrt{50x} - \sqrt{8x} = \sqrt{25 \cdot 2x} - \sqrt{4 \cdot 2x}$

$\qquad = 5\sqrt{2x} - 2\sqrt{2x}$

$\qquad = (5-2)\sqrt{2x}$

$\qquad = 3\sqrt{2x}$

41. $3\sqrt{18} + 5\sqrt{50} = 3\sqrt{9 \cdot 2} + 5\sqrt{25 \cdot 2}$

$\qquad = 3 \cdot 3\sqrt{2} + 5 \cdot 5\sqrt{2}$

$\qquad = 9\sqrt{2} + 25\sqrt{2}$

$\qquad = (9+25)\sqrt{2}$

$\qquad = 34\sqrt{2}$

43. $3\sqrt{8} - \sqrt{32} + 3\sqrt{72} - \sqrt{75}$

$\qquad = 3\sqrt{4 \cdot 2} - \sqrt{16 \cdot 2} + 3\sqrt{36 \cdot 2} - \sqrt{25 \cdot 3}$

$\qquad = 3 \cdot 2\sqrt{2} - 4\sqrt{2} + 3 \cdot 6\sqrt{2} - 5\sqrt{3}$

$\qquad = 6\sqrt{2} - 4\sqrt{2} + 18\sqrt{2} - 5\sqrt{3}$

$\qquad = 20\sqrt{2} - 5\sqrt{3}$

45. $\dfrac{1}{\sqrt{7}} = \dfrac{1}{\sqrt{7}} \cdot \dfrac{\sqrt{7}}{\sqrt{7}} = \dfrac{\sqrt{7}}{7}$

47. $\dfrac{\sqrt{2}}{\sqrt{5}} = \dfrac{\sqrt{2}}{\sqrt{5}} \cdot \dfrac{\sqrt{5}}{\sqrt{5}} = \dfrac{\sqrt{10}}{5}$

49. $\dfrac{13}{3+\sqrt{11}} = \dfrac{13}{3+\sqrt{11}} \cdot \dfrac{3-\sqrt{11}}{3-\sqrt{11}}$

$\qquad = \dfrac{13(3-\sqrt{11})}{3^2 - (\sqrt{11})^2}$

$\qquad = \dfrac{13(3-\sqrt{11})}{9-11}$

$\qquad = \dfrac{13(3-\sqrt{11})}{-2}$

51. $\dfrac{7}{\sqrt{5}-2} = \dfrac{7}{\sqrt{5}-2} \cdot \dfrac{\sqrt{5}+2}{\sqrt{5}+2}$

$= \dfrac{7(\sqrt{5}+2)}{(\sqrt{5})^2 - 2^2}$

$= \dfrac{7(\sqrt{5}+2)}{5-4}$

$= 7(\sqrt{5}+2)$

53. $\dfrac{6}{\sqrt{5}+\sqrt{3}} = \dfrac{6}{\sqrt{5}+\sqrt{3}} \cdot \dfrac{\sqrt{5}-\sqrt{3}}{\sqrt{5}-\sqrt{3}}$

$= \dfrac{6(\sqrt{5}-\sqrt{3})}{(\sqrt{5})^2 - (\sqrt{3})^2}$

$= \dfrac{6(\sqrt{5}-\sqrt{3})}{5-3}$

$= \dfrac{6(\sqrt{5}-\sqrt{3})}{2}$

$= 3(\sqrt{5}-\sqrt{3})$

55. $\sqrt[3]{125} = \sqrt[3]{5^3} = 5$

57. $\sqrt[3]{-8} = \sqrt[3]{(-2)^3} = -2$

59. $\sqrt[4]{-16}$ is not a real number.

61. $\sqrt[4]{(-3)^4} = |-3| = 3$

63. $\sqrt[5]{(-3)^5} = -3$

65. $\sqrt[5]{-\dfrac{1}{32}} = \sqrt[5]{-\dfrac{1}{2^5}} = -\dfrac{1}{2}$

67. $\sqrt[3]{32} = \sqrt[3]{8 \cdot 4} = \sqrt[3]{8}\sqrt[3]{4} = 2 \cdot \sqrt[3]{4}$

69. $\sqrt[3]{x^4} = \sqrt[3]{x^3 \cdot x} = x \cdot \sqrt[3]{x}$

71. $\sqrt[3]{9} \cdot \sqrt[3]{6} = \sqrt[3]{54} = \sqrt[3]{27 \cdot 2} = \sqrt[3]{27}\sqrt[3]{2} = 3\sqrt[3]{2}$

73. $\dfrac{\sqrt[5]{64x^6}}{\sqrt[5]{2x}} = \sqrt[5]{\dfrac{64x^6}{2x}} = \sqrt[5]{32x^5} = 2x$

75. $4\sqrt[5]{2} + 3\sqrt[5]{2} = 7\sqrt[5]{2}$

77. $5\sqrt[3]{16} + \sqrt[3]{54} = 5\sqrt[3]{8 \cdot 2} + \sqrt[3]{27 \cdot 2}$

$= 5 \cdot 2\sqrt[3]{2} + 3\sqrt[3]{2}$

$= 10\sqrt[3]{2} + 3\sqrt[3]{2}$

$= 13\sqrt[3]{2}$

79. $\sqrt[3]{54xy^3} - y\sqrt[3]{128x}$

$= \sqrt[3]{27 \cdot 2xy^3} - y\sqrt[3]{64 \cdot 2x}$

$= 3y\sqrt[3]{2x} - 4y\sqrt[3]{2x}$

$= -y\sqrt[3]{2x}$

81. $\sqrt{2} + \sqrt[3]{8} = \sqrt{2} + 2$

83. $36^{1/2} = \sqrt{36} = 6$

85. $8^{1/3} = \sqrt[3]{8} = 2$

87. $125^{2/3} = \left(\sqrt[3]{125}\right)^2 = 5^2 = 25$

89. $32^{-4/5} = \dfrac{1}{32^{4/5}} = \dfrac{1}{2^4} = \dfrac{1}{16}$

91. $\left(7x^{1/3}\right)\left(2x^{1/4}\right) = 7 \cdot 2x^{1/3} \cdot x^{1/4}$

$= 14 \cdot x^{1/3+1/4}$

$= 14x^{7/12}$

93. $\dfrac{20x^{1/2}}{5x^{1/4}} = \left(\dfrac{20}{5}\right)\left(\dfrac{x^{1/2}}{x^{1/4}}\right)$

$= 4 \cdot x^{1/2-1/4}$

$= 4x^{1/4}$

95. $\left(x^{2/3}\right)^3 = x^{2/3 \cdot 3} = x^2$

97. $(25x^4y^6)^{1/2} = 25^{1/2}x^{4 \cdot 1/2}y^{6 \cdot 1/2} = 5x^2|y|^3$

99. $\dfrac{\left(3y^{\frac{1}{4}}\right)^3}{y^{\frac{1}{12}}} = \dfrac{27y^{\frac{3}{4}}}{y^{\frac{1}{12}}} = 27y^{\frac{3}{4}-\frac{1}{12}}$

$= 27y^{\frac{8}{12}} = 27y^{\frac{2}{3}}$

101. $\sqrt[4]{5^2} = 5^{2/4} = 5^{1/2} = \sqrt{5}$

103. $\sqrt[3]{x^6} = x^{6/3} = x^2$

12

105. $\sqrt[6]{x^4} = \sqrt[6/2]{x^{4/2}} = \sqrt[3]{x^2}$

107. $\sqrt[9]{x^6 y^3} = x^{\frac{6}{9}} y^{\frac{3}{9}} = x^{\frac{2}{3}} y^{\frac{1}{3}} = \sqrt[3]{x^2 y}$

109. $\sqrt[3]{\sqrt[4]{16} + \sqrt{625}} = \sqrt[3]{2 + 25} = \sqrt[3]{27} = 3$

111. $\left(49x^{-2} y^4\right)^{-1/2} \left(xy^{1/2}\right)$

$= (49)^{-1/2} \left(x^{-2}\right)^{-1/2} \left(y^4\right)^{-1/2} \left(xy^{1/2}\right)$

$= \dfrac{1}{49^{1/2}} x^{(-2)(-1/2)} y^{(4)(-1/2)} \left(xy^{1/2}\right)$

$= \dfrac{1}{7} x^1 y^{-2} \cdot xy^{1/2} = \dfrac{1}{7} x^{1+1} y^{-2+(1/2)}$

$= \dfrac{1}{7} x^2 y^{-3/2} = \dfrac{x^2}{7y^{3/2}}$

113. $\left(\dfrac{x^{-5/4} y^{1/3}}{x^{-3/4}}\right)^{-6} = \left(x^{(-5/4)-(-3/4)} y^{1/3}\right)^{-6}$

$= \left(x^{-2/4} y^{1/3}\right)^{-6} = x^{(-2/4)(-6)} y^{(1/3)(-6)}$

$= x^3 y^{-2} = \dfrac{x^3}{y^2}$

115. $d(x) = \sqrt{\dfrac{3x}{2}}$

$d(72) = \sqrt{\dfrac{3(72)}{2}}$

$= \sqrt{3(36)}$

$= \sqrt{3} \cdot \sqrt{36}$

$= 6\sqrt{3} \approx 10.4$ miles

A passenger on the pool deck can see roughly 10.4 miles.

117. $v = \sqrt{20L}; L = 245$

$v = \sqrt{20 \cdot 245} = \sqrt{4900} = 70$

The motorist was traveling 70 miles per hour, so he was speeding.

119. $\dfrac{7\sqrt{2 \cdot 2 \cdot 3}}{6} = \dfrac{7 \cdot 2\sqrt{3}}{6} = \dfrac{14\sqrt{3}}{6} = \dfrac{7}{3}\sqrt{3}$

121. a. $C = 35.74 + 0.6215t - 35.74\sqrt[25]{v^4} + 0.4275t\sqrt[25]{v^4}$

$C = 35.74 + 0.6215t - 35.74v^{\frac{4}{25}} + 0.4275tv^{\frac{4}{25}}$

b. $C = 35.74 + 0.6215(25) - 35.74(30)^{\frac{4}{25}} + 0.4275(25)(30)^{\frac{4}{25}}$

$\approx 8°F$

123. $P = 2l + 2w$

$= 2\left(2\sqrt{20}\right) + 2\left(\sqrt{125}\right)$

$= 4\sqrt{20} + 2\sqrt{125}$

$= 4\sqrt{4 \cdot 5} + 2\sqrt{25 \cdot 5}$

$= 4 \cdot 2\sqrt{5} + 2 \cdot 5\sqrt{5}$

$= 8\sqrt{5} + 10\sqrt{5}$

$= (8 + 10)\sqrt{5} = 18\sqrt{5}$

The perimeter is $18\sqrt{5}$ feet.

$A = lw = 2\sqrt{20} \cdot \sqrt{125}$

$= 2\sqrt{20 \cdot 125} = 2\sqrt{2500}$

$= 2 \cdot 50 = 100$

The area is 100 square feet.

133. a. false; $(-8)^{\frac{1}{3}} = \sqrt[3]{-8} = -2$ is real.

b. false; $\sqrt{x^2 + y^2} \neq x + y$

c. false; $(8)^{-\frac{1}{3}} = \dfrac{1}{(8)^{\frac{1}{3}}} = \dfrac{1}{\sqrt[3]{8}} = \dfrac{1}{2}$

d. true; $2^{\frac{1}{2}} \cdot 2^{\frac{1}{2}} = 2^{\frac{1}{2}+\frac{1}{2}} = 2^1 = 2$

135. $\sqrt{\boxed{25}x^{\boxed{14}}} = 5x^7$

137. a. $3^{\frac{1}{2}} \boxed{>} 3^{\frac{1}{3}}$

Calculator Check: $1.7321 > 1.4422$

b. $\sqrt{7} + \sqrt{18} \boxed{>} \sqrt{7 + 18}$

Calculator Check: $6.8884 > 5$

Section P.4

Check Point Exercises

1. a. $(-17x^3 + 4x^2 - 11x - 5) + (16x^3 - 3x^2 + 3x - 15)$

$= (-17x^3 + 16x^3) + (4x^2 - 3x^2) + (-11x + 3x) + (-5 - 15)$

$= -x^3 + x^2 - 8x - 20$

b. $(13x^2 - 9x^2 - 7x + 1) - (-7x^3 + 2x^2 - 5x + 9)$

$= (13x^3 - 9x^2 - 7x + 1) + (7x^3 - 2x^2 + 5x - 9)$

$= (13x^3 + 7x^3) + (-9x^2 - 2x^2) + (-7x + 5x) + (1 - 9)$

$= 20x^3 - 11x^2 - 2x - 8$

2. $(5x - 2)(3x^2 - 5x + 4)$

$= 5x(3x^2 - 5x + 4) - 2(3x^2 - 5x + 4)$

$= 5x \cdot 3x^2 - 5x \cdot 5x + 5x \cdot 4 - 2 \cdot 3x^2 + 2 \cdot 5x - 2 \cdot 4$

$= 15x^3 - 25x^2 + 20x - 6x^2 + 10x - 8$

$= 15x^3 - 31x^2 + 30x - 8$

3. $(7x - 5)(4x - 3) = 7x \cdot 4x + 7x(-3) + (-5)4x + (-5)(-3)$

$= 28x^2 - 21x - 20x + 15$

$= 28x^2 - 41x + 15$

4. a. Use the special-product formula shown.

$(A + B)(A - B) = A^2 - B^2$

$(7x + 8)(7x - 8) = (7x)^2 - (8)^2$

$= 49x^2 - 64$

b. Use the special-product formula shown.

$(A + B)(A - B) = A^2 - B^2$

$(2y^3 - 5)(2y^3 + 5) = (2y^3 + 5)(2y^3 - 5) = (2y^3)^2 - (5)^2 = 4y^6 - 25$

5. a. Use the special-product formula shown.
$$(A+B)^2 = A^2 + 2AB + B^2$$
$$(x+10)^2 = x^2 + 2(x)(10) + 10^2$$
$$= x^2 + 20x + 100$$

   b. Use the special-product formula shown.
$$(A+B)^2 = A^2 + 2AB + B^2$$
$$(5x+4)^2 = (5x)^2 + 2(5x)(4) + 4^2$$
$$= 25x^2 + 40x + 16$$

6. a. Use the special-product formula shown.
$$(A-B)^2 = A^2 - 2AB + B^2$$
$$(x-9)^2 = x^2 - 2(x)(9) + 9^2$$
$$= x^2 - 18x + 81$$

   b. Use the special-product formula shown.
$$(A-B)^2 = A^2 - 2AB + B^2$$
$$(7x-3)^2 = (7x)^2 - 2(7x)(3) + 3^2$$
$$= 49x^2 - 42x + 9$$

7. $(x^3 - 4x^2y + 5xy^2 - y^3) - (x^3 - 6x^2y + y^3)$
$$= (x^3 - 4x^2y + 5xy^2 - y^3) + (-x^3 + 6x^2y - y^3)$$
$$= (x^3 - x^3) + (-4x^2y + 6x^2y) + (5xy^2) + (-y^3 - y^3)$$
$$= 2x^2y + 5xy^2 - 2y^3$$

8. a. $(7x-6y)(3x-y) = (7x)(3x) + (7x)(-y) + (-6y)(3x) + (-6y)(-y)$
$$= 21x^2 - 7xy - 18xy + 6y^2$$
$$= 21x^2 - 25xy + 6y^2$$

   b. $(2x+4y)^2 = (2x)^2 + 2(2x)(4y) + (4y)^2$
$$= 4x^2 + 16xy + 16y^2$$

Exercise Set P.4

1. Yes; $2x + 3x^2 - 5 = 3x^2 + 2x - 5$

3. No; The form of a polynomial involves addition and subtraction, not division.

5. $3x^2$ has degree 2
    $-5x$ has degree 1
    4 has degree 0
    $3x^2 - 5x + 4$ has degree 2.

7. x^2 has degree 2
    $-4x^3$ has degree 3
    $9x$ has degree 1
    $-12x^4$ has degree 4
    63 has degree 0
    $x^2 - 4x^3 + 9x - 12x^4 + 63$ has degree 4.

9. $(-6x^3 + 5x^2 - 8x + 9) + (17x^3 + 2x^2 - 4x - 13) = (-6x^3 + 17x^3) + (5x^2 + 2x^2) + (-8x - 4x) + (9 - 13)$
    $$= 11x^3 + 7x^2 - 12x - 4$$
    The degree is 3.

11. $(17x^3 - 5x^2 + 4x - 3) - (5x^3 - 9x^2 - 8x + 11) = (17x^3 - 5x^2 + 4x - 3) + (-5x^3 + 9x^2 + 8x - 11)$
    $$= (17x^3 - 5x^3) + (-5x^2 + 9x^2) + (4x + 8x) + (-3 - 11)$$
    $$= 12x^3 + 4x^2 + 12x - 14$$
    The degree is 3.

13. $(5x^2 - 7x - 8) + (2x^2 - 3x + 7) - (x^2 - 4x - 3) = (5x^2 - 7x - 8) + (2x^2 - 3x + 7) + (-x^2 + 4x + 3)$
    $$= (5x^2 + 2x^2 - x^2) + (-7x - 3x + 4x) + (-8 + 7 + 3)$$
    $$= 6x^2 - 6x + 2$$
    The degree is 2.

15. $(x + 1)(x^2 - x + 1) = x(x^2) - x \cdot x + x \cdot 1 + 1(x^2) - 1 \cdot x + 1 \cdot 1$
    $$= x^3 - x^2 + x + x^2 - x + 1$$
    $$= x^3 + 1$$

17. $(2x - 3)(x^2 - 3x + 5) = (2x)(x^2) + (2x)(-3x) + (2x)(5) + (-3)(x^2) + (-3)(-3x) + (-3)(5)$
    $$= 2x^3 - 6x^2 + 10x - 3x^2 + 9x - 15$$
    $$= 2x^3 - 9x^2 + 19x - 15$$

19. $(x + 7)(x + 3) = x^2 + 3x + 7x + 21 = x^2 + 10x + 21$

21. $(x - 5)(x + 3) = x^2 + 3x - 5x - 15 = x^2 - 2x - 15$

23. $(3x + 5)(2x + 1) = (3x)(2x) + 3x(1) + 5(2x) + 5 = 6x^2 + 3x + 10x + 5 = 6x^2 + 13x + 5$

25. $(2x - 3)(5x + 3) = (2x)(5x) + (2x)(3) + (-3)(5x) + (-3)(3) = 10x^2 + 6x - 15x - 9 = 10x^2 - 9x - 9$

27. $(5x^2 - 4)(3x^2 - 7) = (5x^2)(3x^2) + (5x^2)(-7) + (-4)(3x^2) + (-4)(-7) = 15x^4 - 35x^2 - 12x^2 + 28 = 15x^4 - 47x^2 + 28$

29. $(8x^3 + 3)(x^2 - 5) = (8x^3)(x^2) + (8x^3)(-5) + (3)(x^2) + (3)(-5) = 8x^5 - 40x^3 + 3x^2 - 15$

31. $(x + 3)(x - 3) = x^2 - 3^2 = x^2 - 9$

33. $(3x + 2)(3x - 2) = (3x)^2 - 2^2 = 9x^2 - 4$

35. $(5 - 7x)(5 + 7x) = 5^2 - (7x)^2 = 25 - 49x^2$

37. $(4x^2 + 5x)(4x^2 - 5x) = (4x^2)^2 - (5x)^2 = 16x^4 - 25x^2$

39. $\left(1-y^5\right)\left(1+y^5\right) = \left(1\right)^2 - \left(y^5\right)^2 = 1 - y^{10}$

41. $(x+2)^2 = x^2 + 2 \cdot x \cdot 2 + 2^2 = x^2 + 4x + 4$

43. $(2x+3)^2 = (2x)^2 + 2(2x)(3) + 3^2 = 4x^2 + 12x + 9$

45. $(x-3)^2 = x^2 - 2 \cdot x \cdot 3 + 3^2 = x^2 - 6x + 9$

47. $(4x^2 - 1)^2 = (4x^2)^2 - 2(4x^2)(1) + 1^2 = 16x^4 - 8x^2 + 1$

49. $(7-2x)^2 = 7^2 - 2(7)(2x) + (2x)^2 = 49 - 28x + 4x^2 = 4x^2 - 28x + 49$

51. $(x+1)^3 = x^3 + 3 \cdot x^2 \cdot 1 + 3x \cdot 1^2 + 1^3 = x^3 + 3x^2 + 3x + 1$

53. $(2x+3)^3 = (2x)^3 + 3 \cdot (2x)^2 \cdot 3 + 3(2x) \cdot 3^2 + 3^3 = 8x^3 + 36x^2 + 54x + 27$

55. $(x-3)^3 = x^3 - 3 \cdot x^3 \cdot 3 + 3 \cdot x \cdot 3^2 - 3^3 = x^3 - 9x^2 + 27x - 27$

57. $(3x-4)^3 = (3x)^3 - 3(3x)^2 \cdot 4 + 3(3x) \cdot 4^2 - 4^3 = 27x^3 - 108x^2 + 144x - 64$

59. $(5x^2 y - 3xy) + (2x^2 y - xy) = (5x^2 y + 2x^2 y) + (-3xy - xy)$
$$= (5+2)x^2 y + (-3-1)xy$$
$$= 7x^2 y - 4xy \text{ is of degree 3.}$$

61. $(4x^2 y + 8xy + 11) + (-2x^2 y + 5xy + 2) = (4x^2 y - 2x^2 y) + (8xy + 5xy) + (11+2)$
$$= (4-2)x^2 y + (8+5)xy + 13$$
$$= 2x^2 y + 13xy + 13 \text{ is of degree 3.}$$

63. $(x^3 + 7xy - 5y^2) - (6x^3 - xy + 4y^2) = (x^3 + 7xy - 5y^2)$
$$= (x^3 - 6x^3) + (7xy + xy) + (-5y^2 - 4y^2)$$
$$= (1-6)x^3 + (7+1)xy + (-5-4)y^2$$
$$= -5x^3 + 8xy - 9y^2 \text{ is of degree 3.}$$

65. $(3x^4 y^2 + 5x^3 y - 3y) - (2x^4 y^2 - 3x^3 y - 4y + 6x) = (3x^4 y^2 + 5x^3 y - 3y) + (-2x^4 y^2 + 3x^3 y + 4y - 6x)$
$$= (3x^4 y^2 - 2x^4 y^2) + (5x^3 y + 3x^3 y) + (-3y + 4y) - 6x$$
$$= (3-2)x^4 y^2 + (5+3)x^3 y + (-3+4)y - 6x$$
$$= x^4 y^2 + 8x^3 y + y - 6x \text{ is of degree 6.}$$

67. $(x+5y)(7x+3y) = x(7x) + x(3y) + (5y)(7x) + (5y)(3y)$
$$= 7x^2 + 3xy + 35xy + 15y^2$$
$$= 7x^2 + 38xy + 15y^2$$

69. $(x-3y)(2x+7y) = x(2x) + x(7y) + (-3y)(2x) + (-3y)(7y)$
$$= 2x^2 + 7xy - 6xy - 21y^2$$
$$= 2x^2 + xy - 21y^2$$

71. $(3xy-1)(5xy+2) = (3xy)(5xy)+(3xy)(2)+(-1)(5xy)+(-1)(2)$
$$= 15x^2y^2+6xy-5xy-2$$
$$= 15x^2y^2+xy-2$$

73. $(7x+5y)^2 = (7x)^2+2(7x)(5y)+(5y)^2 = 49x^2+70xy+25y^2$

75. $(x^2y^2-3)^2 = (x^2y^2)^2-2(x^2y^2)(3)+3^2 = x^4y^4-6x^2y^2+9$

77. $(x-y)(x^2+xy+y^2) = x(x^2)+x(xy)+x(y^2)+(-y)(x^2)+(-y)(xy)+(-y)(y^2)$
$$= x^3+x^2y+xy^2-x^2y-xy^2-y^3$$
$$= x^3-y^3$$

79. $(3x+5y)(3x-5y) = (3x)^2-(5y)^2 = 9x^2-25y^2$

81. $\left(7xy^2-10y\right)\left(7xy^2+10y\right) = \left(7xy^2\right)^2-(10y)^2 = 49x^2y^4-100y^2$

83. $(3x+4y)^2-(3x-4y)^2 = \left[(3x)^2+2(3x)(4y)+(4y)^2\right]-\left[(3x)^2-2(3x)(4y)+(4y)^2\right]$
$$= \left(9x^2+24xy+16y^2\right)-\left(9x^2-24xy+16y^2\right)$$
$$= 9x^2+24xy+16y^2-9x^2+24xy-16y^2$$
$$= 48xy$$

85. $(5x-7)(3x-2)-(4x-5)(6x-1)$
$$= \left[15x^2-10x-21x+14\right]-\left[24x^2-4x-30x+5\right]$$
$$= \left(15x^2-31x+14\right)-\left(24x^2-34x+5\right)$$
$$= 15x^2-31x+14-24x^2+34x-5$$
$$= -9x^2+3x+9$$

87. $(2x+5)(2x-5)\left(4x^2+25\right)$
$$= \left[(2x)^2-5^2\right]\left(4x^2+25\right)$$
$$= \left(4x^2-25\right)\left(4x^2+25\right)$$
$$= \left(4x^2\right)^2-(25)^2$$
$$= 16x^4-625$$

89. $\dfrac{(2x-7)^5}{(2x-7)^3} = (2x-7)^{5-3}$
$$= (2x-7)^2$$
$$= (2x)^2-2(2x)(7)+(7)^2$$
$$= 4x^2-28x+49$$

92. Model 2 is not a polynomial model

93. Model 1:

$$N = 1.8x + 5.1$$
$$N = 1.8(2) + 5.1$$
$$N = 8.7$$

Model 2:

$$N = 5.6(1.2)^x$$
$$N = 5.6(1.2)^2$$
$$N = 8.064$$

Model 3:

$$N = 0.17x^2 + 0.95x + 5.68$$
$$N = 0.17(2)^2 + 0.95(2) + 5.68$$
$$N = 8.26$$

Model 4:

$$N = 0.09x^2 + 0.01x^3 + 1.1x + 5.64$$
$$N = 0.09(2)^2 + 0.01(2)^3 + 1.1(2) + 5.64$$
$$N = 8.28$$

Model 1 best describes the data in 2000.

109. $[(7x+5) + 4y][(7x+5) - 4y] = (7x+5)^2 - 4y^2$
$$= (7x)^2 + 2(7x)(5) + 5^2 - 16y^2$$
$$= 49x^2 + 70x + 25 - 16y^2$$

111. $(x^n + 2)(x^n - 2) - (x^n - 3)^2$
$$(x^n + 2)(x^n - 2) - (x^n - 3)^2$$
$$= (x^{2n} - 4) - (x^{2n} - 6x^n + 9)$$
$$= x^{2n} - 4 - x^{2n} + 6x^n - 9$$
$$= 6x^n - 13$$

95. Model 3 is the model of degree 2.

$$N = 0.17x^2 + 0.95x + 5.68$$
$$N = 0.17(5)^2 + 0.95(5) + 5.68$$
$$N = 14.68$$

Model 3 best describes the data in 2003 very well.

97. $x(8 - 2x)(10 - 2x) = x(80 - 36x + 4x^2)$
$$= 80x - 36x^2 + 4x^3$$
$$= 4x^3 - 36x^2 + 80x$$

99. $(x+9)(x+3) - (x+5)(x+1)$
$$= x^2 + 12x + 27 - (x^2 + 6x + 5)$$
$$= x^2 + 12x + 27 - x^2 - 6x - 5$$
$$= 6x + 22$$

Mid Chapter P Check Point

1. $(3x+5)(4x-7) = (3x)(4x) + (3x)(-7) + (5)(4x) + (5)(-7)$
$$= 12x^2 - 21x + 20x - 35$$
$$= 12x^2 - x - 35$$

2. $(3x+5) - (4x-7) = 3x + 5 - 4x + 7$
$$= 3x - 4x + 5 + 7$$
$$= -x + 12$$

3. $\sqrt{6} + 9\sqrt{6} = 10\sqrt{6}$

4. $3\sqrt{12} - \sqrt{27} = 3 \cdot 2\sqrt{3} - 3\sqrt{3} = 6\sqrt{3} - 3\sqrt{3} = 3\sqrt{3}$

5. $7x + 3[9 - (2x - 6)] = 7x + 3[9 - 2x + 6] = 7x + 3[15 - 2x] = 7x + 45 - 6x = x + 45$

6. $(8x - 3)^2 = (8x)^2 - 2(8x)(3) + (3)^2 = 64x^2 - 48x + 9$

7. $\left(x^{\frac{1}{3}}y^{-\frac{1}{2}}\right)^6 = x^{\frac{1}{3}\cdot 6}y^{-\frac{1}{2}\cdot 6} = x^2 y^{-3} = \dfrac{x^2}{y^3}$

8. $\left(\dfrac{2}{7}\right)^0 - 32^{-\frac{2}{5}} = 1 - \dfrac{1}{\left(\sqrt[5]{32}\right)^2} = 1 - \dfrac{1}{(2)^2} = 1 - \dfrac{1}{4} = \dfrac{3}{4}$

9. $(2x-5)-(x^2-3x+1) = 2x-5-x^2+3x-1 = -x^2+5x-6$

10. $(2x-5)(x^2-3x+1) = 2x(x^2-3x+1)-5(x^2-3x+1)$
$$= 2x(x^2-3x+1)-5(x^2-3x+1)$$
$$= 2x^3-6x^2+2x-5x^2+15x-5$$
$$= 2x^3-6x^2-5x^2+2x+15x-5$$
$$= 2x^3-11x^2+17x-5$$

11. $x^3+x^3-x^3\cdot x^3 = 2x^3-x^6 = -x^6+2x^3$

12. $(9a-10b)(2a+b) = (9a)(2a)+(9a)(b)+(-10b)(2a)+(-10b)(b)$
$$= (9a)(2a)+(9a)(b)+(-10b)(2a)+(-10b)(b)$$
$$= 18a^2+9ab-20ab-10b^2$$
$$= 18a^2-11ab-10b^2$$

13. $\{a,c,d,e\}\cup\{c,d,f,h\} = \{a,c,d,e,f,h\}$

14. $\{a,c,d,e\}\cap\{c,d,f,h\} = \{c,d\}$

15. $\left(3x^2y^3-xy+4y^2\right)-\left(-2x^2y^3-3xy+5y^2\right) = 3x^2y^3-xy+4y^2+2x^2y^3+3xy-5y^2$
$$= 3x^2y^3-xy+4y^2+2x^2y^3+3xy-5y^2$$
$$= 3x^2y^3+2x^2y^3-xy+3xy+4y^2-5y^2$$
$$= 5x^2y^3+2xy-y^2$$

16. $\dfrac{24x^2y^{13}}{-2x^5y^{-2}} = -12x^{2-5}y^{13-(-2)} = -12x^{-3}y^{15} = -\dfrac{12y^{15}}{x^3}$

17. $\left(\dfrac{1}{3}x^{-5}y^4\right)\left(18x^{-2}y^{-1}\right) = 6x^{-5-2}y^{4-1} = \dfrac{6y^3}{x^7}$

18. $\sqrt[12]{x^4} = x^{\frac{4}{12}} = \left|x^{\frac{1}{3}}\right| = \left|\sqrt[3]{x}\right|$

19. $\dfrac{24\times 10^3}{2\times 10^6} = \dfrac{24}{2}\cdot\dfrac{10^3}{10^6} = 12\times 10^{-3} = \left(1.2\times 10^1\right)\times 10^{-3} = 1.2\times\left(10^1\times 10^{-3}\right) = 1.2\times 10^{-2}$

20. $\dfrac{\sqrt[3]{32}}{\sqrt[3]{2}} = \sqrt[3]{\dfrac{32}{2}} = \sqrt[3]{16} = \sqrt[3]{2^4} = 2\sqrt[3]{2}$

21. $(x^3 + 2)(x^3 - 2) = x^6 - 4$

22. $(x^2 + 2)^2 = (x^2)^2 + 2(x^2)(2) + (2)^2 = x^4 + 4x^2 + 4$

23. $\sqrt{50} \cdot \sqrt{6} = 5\sqrt{2} \cdot \sqrt{6} = 5\sqrt{2 \cdot 6} = 5\sqrt{12} = 5 \cdot 2\sqrt{3} = 10\sqrt{3}$

24. $\dfrac{11}{7 - \sqrt{3}} = \dfrac{11}{7 - \sqrt{3}} \cdot \dfrac{7 + \sqrt{3}}{7 + \sqrt{3}} = \dfrac{77 + 11\sqrt{3}}{49 - 3} = \dfrac{77 + 11\sqrt{3}}{46}$

25. $\dfrac{11}{\sqrt{3}} = \dfrac{11}{\sqrt{3}} \cdot \dfrac{\sqrt{3}}{\sqrt{3}} = \dfrac{11\sqrt{3}}{3}$

26. $\left\{ -11, \ -\dfrac{3}{7}, \ 0, \ 0.45, \ \sqrt{25} \right\}$

27. Since $2 - \sqrt{13} < 0$ then $\left| 2 - \sqrt{13} \right| = \sqrt{13} - 2$

28. Since $x < 0$ then $|x| = -x$. Thus $x^2 |x| = -x^2 x = -x^3$

29. $120 \cdot 2.9 \times 10^8 = 348 \times 10^8 = 3.48 \times 10^2 \times 10^8 = 3.48 \times 10^{10}$
The total annual spending on ice cream is $\$3.48 \times 10^{10}$

30. $\dfrac{3 \times 10^{10}}{7.5 \times 10^9} = \dfrac{3}{7.5} \cdot \dfrac{10^{10}}{10^9} = 0.4 \times 10 = 4$
A human brain has 4 times as many neurons as a gorilla brain.

31.   **a.**   Model 1:

$D = 236(1.5)^x$

$D = 236(1.5)^2$

$D = 531$

Model 2:

$D = 127x + 239$

$D = 127(2) + 239$

$D = 493$

Model 3:

$D = -54x^2 + 234x + 220$

$D = -54(2)^2 + 234(2) + 220$

$D = 472$

Model 3 best describes the data in 2004.

  b.   Model 2 is the polynomial of degree 1:

$D = 127x + 239$

$D = 127(6) + 239$

$D = 1001$

Model 2 predicts Americans will spend 1001 million dollars on online dating in 2008.

Section P.5

Check Point Exercises

1. **a.** $10x^3 - 4x^2$
    $= 2x^2(5x) - 2x^2(2)$
    $= 2x^2(5x - 2)$

    b. $2x(x - 7) + 3(x - 7)$
    $= (x - 7)(2x + 3)$

2. $x^3 + 5x^2 - 2x - 10$
    $= (x^3 + 5x^2) - (2x + 10)$
    $= x^2(x + 5) - 2(x + 5)$
    $= (x + 5)(x^2 - 2)$

3. **a.** Find two numbers whose product is 40 and whose sum is 13. The required integers are 8 and 5. Thus,
    $x^2 + 13x + 40 = (x + 5)(x + 8)$ or $(x + 8)(x + 5)$

    b. Find two numbers whose product is –14 and whose sum is –5. The required integers are –7 and 2. Thus,
    $x^2 - 5x - 14 = (x - 7)(x + 2)$ or $(x + 2)(x - 7)$.

4. Find two First terms whose product is $6x^2$.
    $6x^2 + 19x - 7 = (6x \quad)(x \quad)$
    $6x^2 + 19x - 7 = (3x \quad)(2x \quad)$

    Find two Last terms whose product is –7.
    The possible factors are $1(-7)$ and $-1(7)$.

    Try various combinations of these factors to find the factorization in which the sum of the Outside and Inside products is $19x$.

Possible Factors of $6x^2 + 19x - 7$	Sum of Outside and Inside Products (Should Equal $19x$)
$(6x + 1)(x - 7)$	$-42x + x = -41x$
$(6x - 7)(x + 1)$	$6x - 7x = -x$
$(6x - 1)(x + 7)$	$42x - x = 41x$
$(6x + 7)(x - 1)$	$-6x + 7x = x$
$(3x + 1)(2x - 7)$	$-21x + 2x = -19x$
$(3x - 7)(2x + 1)$	$3x - 14x = -11x$
$(3x - 1)(2x + 7)$	$21x - 2x = 19x$
$(3x + 7)(2x - 1)$	$-3x + 14x = 11x$

    Thus, $6x^2 + 19x - 7 = (3x - 1)(2x + 7)$ or $(2x + 7)(3x - 1)$.

5. Find two First terms whose product is $3x^2$.

$3x^2 - 13xy + 4y^2 = (3x\quad)(x\quad)$

Find two Last terms whose product is $4y^2$.
The possible factors are $(2y)(2y)$, $(-2y)(-2y)$, $(4y)(y)$, and $(-4y)(-y)$.

Try various combinations of these factors to find the factorization in which the sum of the Outside and Inside products is $-13xy$.

$3x^2 - 13xy + y^2 = (3x - y)(x - 4y)$ or $(x - 4y)(3x - y)$.

6. Express each term as the square of some monomial. Then use the formula for factoring $A^2 - B^2$.

a. $x^2 - 81 = x^2 - 9^2 = (x + 9)(x - 9)$

b. $36x^2 - 25 = (6x)^2 - 5^2 = (6x + 5)(6x - 5)$

7. Express $81x^4 - 16$ as the difference of two squares and use the formula for factoring $A^2 - B^2$.
$81x^4 - 16 = (9x^2)^2 - 4^2 = (9x^2 + 4)(9x^2 - 4)$

The factor $9x^2 - 4$ is the difference of two squares and can be factored. Express $9x^2 - 4$ as the difference of two squares and again use the formula for factoring $A^2 - B^2$.
$(9x^2 + 4)(9x^2 - 4) = (9x^2 + 4)\left[(3x)^2 - 2^2\right] = (9x^2 + 4)(3x + 2)(3x - 2)$

Thus, factored completely,
$81x^4 - 16 = (9x^2 + 4)(3x + 2)(3x - 2)$.

8. **a.** $x^2 + 14x + 49 = x^2 + 2 \cdot x \cdot 7 + 7^2 = (x + 7)^2$

b. Since $16x^2 = (4x)^2$ and $49 = 7^2$, check to see if the middle term can be expressed as twice the product of $4x$ and 7. Since $2 \cdot 4x \cdot 7 = 56x$, $16x^2 - 56x + 49$ is a perfect square trinomial. Thus,
$$16x^2 - 56x + 49 = (4x)^2 - 2 \cdot 4x \cdot 7 + 7^2$$
$$= (4x - 7)^2$$

9. **a.** $\quad = x^3 + 1^3$
$= (x + 1)(x^2 - x \cdot 1 + 1^2)$
$= (x + 1)(x^2 - x + 1)$

b. $\quad -8 = (5x)^3 - 2^3$
$= (5x - 2)\left[(5x)^2 + (5x)(2) + 2^2\right]$
$= (5x - 2)(25x^2 + 10x + 4)$

10. Factor out the greatest common factor.
$3x^3 - 30x^2 + 75x = 3x(x^2 - 10x + 25)$
Factor the perfect square trinomial.
$3x(x^2 - 10x + 25) = 3x(x - 5)^2$

11. Reorder to write as a difference of squares.
$x^2 - 36a^2 + 20x + 100$
$= x^2 + 20x + 100 - 36a^2$
$= (x^2 + 20x + 100) - 36a^2$
$= (x + 10)^2 - 36a^2$
$= (x + 10 + 6a)(x + 10 - 6a)$

12. $x(x-1)^{-\frac{1}{2}} + (x-1)^{\frac{1}{2}}$

$\quad = (x-1)^{-\frac{1}{2}}\left[x + (x-1)^{\frac{1}{2}-(-\frac{1}{2})}\right]$

$\quad = (x-1)^{-\frac{1}{2}}\left[x + (x-1)\right]$

$\quad = (x-1)^{-\frac{1}{2}}(2x-1)$

$\quad = \dfrac{(2x-1)}{(x-1)^{\frac{1}{2}}}$

Exercise Set P.5

1. $18x + 27 = 9 \cdot 2x + 9 \cdot 3 = 9(2x+3)$

3. $3x^2 + 6x = 3x \cdot x + 3x \cdot 2 = 3x(x+2)$

5. $9x^4 - 18x^3 + 27x^2$

$\quad = 9x^2(x^2) + 9x^2(-2x) + 9x^2(3)$

$\quad = 9x^2(x^2 - 2x + 3)$

7. $x(x+5) + 3(x+5) = (x+5)(x+3)$

9. $x^2(x-3) + 12(x-3) = (x-3)(x^2+12)$

11. $x^3 - 2x^2 + 5x - 10 = x^2(x-2) + 5(x-2)$

$\quad = (x^2+5)(x-2)$

13. $x^3 - x^2 + 2x - 2 = x^2(x-1) + 2(x-1)$

$\quad = (x-1)(x^2+2)$

15. $3x^3 - 2x^2 - 6x + 4 = x^2(3x-2) - 2(3x-2)$

$\quad = (3x-2)(x^2-2)$

17. $x^2 + 5x + 6 = (x+2)(x+3)$

19. $x^2 - 2x - 15 = (x-5)(x+3)$

21. $x^2 - 8x + 15 = (x-5)(x-3)$

23. $3x^2 - x - 2 = (3x+2)(x-1)$

25. $3x^2 - 25x - 28 = (3x-28)(x+1)$

27. $6x^2 - 11x + 4 = (2x-1)(3x-4)$

29. $4x^2 + 16x + 15 = (2x+3)(2x+5)$

31. $9x^2 - 9x + 2 = (3x-1)(3x-2)$

33. $20x^2 + 27x - 8 = (5x+8)(4x-1)$

35. $2x^2 + 3xy + y^2 = (2x+y)(x+y)$

37. $6x^2 - 5xy - 6y^2 = (3x+2y)(2x-3y)$

39. $x^2 - 100 = x^2 - 10^2 = (x+10)(x-10)$

41. $36x^2 - 49 = (6x)^2 - 7^2 = (6x+7)(6x-7)$

43. $9x^2 - 25y^2 = (3x)^2 - (5y)^2$

$\quad = (3x+5y)(3x-5y)$

45. $x^4 - 16 = (x^2)^2 - 4^2$

$\quad = (x^2+4)(x^2-4)$

$\quad = (x^2+4)(x+2)(x-2)$

47. $16x^4 - 81 = (4x^2)^2 - 9^2$

$\quad = (4x^2+9)(4x^2-9)$

$\quad = (4x^2+9)[(2x)^2 - 3^2]$

$\quad = (4x^2+9)(2x+3)(2x-3)$

49. $x^2 + 2x + 1 = x^2 + 2 \cdot x \cdot 1 + 1^2 = (x+1)^2$

51. $x^2 - 14x + 49 = x^2 - 2 \cdot x \cdot 7 + 7^2$

$\quad = (x-7)^2$

53. $4x^2 + 4x + 1 = (2x)^2 + 2 \cdot 2x \cdot 1 + 1^2$

$\quad = (2x+1)^2$

55. $9x^2 - 6x + 1 = (3x)^2 - 2 \cdot 3x \cdot 1 + 1^2$

$\quad = (3x-1)^2$

57. $x^3 + 27 = x^3 + 3^3$

$\quad = (x+3)(x^2 - x \cdot 3 + 3^2)$

$\quad = (x+3)(x^2 - 3x + 9)$

59. $x^3 - 64 = x^3 - 4^3$

$\quad = (x-4)(x^2 + x \cdot 4 + 4^2)$

$\quad = (x-4)(x^2 + 4x + 16)$

61. $8x^3 - 1 = (2x)^3 - 1^3$

$\quad = (2x-1)[(2x)^2 + (2x)(1) + 1^2]$

$\quad = (2x-1)(4x^2 + 2x + 1)$

63. $64x^3 + 27 = (4x)^3 + 3^3$
$$= (4x+3)[(4x)^2 - (4x)(3) + 3^2]$$
$$= (4x+3)(16x^2 - 12x + 9)$$

65. $3x^3 - 3x = 3x(x^2 - 1) = 3x(x+1)(x-1)$

67. $4x^2 - 4x - 24 = 4(x^2 - x - 6)$
$$= 4(x+2)(x-3)$$

69. $2x^4 - 162 = 2(x^4 - 81)$
$$= 2[(x^2)^2 - 9^2]$$
$$= 2(x^2 + 9)(x^2 - 9)$$
$$= 2(x^2 + 9)(x^2 - 3^2)$$
$$= 2(x^2 + 9)(x+3)(x-3)$$

71. $x^3 + 2x^2 - 9x - 18 = (x^3 + 2x^2) - (9x + 18)$
$$= x^2(x+2) - 9(x+2)$$
$$= (x^2 - 9)(x+2)$$
$$= (x^2 - 3^2)(x+2)$$
$$= (x-3)(x+3)(x+2)$$

73. $2x^2 - 2x - 112 = 2(x^2 - x - 56) = 2(x-8)(x+7)$

75. $x^3 - 4x = x(x^2 - 4)$
$$= x(x^2 - 2^2)$$
$$= x(x-2)(x+2)$$

77. $x^2 + 64$ is prime.

79. $x^3 + 2x^2 - 4x - 8 = (x^3 + 2x^2) + (-4x - 8)$
$$= x^2(x+2) - 4(x+2) = (x^2 - 4)(x+2) = (x^2 - 2^2)(x+2) = (x-2)(x+2)(x+2) = (x-2)(x+2)^2$$

81. $y^5 - 81y$
$$= y(y^4 - 81) = y[(y^2)^2 - 9^2] = y(y^2 + 9)(y^2 - 9) = y(y^2 + 9)(y^2 - 3^2) = y(y^2 + 9)(y+3)(y-3)$$

83. $20y^4 - 45y^2 = 5y^2(4y^2 - 9) = 5y^2[(2y)^2 - 3^2] = 5y^2(2y+3)(2y-3)$

85. $x^2 - 12x + 36 - 49y^2$
$$= \left(x^2 - 12x + 36\right) - 49y^2 = (x-6)^2 - 49y^2 = (x-6+7y)(x-6-7y)$$

87. $9b^2 x - 16y - 16x + 9b^2 y$
$$= \left(9b^2 x + 9b^2 y\right) + (-16x - 16y) = 9b^2(x+y) - 16(x+y) = (x+y)\left(9b^2 - 16\right) = (x+y)(3b+4)(3b-4)$$

89. $x^2 y - 16y + 32 - 2x^2$
$$= \left(x^2 y - 16y\right) + \left(-2x^2 + 32\right) = y\left(x^2 - 16\right) - 2\left(x^2 - 16\right) = \left(x^2 - 16\right)(y-2) = (x+4)(x-4)(y-2)$$

91. $2x^3 - 8a^2 x + 24x^2 + 72x$
$$= 2x\left(x^2 - 4a^2 + 12x + 36\right) = 2x\left[\left(x^2 + 12x + 36\right) - 4a^2\right] = 2x\left[(x+6)^2 - 4a^2\right] = 2x(x+6-2a)(x+6+2a)$$

93. $x^{\frac{3}{2}} - x^{\frac{1}{2}} = x^{\frac{1}{2}}\left(x^{\frac{3}{2} - \frac{1}{2}}\right) - 1 = x^{\frac{1}{2}}(x-1)$

95. $4x^{-\frac{2}{3}} + 8x^{\frac{1}{3}} = 4x^{-\frac{2}{3}}\left(1 + 2x^{\frac{1}{3} - \left(-\frac{2}{3}\right)}\right) = 4x^{-\frac{2}{3}}(1 + 2x) = \dfrac{4(1+2x)}{x^{\frac{2}{3}}}$

97. $(x+3)^{\frac{1}{2}} - (x+3)^{\frac{3}{2}} = (x+3)^{\frac{1}{2}}\left[1 - (x+3)^{\frac{3}{2} - \frac{1}{2}}\right] = (x+3)^{\frac{1}{2}}\left[1 - (x+3)\right] = (x+3)^{\frac{1}{2}}(-x-2) = -(x+3)^{\frac{1}{2}}(x+2)$

99. $(x+5)^{-\frac{1}{2}} - (x+5)^{-\frac{3}{2}} = (x+5)^{-\frac{3}{2}} \left[(x+5)^{-\frac{1}{2}-\left(-\frac{3}{2}\right)} - 1 \right] = (x+5)^{-\frac{3}{2}} \left[(x+5) - 1 \right] = (x+5)^{-\frac{3}{2}} (x+4) = \dfrac{x+4}{(x+5)^{\frac{3}{2}}}$

101. $(4x-1)^{\frac{1}{2}} - \dfrac{1}{3}(4x-1)^{\frac{3}{2}}$

$= (4x-1)^{\frac{1}{2}} \left[1 - \dfrac{1}{3}(4x-1)^{\frac{3}{2}-\frac{1}{2}} \right] = (4x-1)^{\frac{1}{2}} \left[1 - \dfrac{1}{3}(4x-1) \right] = (4x-1)^{\frac{1}{2}} \left[1 - \dfrac{4}{3}x + \dfrac{1}{3} \right]$

$= (4x-1)^{\frac{1}{2}} \left(\dfrac{4}{3} - \dfrac{4}{3}x \right) = (4x-1)^{\frac{1}{2}} \dfrac{4}{3}(1-x) = \dfrac{-4(4x-1)(x-1)}{3}$

103. $10x^2(x+1) - 7x(x+1) - 6(x+1) = (x+1)\left(10x^2 - 7x - 6\right) = (x+1)(5x-6)(2x+1)$

105. $6x^4 + 35x^2 - 6 = \left(x^2+6\right)\left(6x^2-1\right)$

107. $y^7 + y = y\left(y^6 + 1\right) = y\left[\left(y^2\right)^3 + 1^3 \right] = y\left(y^2+1\right)\left(y^4 - y^2 + 1\right)$

109. $x^4 - 5x^2y^2 + 4y^4 = \left(x^2 - 4y^2\right)\left(x^2 - y^2\right) = (x+2y)(x-2y)(x+y)(x-y)$

111. $(x-y)^4 - 4(x-y)^2$

$= (x-y)^2 \left((x-y)^2 - 4\right) = (x-y)^2 \left((x-y)+2\right)\left((x-y)-2\right) = (x-y)^2 (x-y+2)(x-y-2)$

113. $2x^2 - 7xy^2 + 3y^4 = \left(2x - y^2\right)\left(x - 3y^2\right)$

115. a. $(x - 0.4x) - 0.4(x - 0.4x) = (x - 0.4x)(1 - 0.4) = (0.6x)(0.6) = 0.36x$

   b. No, the computer is selling at 36% of its original price.

117. a. $(3x)^2 - 4 \cdot 2^2 = 9x^2 - 16$

   b. $9x^2 - 16 = (3x+4)(3x-4)$

119. a. $x(x+y) - y(x+y)$

   b. $x(x+y) - y(x+y) = (x+y)(x-y)$

121. $V_{shaded} = V_{outside} - V_{inside}$

$= a \cdot a \cdot 4a - b \cdot b \cdot 4a$

$= 4a^3 - 4ab^2$

$= 4a\left(a^2 - b^2\right)$

$= 4a(a+b)(a-b)$

131. $x^{2n} + 6x^n + 8 = \left(x^n + 4\right)\left(x^n + 2\right)$

133. $x^4 - y^4 - 2x^3 y + 2xy^3$
$= \left(x^4 - y^4\right) + \left(-2x^3 y + 2xy^3\right)$
$= \left(x^2 - y^2\right)\left(x^2 + y^2\right) - 2xy\left(x^2 - y^2\right)$
$= \left(x^2 - y^2\right)\left(x^2 + y^2 - 2xy\right)$
$= (x - y)(x + y)\left(x^2 - 2xy + y^2\right)$
$= (x - y)(x + y)(x - y)^2$
$= (x - y)^3 (x + y)$

135. $x^2 + bx + 15$, $b = 16,\ -16,\ 8$ or -8

Section P.6

Check Point Exercises

1.　a. The denominator would equal zero if $x = -5$, so -5 must be excluded from the domain.

**　　b.**　$x^2 - 36 = (x + 6)(x - 6)$
The denominator would equal zero if $x = -6$ or $x = 6$, so -6 and 6 must both must be excluded from the domain.

2.　a.
$$\frac{x^3 + 3x^2}{x + 3} = \frac{x^2(x + 3)}{x + 3}$$
$$= \frac{x^2(x + 3)}{x + 3}$$
$$= x^2,\ x \neq -3$$

Because the denominator is $x + 3$,
　　　$x \neq -3$

**　　b.**
$$\frac{x^2 - 1}{x^2 + 2x + 1} = \frac{(x - 1)(x + 1)}{(x + 1)(x + 1)}$$
$$= \frac{x - 1}{x + 1}, x \neq -1$$

Because the denominator is
$(x + 1)(x + 1), x \neq -1$

3.
$$\frac{x + 3}{x^2 - 4} \cdot \frac{x^2 - x - 6}{x^2 + 6x + 9}$$
$$= \frac{x + 3}{(x + 2)(x - 2)} \cdot \frac{(x - 3)(x + 2)}{(x + 3)(x + 3)}$$
$$= \frac{x + 3}{(x + 2)(x - 2)} \cdot \frac{(x - 3)(x + 2)}{(x + 3)(x + 3)}$$
$$= \frac{x - 3}{(x - 2)(x + 3)},\ x \neq -2,\ x \neq 2,\ x \neq -3$$

Because the denominator has factors of
$x + 2$, $x - 2$, and $x + 3$, $x \neq -2$, $x \neq 2$,
and $x \neq -3$.

4. $\dfrac{x^2 - 2x + 1}{x^3 + x} \div \dfrac{x^2 + x - 2}{3x^2 + 3}$

$= \dfrac{x^2 - 2x + 1}{x^3 + x} \cdot \dfrac{3x^2 + 3}{x^2 + x - 2}$

$= \dfrac{(x-1)(x-1)}{x(x^2 + 1)} \cdot \dfrac{3(x^2 + 1)}{(x+2)(x-1)}$

$= \dfrac{3(x-1)}{x(x+2)}, \; x \neq 0, \; x \neq -2, \; x \neq 1$

5. $\dfrac{x}{x+1} - \dfrac{3x+2}{x+1} = \dfrac{x - 3x - 2}{x+1}$

$= \dfrac{-2x - 2}{x+1}$

$= \dfrac{-2(x+1)}{x+1}$

$= -2, \; x \neq -1$

6. $\dfrac{3}{x+1} + \dfrac{5}{x-1}$

$= \dfrac{3x(x-1) + 5(x+1)}{(x+1)(x-1)}$

$= \dfrac{3x - 3 + 5x + 5}{(x+1)(x-1)}$

$= \dfrac{8x + 2}{(x+1)(x-1)}$

$= \dfrac{2(4x+1)}{(x+1)(x-1)}$

$= \dfrac{2(4x+1)}{(x+1)(x-1)}, \; x \neq -1 \text{ and } x \neq 1.$

7. Factor each denominator completely.
$x^2 - 6x + 9 = (x-3)^2$
$x^2 - 9 = (x+3)(x-3)$

List the factors of the first denominator.
$x - 3, \; x - 3$

Add any unlisted factors from the second denominator.
$x - 3, \; x - 3, \; x + 3$

The least common denominator is the product of all factors in the final list.
$(x-3)(x-3)(x+3)$ or $(x-3)^2(x+3)$ is the least common denominator.

8. Find the least common denominator.

$$x^2 - 10x + 25 = (x-5)^2$$
$$2x - 10 = 2(x-5)$$

The least common denominator is $2(x-5)(x-5)$.
Write all rational expressions in terms of the least common denominator.

$$\frac{x}{x^2 - 10x + 25} - \frac{x-4}{2x-10}$$

$$= \frac{x}{(x-5)(x-5)} - \frac{x-4}{2(x-5)}$$

$$= \frac{2x}{2(x-5)(x-5)} - \frac{(x-4)(x-5)}{2(x-5)(x-5)}$$

Add numerators, putting this sum over the least common denominator.

$$= \frac{2x - (x-4)(x-5)}{2(x-5)(x-5)}$$

$$= \frac{2x - (x^2 - 5x - 4x + 20)}{2(x-5)(x-5)}$$

$$= \frac{2x - x^2 + 5x + 4x - 20}{2(x-5)(x-5)}$$

$$= \frac{2x - x^2 + 5x + 4x - 20}{2(x-5)(x-5)}$$

$$= \frac{-x^2 + 11x - 20}{2(x-5)(x-5)}$$

$$= \frac{-x^2 + 11x - 20}{2(x-5)^2}, \ x \neq 5$$

9.
$$\frac{\dfrac{1}{x} - \dfrac{3}{2}}{\dfrac{1}{x} + \dfrac{3}{4}} = \frac{\dfrac{2}{2x} - \dfrac{3x}{2x}}{\dfrac{4}{4x} + \dfrac{3x}{4x}}, \ x \neq 0$$

$$= \frac{\dfrac{2-3x}{2x}}{\dfrac{4+3x}{4x}}, \ x \neq \frac{-4}{3}$$

$$= \frac{2-3x}{2x} \div \frac{4+3x}{4x}$$

$$= \frac{2-3x}{2x} \cdot \frac{4x}{4+3x}$$

$$= \frac{2-3x}{4+3x} \cdot \frac{4}{2}$$

$$= \frac{2-3x}{4+3x} \cdot \frac{2}{1}$$

$$= \frac{2(2-3x)}{4+3x}, \ x \neq 0 \text{ and } x \neq \frac{-4}{3}$$

10. Multiply each of the three terms, $\dfrac{1}{x+7}$, $\dfrac{1}{x}$, and 7 by the least common denominator of $x(x+7)$.

$$\frac{\dfrac{1}{x+7} - \dfrac{1}{x}}{7} = \frac{x(x+7)\left(\dfrac{1}{x+7}\right) - x(x+7)\left(\dfrac{1}{x}\right)}{7x(x+7)}$$

$$= \frac{x - (x+7)}{7x(x+7)}$$

$$= \frac{-7}{7x(x+7)}$$

$$= -\frac{1}{x(x+7)}, \ x \neq 0, \ x \neq -7$$

29

Exercise Set P.6

1. $\dfrac{7}{x-3}$, $x \neq 3$

3. $\dfrac{x+5}{x^2-25} = \dfrac{x+5}{(x+5)(x-5)}$, $x \neq 5, -5$

5. $\dfrac{x-1}{x^2+11x+10} = \dfrac{x-1}{(x+1)(x+10)}$, $x \neq -1, -10$

7. $\dfrac{3x-9}{x^2-6x+9} = \dfrac{3(x-3)}{(x-3)(x-3)}$

$\qquad = \dfrac{3}{x-3}$, $x \neq 3$

9. $\dfrac{x^2-12x+36}{4x-24} = \dfrac{(x-6)(x-6)}{4(x-6)} = \dfrac{x-6}{4}$.

$x \neq 6$

11. $\dfrac{y^2+7y-18}{y^2-3y+2} = \dfrac{(y+9)(y-2)}{(y-2)(y-1)} = \dfrac{y+9}{y-1}$,

$y \neq 1, 2$

13. $\dfrac{x^2+12x+36}{x^2-36} = \dfrac{(x+6)^2}{(x+6)(x-6)} = \dfrac{x+6}{x-6}$,

$x \neq 6, -6$

15. $\dfrac{x-2}{3x+9} \cdot \dfrac{2x+6}{2x-4} = \dfrac{x-2}{3(x+3)} \cdot \dfrac{2(x+3)}{2(x-2)}$

$\qquad\qquad = \dfrac{2}{6} = \dfrac{1}{3}$, $x \neq 2, -3$

17. $\dfrac{x^2-9}{x^2} \cdot \dfrac{x^2-3x}{x^2+x-12}$

$\qquad = \dfrac{(x-3)(x+3)}{x^2} \cdot \dfrac{x(x-3)}{(x+4)(x-3)}$

$\qquad = \dfrac{(x-3)(x+3)}{x(x+4)}$, $x \neq 0, -4, 3$

19. $\dfrac{x^2-5x+6}{x^2-2x-3} \cdot \dfrac{x^2-1}{x^2-4}$

$\qquad = \dfrac{(x-3)(x-2)}{(x-3)(x+1)} \cdot \dfrac{(x+1)(x-1)}{(x-2)(x+2)}$

$\qquad = \dfrac{x-1}{x+2}$, $x \neq -2, -1, 2, 3$

21. $\dfrac{x^3-8}{x^2-4} \cdot \dfrac{x+2}{3x} = \dfrac{(x-2)(x^2+2x+4)}{(x-2)(x+2)} \cdot \dfrac{x+2}{3x}$

$\qquad = \dfrac{x^2+2x+4}{3x}$, $x \neq -2, 0, 2$

23. $\dfrac{x+1}{3} \div \dfrac{3x+3}{7} = \dfrac{x+1}{3} \div \dfrac{3(x+1)}{7}$

$\qquad = \dfrac{x+1}{3} \cdot \dfrac{7}{3(x+1)}$

$\qquad = \dfrac{7}{9}$, $x \neq -1$

25. $\dfrac{x^2-4}{x} \div \dfrac{x+2}{x-2} = \dfrac{(x-2)(x+2)}{x} \cdot \dfrac{x-2}{x+2}$

$\qquad = \dfrac{(x-2)^2}{x}$; $x \neq 0, -2, 2$

27. $\dfrac{4x^2+10}{x-3} \div \dfrac{6x^2+15}{x^2-9}$

$\qquad = \dfrac{2(2x^2+5)}{x-3} \div \dfrac{3(2x^2+5)}{(x-3)(x+3)}$

$\qquad = \dfrac{2(2x^2+5)}{x-3} \cdot \dfrac{(x-3)(x+3)}{3(2x^2+5)}$

$\qquad = \dfrac{2(x+3)}{3}$, $x \neq 3, -3$

29. $\dfrac{x^2-25}{2x-2} \div \dfrac{x^2+10x+25}{x^2+4x-5}$

$\qquad = \dfrac{(x-5)(x+5)}{2(x-1)} \div \dfrac{(x+5)^2}{(x+5)(x-1)}$

$\qquad = \dfrac{(x-5)(x+5)}{2(x-1)} \cdot \dfrac{(x+5)(x-1)}{(x+5)^2}$

$\qquad = \dfrac{x-5}{2}$, $x \neq 1, -5$

31. $\dfrac{x^2+x-12}{x^2+x-30} \cdot \dfrac{x^2+5x+6}{x^2-2x-3} \div \dfrac{x+3}{x^2+7x+6}$

$\qquad = \dfrac{(x+4)(x-3)}{(x+6)(x-5)} \cdot \dfrac{(x+2)(x+3)}{(x+1)(x-3)} \cdot \dfrac{(x+6)(x+1)}{x+3}$

$\qquad = \dfrac{(x+4)(x+2)}{x-5}$

$x \neq -6, -3, -1, 3, 5$

33. $\dfrac{4x+1}{6x+5}+\dfrac{8x+9}{6x+5}=\dfrac{4x+1+8x+9}{6x+5}$

$\qquad\qquad\qquad\quad =\dfrac{12x+10}{6x+5}$

$\qquad\qquad\qquad\quad =\dfrac{2(6x+5)}{6x+5}=2,\ x\neq -\dfrac{5}{6}$

35. $\dfrac{x^2-2x}{x^2+3x}+\dfrac{x^2+x}{x^2+3x}=\dfrac{x^2-2x+x^2+x}{x^2+3x}$

$\qquad\qquad\qquad\quad =\dfrac{2x^2-x}{x^2+3x}$

$\qquad\qquad\qquad\quad =\dfrac{x(2x-1)}{x(x+3)}$

$\qquad\qquad\qquad\quad =\dfrac{2x-1}{x+3},\ x\neq 0,-3$

37. $\dfrac{4x-10}{x-2}-\dfrac{x-4}{x-2}=\dfrac{4x-10-(x-4)}{x-2}$

$\qquad\qquad\qquad\quad =\dfrac{4x-10-x+4}{x-2}$

$\qquad\qquad\qquad\quad =\dfrac{3x-6}{x-2}$

$\qquad\qquad\qquad\quad =\dfrac{3(x-2)}{x-2}$

$\qquad\qquad\qquad\quad =3,\ x\neq 2$

39. $\dfrac{x^2+3x}{x^2+x-12}-\dfrac{x^2-12}{x^2+x-12}$

$\quad =\dfrac{x^2+3x-(x^2-12)}{x^2+x-12}$

$\quad =\dfrac{x^2+3x-x^2+12}{x^2+x-12}$

$\quad =\dfrac{3x+12}{x^2+x-12}$

$\quad =\dfrac{3(x+4)}{(x+4)(x-3)}$

$\quad =\dfrac{3}{x-3},\ x\neq 3,-4$

41. $\dfrac{3}{x+4}+\dfrac{6}{x+5}=\dfrac{3(x+5)+6(x+4)}{(x+4)(x+5)}$

$\quad =\dfrac{3x+15+6x+24}{(x+4)(x+5)}$

$\quad =\dfrac{9x+39}{(x+4)(x+5)},\ x\neq -4,-5$

43. $\dfrac{3}{x+1}-\dfrac{3}{x}=\dfrac{3x-3(x+1)}{x(x+1)}$

$\quad =\dfrac{3x-3x-3}{x(x+1)}=-\dfrac{3}{x(x+1)},\ x\neq -1,0$

45. $\dfrac{2x}{x+2}+\dfrac{x+2}{x-2}=\dfrac{2x(x-2)+(x+2)(x+2)}{(x+2)(x-2)}$

$\quad =\dfrac{2x^2-4x+x^2+4x+4}{(x+2)(x-2)}$

$\quad =\dfrac{3x^2+4}{(x+2)(x-2)},\ x\neq -2,2$

47. $\dfrac{x+5}{x-5}+\dfrac{x-5}{x+5}$

$\quad =\dfrac{(x+5)(x+5)+(x-5)(x-5)}{(x-5)(x+5)}$

$\quad =\dfrac{x^2+10x+25+x^2-10x+25}{(x-5)(x+5)}$

$\quad =\dfrac{2x^2+50}{(x-5)(x+5)},\ x\neq -5,5$

49. $\dfrac{4}{x^2+6x+9}+\dfrac{4}{x+3}=\dfrac{4}{(x+3)^2}+\dfrac{4}{x+3}$

$\quad =\dfrac{4+4(x+3)}{(x+3)^2}=\dfrac{4+4x+12}{(x+3)^2}=\dfrac{4x+16}{(x+3)^2},$

$\quad x\neq -3$

51. $\dfrac{3x}{x^2+3x-10}-\dfrac{2x}{x^2+x-6}$

$\quad =\dfrac{3x}{(x+5)(x-2)}-\dfrac{2x}{(x+3)(x-2)}$

$\quad =\dfrac{3x(x+3)-2x(x+5)}{(x+5)(x-2)(x+3)}$

$\quad =\dfrac{3x^2+9x-2x^2-10x}{(x+5)(x-2)(x+3)}$

$\quad =\dfrac{x^2-x}{(x+5)(x-2)(x+3)},\ x\neq -5,2,-3$

53. $\dfrac{4x^2+x-6}{x^2+3x+2}-\dfrac{3x}{x+1}+\dfrac{5}{x+2}$

$=\dfrac{4x^2+x-6}{(x+1)(x+2)}+\dfrac{-3x}{x+1}+\dfrac{5}{x+2}$

$=\dfrac{4x^2+x-5}{(x+1)(x+2)}+\dfrac{-3x(x+2)}{(x+1)(x+2)}+\dfrac{5(x+1)}{(x+1)(x+2)}$

$=\dfrac{4x^2+x-6-3x^2-6x+5x+5}{(x+1)(x+2)}$

$=\dfrac{x^2-1}{(x+1)(x+2)}$

$=\dfrac{(x-1)(x+1)}{(x+1)(x+2)}$

$=\dfrac{x-1}{x+2}; x\ne -2,-1$

55. $\dfrac{\frac{x}{3}-1}{x-3}=\dfrac{3\left[\frac{x}{3}-1\right]}{3[x-3]}=\dfrac{x-3}{3(x-3)}=\dfrac{1}{3},\ x\ne 3$

57. $\dfrac{1+\frac{1}{x}}{3-\frac{1}{x}}=\dfrac{x\left[1+\frac{1}{x}\right]}{x\left[3-\frac{1}{x}\right]}=\dfrac{x+1}{3x-1}, x\ne 0,\frac{1}{3}$

59. $\dfrac{\frac{1}{x}+\frac{1}{y}}{x+y}=\dfrac{xy\left[\frac{1}{x}+\frac{1}{y}\right]}{xy[x+y]}=\dfrac{y+x}{xy(x+y)}=\dfrac{1}{xy}$,

$x\ne 0, y\ne 0, x\ne -y$

61. $\dfrac{x-\frac{x}{x+3}}{x+2}=\dfrac{(x+3)\left[x-\frac{x}{x+3}\right]}{(x+3)(x+2)}=\dfrac{x(x+3)-x}{(x+3)(x+2)}$

$=\dfrac{x^2+3x-x}{(x+3)(x+2)}=\dfrac{x^2+2x}{(x+3)(x+2)}$

$=\dfrac{x(x+2)}{(x+3)(x+2)}=\dfrac{x}{x+3}, x\ne -2,-3$

63. $\dfrac{\frac{3}{x-2}-\frac{4}{x+2}}{\frac{7}{x^2-4}}=\dfrac{\frac{3}{x-2}-\frac{4}{x+2}}{\frac{7}{(x-2)(x+2)}}$

$=\dfrac{\left[\frac{3}{x-2}-\frac{4}{x+2}\right](x-2)(x+2)}{\left[\frac{7}{(x-2)(x+2)}\right](x-2)(x+2)}$

$=\dfrac{3(x+2)-4(x-2)}{7}$

$=\dfrac{3x+6-4x+8}{7}=\dfrac{-x+14}{7}$

$=-\dfrac{x-14}{7}\ \ x\ne -2,2$

65. $\dfrac{\frac{1}{x+1}}{\frac{1}{x^2-2x-3}+\frac{1}{x-3}}=\dfrac{\frac{1}{x+1}}{\frac{1}{(x+1)(x-3)}+\frac{1}{x-3}}$

$=\dfrac{\frac{(x+1)(x-3)}{x+1}}{\frac{(x+1)(x-3)}{(x+1)(x-3)}+\frac{(x+1)(x-3)}{x-3}}$

$=\dfrac{x-3}{1+x+1}$

$=\dfrac{x-3}{x+2}\ \ x\ne -2,-1,3$

67. $\dfrac{\frac{1}{(x+h)^2}-\frac{1}{x^2}}{h}=\dfrac{\frac{x^2(x+h)^2}{(x+h)^2}-\frac{x^2(x+h)^2}{x^2}}{hx^2(x+h)^2}$

$=\dfrac{x^2-(x+h)^2}{hx^2(x+h)^2}$

$=\dfrac{x^2-(x^2+2hx+h^2)}{hx^2(x+h)^2}$

$=\dfrac{x^2-x^2-2hx-h^2}{hx^2(x+h)^2}$

$=\dfrac{-2hx-h^2}{hx^2(x+h)^2}$

$=\dfrac{-h(2x+h)}{hx^2(x+h)^2}$

$=-\dfrac{(2x+h)}{x^2(x+h)^2}$

69. $\left(\dfrac{2x+3}{x+1}\cdot\dfrac{x^2+4x-5}{2x^2+x-3}\right)-\dfrac{2}{x+2}=\left(\dfrac{\cancel{(2x+3)}}{x+1}\cdot\dfrac{(x+5)\cancel{(x-1)}}{\cancel{(2x+3)}\cancel{(x-1)}}\right)-\dfrac{2}{x+2}=\dfrac{x+5}{x+1}-\dfrac{2}{x+2}$

$=\dfrac{(x+5)(x+2)}{(x+1)(x+2)}-\dfrac{2(x+1)}{(x+1)(x+2)}=\dfrac{(x+5)(x+2)-2(x+1)}{(x+1)(x+2)}=\dfrac{x^2+2x+5x+10-2x-2}{(x+1)(x+2)}=\dfrac{x^2+5x+8}{(x+1)(x+2)}$

71. $\left(2-\dfrac{6}{x+1}\right)\left(1+\dfrac{3}{x-2}\right)=\left(\dfrac{2(x+1)}{(x+1)}-\dfrac{6}{(x+1)}\right)\left(\dfrac{(x-2)}{(x-2)}+\dfrac{3}{(x-2)}\right)$

$=\left(\dfrac{2x+2-6}{x+1}\right)\left(\dfrac{x-2+3}{x-2}\right)=\left(\dfrac{2x-4}{x+1}\right)\left(\dfrac{x+1}{x-2}\right)=\dfrac{2\cancel{(x-2)}\cancel{(x+1)}}{\cancel{(x+1)}\cancel{(x-2)}}=2$

73. $\dfrac{y^{-1}-(y+5)^{-1}}{5}=\dfrac{\dfrac{1}{y}-\dfrac{1}{y+5}}{5}$

$\text{LCD}=y(y+5)$

$\dfrac{\dfrac{1}{y}-\dfrac{1}{y+5}}{5}=\dfrac{y(y+5)\left(\dfrac{1}{y}-\dfrac{1}{y+5}\right)}{y(y+5)(5)}=\dfrac{y+5-y}{5y(y+5)}=\dfrac{5}{5y(y+5)}=\dfrac{1}{y(y+5)}$

75. $\left(\dfrac{1}{a^3-b^3}\cdot\dfrac{ac+ad-bc-bd}{1}\right)-\dfrac{c-d}{a^2+ab+b^2}=\left(\dfrac{1}{(a-b)(a^2+ab+b^2)}\cdot\dfrac{a(c+d)-b(c+d)}{1}\right)-\dfrac{c-d}{a^2+ab+b^2}$

$=\left(\dfrac{1}{\cancel{(a-b)}(a^2+ab+b^2)}\cdot\dfrac{(c+d)\cancel{(a-b)}}{1}\right)-\dfrac{c-d}{a^2+ab+b^2}=\dfrac{c+d}{a^2+ab+b^2}-\dfrac{c-d}{a^2+bd+b^2}$

$=\dfrac{c+d-c+d}{a^2+ab+b^2}=\dfrac{2d}{a^2+ab+b^2}$

77. a. $\dfrac{130x}{100-x}$ is equal to

   1. $\dfrac{130\cdot40}{100-40}=\dfrac{130\cdot40}{60}=86.67,$

      when $x=40$

   2. $\dfrac{130\cdot80}{100-80}=\dfrac{130\cdot80}{20}=520,$

      when $x=80$

   3. $\dfrac{130\cdot90}{100-90}=\dfrac{130\cdot90}{10}=1170,$

      when $x=90$

It costs $86,670,000 to inoculate 40% of the population against this strain of flu, and $520,000,000 to inoculate 80% of the population, and $1,170,000,000 to inoculate 90% of the population.

b. For $x=100$, the function is not defined.

c. As x approaches 100, the value of the function increases rapidly. So it costs an astronomical amount of money to inoculate almost all of the people, and it is impossible to inoculate 100% of the population.

79. a. The crime rate is the number of crimes per person. Thus the rational expression is the number of crimes divided by the total population

$$\frac{-0.3t+14}{3.6t+260}$$

b. $\dfrac{-0.3t+14}{3.6t+260} = \dfrac{-0.3(8)+14}{3.6(8)+260} \approx 0.04$

The crime rate in 2002 was 0.04.
That is 4000 per 100,000 people.

c. The rational expression models the crime rate in 2002 fairly well.

81. $P = 2L + 2W$

$$= 2\left(\frac{x}{x+3}\right) + 2\left(\frac{x}{x-4}\right)$$

$$= \frac{2x}{x+3} + \frac{2x}{x+4}$$

$$= \frac{2x(x+4)}{(x+3)(x+4)} + \frac{2x(x+3)}{(x+3)(x+4)}$$

$$= \frac{2x^2 + 8x + 2x^2 + 6x}{(x+3)(x+4)}$$

$$= \frac{4x^2 + 14x}{(x+3)(x+4)}$$

97. $\dfrac{1}{x^n-1} - \dfrac{1}{x^n+1} - \dfrac{1}{x^{2n}-1}$

$$= \frac{x^n+1}{x^{2n}-1} - \frac{x^n-1}{x^{2n}-1} - \frac{1}{x^{2n}-1}$$

$$= \frac{x^n+1-x^n+1-1}{x^{2n}-1}$$

$$= \frac{1}{x^{2n}-1}$$

99. $(x-y)^{-1} + (x-y)^{-2} = \dfrac{1}{(x-y)} + \dfrac{1}{(x-y)^2} = \dfrac{(x-y)}{(x-y)(x-y)} + \dfrac{1}{(x-y)^2} = \dfrac{x-y+1}{(x-y)^2}$

Chapter P Review Exercises

1. $3 + 6(x-2)^3 = 3 + 6(4-2)^3$

$$= 3 + 6(2)^3$$
$$= 3 + 6(8)$$
$$= 3 + 48$$
$$= 51$$

2. $x^2 - 5(x-y) = 6^2 - 5(6-2)$

$$= 36 - 5(4)$$
$$= 36 - 20$$
$$= 16$$

3. $S = 0.015x^2 + x + 10$

$$S = 0.015(60)^2 + (60) + 10$$
$$= 0.015(3600) + 60 + 10$$
$$= 54 + 60 + 10$$
$$= 124$$

4. $A = \{a,b,c\} \quad B = \{a,c,d,e\}$

$$\{a,b,c\} \cap \{a,c,d,e\} = \{a,c\}$$

5. $A = \{a,b,c\} \quad B = \{a,c,d,e\}$

$$\{a,b,c\} \cup \{a,c,d,e\} = \{a,b,c,d,e\}$$

34

6. $A = \{a,b,c\}$ $C = \{a,d,f,g\}$

      $\{a,b,c\} \cup \{a,d,f,g\} = \{a,b,c,d,f,g\}$

7. $A = \{a,b,c\}$ $C = \{a,d,f,g\}$

      $\{a,d,f,g\} \cap \{a,b,c\} = \{a\}$

8.   **a.** $\sqrt{81}$

      b. $0, \sqrt{81}$

      c. $-17, 0, \sqrt{81}$

      d. $-17, -\dfrac{9}{13}, 0, 0.75, \sqrt{81}$

      e. $\sqrt{2}, \pi$

      f. $-17, -\dfrac{9}{13}, 0, 0.75, \sqrt{2}, \pi, \sqrt{81}$

9. $|-103| = 103$

10. $\left|\sqrt{2}-1\right| = \sqrt{2}-1$

11. $\left|3 - \sqrt{17}\right| = \sqrt{17} - 3$ since $\sqrt{17}$ is greater than 3.

12. $|4-(-17)| = |4+17| = |21| = 21$

13. $3 + 17 = 17 + 3$;

      commutative property of addition.

14. $(6\cdot3)\cdot9 = 6\cdot(3\cdot9)$;

      associative property of multiplication.

15. $\sqrt{3}(\sqrt{5}+\sqrt{3}) = \sqrt{15}+3$;

      distributive property of multiplication over addition.

16. $(6\cdot9)\cdot2 = 2\cdot(6\cdot9)$;

      commutative property of multiplication.

17. $\sqrt{3}(\sqrt{5}+\sqrt{3}) = (\sqrt{5}+\sqrt{3})\sqrt{3}$;

      commutative property of multiplication.

18. $(3\cdot7)+(4\cdot7) = (4\cdot7)+(3\cdot7)$;

      commutative property of addition.

19. $5(2x-3)+7x = 10x-15+7x = 17x-15$

20. $\dfrac{1}{5}(5x)+[(3y)+(-3y)]-(-x) = x+[0]+x = 2x$

21. $3(4y-5)-(7y+2) = 12y-15-7y-2 = 5y-17$

22. $8-2[3-(5x-1)] = 8-2[3-5x+1]$

                      $= 8-2[4-5x]$

                      $= 8-8+10x$

                      $= 10x$

23. $E = 10x+166$

      $E = 10(20)+166 = 366$

      $E = 0.04x^2+9.2x+169$

      $E = 0.04(20)^2+9.2(20)+169 = 369$

      The actual number was 368 so the better formula was $E = 0.04x^2+9.2x+169$.

24. $(-3)^3(-2)^2 = (-27)\cdot(4) = -108$

25. $2^{-4}+4^{-1} = \dfrac{1}{2^4}+\dfrac{1}{4}$

               $= \dfrac{1}{16}+\dfrac{1}{4}$

               $= \dfrac{1}{16}+\dfrac{4}{16}$

               $= \dfrac{5}{16}$

26. $5^{-3}\cdot5 = 5^{-3}5^1 = 5^{-3+1} = 5^{-2} = \dfrac{1}{5^2} = \dfrac{1}{25}$

27. $\dfrac{3^3}{3^6} = 3^{3-6} = 3^{-3} = \dfrac{1}{3^3} = \dfrac{1}{27}$

28. $(-2x^4y^3)^3 = (-2)^3(x^4)^3(y^3)^3$

                   $= (-2)^3 x^{4\cdot3}y^{3\cdot3}$

                   $= -8x^{12}y^9$

29. $(-5x^3y^2)(-2x^{-11}y^{-2})$

      $= (-5)(-2)x^3x^{-11}y^2y^{-2}$

      $= 10\cdot x^{3-11}y^{2-2}$

      $= 10x^{-8}y^0$

      $= \dfrac{10}{x^8}$

30. $(2x^3)^{-4} = (2)^{-4}(x^3)^{-4}$

$\quad = 2^{-4}x^{-12}$

$\quad = \dfrac{1}{2^4 x^{12}}$

$\quad = \dfrac{1}{16x^{12}}$

31. $\dfrac{7x^5 y^6}{28x^{15}y^{-2}} = \left(\dfrac{7}{28}\right)(x^{5-15})(y^{6-(-2)})$

$\quad = \dfrac{1}{4}x^{-10}y^8$

$\quad = \dfrac{y^8}{4x^{10}}$

32. $3.74 \times 10^4 = 37,400$

33. $7.45 \times 10^{-5} = 0.0000745$

34. $3,590,000 = 3.59 \times 10^6$

35. $0.00725 = 7.25 \times 10^{-3}$

36. $(3 \times 10^3)(1.3 \times 10^2) = (3 \times 1.3) \times (10^3 \times 10^2)$

$\quad = 3.9 \times 10^5$

$\quad = 390,000$

37. $\dfrac{6.9 \times 10^3}{3 \times 10^5} = \left(\dfrac{6.9}{3}\right) \times 10^{3-5}$

$\quad = 2.3 \times 10^{-2}$

$\quad = 0.023$

38. $\dfrac{10^9}{10^6} = 10^{9-6} = 10^3$

It would take 10^3 or 1000 years to accumulate $1 billion.

39. $(2.9 \times 10^8) \times 150$

$\quad = (2.9 \times 10^8) \times (1.5 \times 10^2)$

$\quad = (2.9 \times 1.5) \times (10^8 \times 10^2)$

$\quad = 4.35 \times 10^{10}$

The total annual spending on movies is 4.35×10^{10}.

40. $\sqrt{300} = \sqrt{100 \cdot 3} = \sqrt{100} \cdot \sqrt{3} = 10\sqrt{3}$

41. $\sqrt{12x^2} = \sqrt{4x^2 \cdot 3} = \sqrt{4x^2} \cdot \sqrt{3} = 2|x|\sqrt{3}$

42. $\sqrt{10x} \cdot \sqrt{2x} = \sqrt{20x^2}$

$\quad = \sqrt{4x^2} \cdot \sqrt{5}$

$\quad = 2x\sqrt{5}$

43. $\sqrt{r^3} = \sqrt{r^2} \cdot \sqrt{r} = r\sqrt{r}$

44. $\sqrt{\dfrac{121}{4}} = \dfrac{\sqrt{121}}{\sqrt{4}} = \dfrac{11}{2}$

45. $\dfrac{\sqrt{96x^3}}{\sqrt{2x}} = \sqrt{\dfrac{96x^3}{2x}}$

$\quad = \sqrt{48x^2}$

$\quad = \sqrt{16x^2} \cdot \sqrt{3}$

$\quad = 4x\sqrt{3}$

46. $7\sqrt{5} + 13\sqrt{5} = (7+13)\sqrt{5} = 20\sqrt{5}$

47. $2\sqrt{50} + 3\sqrt{8} = 2\sqrt{25 \cdot 2} + 3\sqrt{4 \cdot 2}$

$\quad = 2 \cdot 5\sqrt{2} + 3 \cdot 2\sqrt{2}$

$\quad = 10\sqrt{2} + 6\sqrt{2}$

$\quad = 16\sqrt{2}$

48. $4\sqrt{72} - 2\sqrt{48} = 4\sqrt{36 \cdot 2} - 2\sqrt{16 \cdot 3}$

$\quad = 4 \cdot 6\sqrt{2} - 2 \cdot 4\sqrt{3}$

$\quad = 24\sqrt{2} - 8\sqrt{3}$

49. $\dfrac{30}{\sqrt{5}} = \dfrac{30}{\sqrt{5}} \cdot \dfrac{\sqrt{5}}{\sqrt{5}} = \dfrac{30\sqrt{5}}{5} = 6\sqrt{5}$

50. $\dfrac{\sqrt{2}}{\sqrt{3}} = \dfrac{\sqrt{2}}{\sqrt{3}} \cdot \dfrac{\sqrt{3}}{\sqrt{3}} = \dfrac{\sqrt{6}}{3}$

51. $\dfrac{5}{6+\sqrt{3}} = \dfrac{5}{6+\sqrt{3}} \cdot \dfrac{6-\sqrt{3}}{6-\sqrt{3}}$

$\quad = \dfrac{5(6-\sqrt{3})}{36-3}$

$\quad = \dfrac{5(6-\sqrt{3})}{33}$

52. $\dfrac{14}{\sqrt{7}-\sqrt{5}} = \dfrac{14}{\sqrt{7}-\sqrt{5}} \cdot \dfrac{\sqrt{7}+\sqrt{5}}{\sqrt{7}+\sqrt{5}}$

$= \dfrac{14(\sqrt{7}+\sqrt{5})}{7-5}$

$= \dfrac{14(\sqrt{7}+\sqrt{5})}{2}$

$= 7(\sqrt{7}+\sqrt{5})$

53. $\sqrt[3]{125} = 5$

54. $\sqrt[5]{-32} = -2$

55. $\sqrt[4]{-125}$ is not a real number.

56. $\sqrt[4]{(-5)^4} = \sqrt[4]{625} = \sqrt[4]{5^4} = 5$

57. $\sqrt[3]{81} = \sqrt[3]{27\cdot 3} = \sqrt[3]{27}\cdot\sqrt[3]{3} = 3\sqrt[3]{3}$

58. $\sqrt[3]{y^5} = \sqrt[3]{y^3 y^2} = y\sqrt[3]{y^2}$

59. $\sqrt[4]{8}\cdot\sqrt[4]{10} = \sqrt[4]{80} = \sqrt[4]{16\cdot 5} = \sqrt[4]{16}\cdot\sqrt[4]{5} = 2\sqrt[4]{5}$

61. $4\sqrt[3]{16} + 5\sqrt[3]{2} = 4\sqrt[3]{8\cdot 2} + 5\sqrt[3]{2}$

$= 4\cdot 2\sqrt[3]{2} + 5\sqrt[3]{2}$

$= 8\sqrt[3]{2} + 5\sqrt[3]{2}$

$= 13\sqrt[3]{2}$

61. $\dfrac{\sqrt[4]{32x^5}}{\sqrt[4]{16x}} = \sqrt[4]{\dfrac{32x^5}{16x}} = \sqrt[4]{2x^4} = x\sqrt[4]{2}$

62. $16^{1/2} = \sqrt{16} = 4$

63. $25^{-1/2} = \dfrac{1}{25^{1/2}} = \dfrac{1}{\sqrt{25}} = \dfrac{1}{5}$

64. $125^{1/3} = \sqrt[3]{125} = 5$

65. $27^{-1/3} = \dfrac{1}{27^{1/3}} = \dfrac{1}{\sqrt[3]{27}} = \dfrac{1}{3}$

66. $64^{2/3} = (\sqrt[3]{64})^2 = 4^2 = 16$

67. $27^{-4/3} = \dfrac{1}{27^{4/3}} = \dfrac{1}{(\sqrt[3]{27})^4} = \dfrac{1}{3^4} = \dfrac{1}{81}$

68. $(5x^{2/3})(4x^{1/4}) = 5\cdot 4x^{2/3+1/4} = 20x^{11/12}$

69. $\dfrac{15x^{3/4}}{5x^{1/2}} = \left(\dfrac{15}{5}\right)x^{3/4-1/2} = 3x^{1/4}$

70. $(125\cdot x^6)^{2/3} = (\sqrt[3]{125x^6})^2$

$= (5x^2)^2$

$= 25x^4$

71. $\sqrt[6]{y^3} = (y^3)^{1/6} = y^{3\cdot 1/6} = y^{1/2} = \sqrt{y}$

72. $(-6x^3 + 7x^2 - 9x + 3) + (14x^3 + 3x^2 - 11x - 7) = (-6x^3 + 14x^3) + (7x^2 + 3x^2) + (-9x - 11x) + (3 - 7)$
$$= 8x^3 + 10x^2 - 20x - 4$$
The degree is 3.

73. $(13x^4 - 8x^3 + 2x^2) - (5x^4 - 3x^3 + 2x^2 - 6) = (13x^4 - 8x^3 + 2x^2) + (-5x^4 + 3x^3 - 2x^2 + 6)$
$$= (13x^4 - 5x^4) + (-8x^3 + 3x^3) + (2x^2 - 2x^2) + 6$$
$$= 8x^4 - 5x^3 + 6$$
The degree is 4.

74. $(3x - 2)(4x^2 + 3x - 5) = (3x)(4x^2) + (3x)(3x) + (3x)(-5) + (-2)(4x^2) + (-2)(3x) + (-2)(-5)$
$$= 12x^3 + 9x^2 - 15x - 8x^2 - 6x + 10$$
$$= 12x^3 + x^2 - 21x + 10$$

75. $(3x - 5)(2x + 1) = (3x)(2x) + (3x)(1) + (-5)(2x) + (-5)(1)$
$$= 6x^2 + 3x - 10x - 5$$
$$= 6x^2 - 7x - 5$$

76. $(4x + 5)(4x - 5) = (4x^2) - 5^2 = 16x^2 - 25$

77. $(2x + 5)^2 = (2x)^2 + 2(2x) \cdot 5 + 5^2 = 4x^2 + 20x + 25$

78. $(3x - 4)^2 = (3x)^2 - 2(3x) \cdot 4 + (-4)^2 = 9x^2 - 24x + 16$

79. $(2x + 1)^3 = (2x)^3 + 3(2x)^2(1) + 3(2x)(1)^2 + 1^3 = 8x^3 + 12x^2 + 6x + 1$

80. $(5x - 2)^3 = (5x)^3 - 3(5x)^2(2) + 3(5x)(2)^2 - 2^3 = 125x^3 - 150x^2 + 60x - 8$

81. $(7x^2 - 8xy + y^2) + (-8x^2 - 9xy - 4y^2) = (7x^2 - 8x^2) + (-8xy - 9xy) + (y^2 - 4y^2)$
$$= -x^2 - 17xy - 3y^2$$
The degree is 2.

82. $(13x^3y^2 - 5x^2y - 9x^2) - (-11x^3y^2 - 6x^2y + 3x^2 - 4)$
$= (13x^3y^2 - 5x^2y - 9x^2) + (11x^3y^2 + 6x^2y - 3x^2 + 4)$
$= (13x^3y^2 + 11x^3y^2) + (-5x^2y + 6x^2y) + (-9x^2 - 3x^2) + 4$
$= 24x^3y^2 + x^2y - 12x^2 + 4$
The degree is 5.

83. $(x + 7y)(3x - 5y) = x(3x) + (x)(-5y) + (7y)(3x) + (7y)(-5y)$
$$= 3x^2 - 5xy + 21xy - 35y^2$$
$$= 3x^2 + 16xy - 35y^2$$

84. $(3x - 5y)^2 = (3x)^2 - 2(3x)(5y) + (-5y)^2$
$$= 9x^2 - 30xy + 25y^2$$

85. $(3x^2 + 2y)^2 = (3x^2)^2 + 2(3x^2)(2y) + (2y)^2$
$$= 9x^4 + 12x^2y + 4y^2$$

86. $(7x+4y)(7x-4y)=(7x)^2-(4y)^2$
$$=49x^2-16y^2$$

87. $(a-b)(a^2+ab+b^2)$
$$=a(a^2)+a(ab)+a(b^2)+(-b)(a^2)$$
$$+(-b)(ab)+(-b)(b^2)$$
$$=a^3+a^2b+ab^2-a^2b-ab^2-b^3$$
$$=a^3-b^3$$

88. $15x^3+3x^2=3x^2\cdot5x+3x^2\cdot1$
$$=3x^2(5x+1)$$

89. $x^2-11x+28=(x-4)(x-7)$

90. $15x^2-x-2=(3x+1)(5x-2)$

91. $64-x^2=8^2-x^2=(8-x)(8+x)$

92. x^2+16 is prime.

93. $3x^4-9x^3-30x^2=3x^2(x^2-3x-10)$
$$=3x^2(x-5)(x+2)$$

94. $20x^7-36x^3=4x^3(5x^4-9)$

95. $x^3-3x^2-9x+27=x^2(x-3)-9(x-3)$
$$=(x^2-9)(x-3)$$
$$=(x+3)(x-3)(x-3)$$
$$=(x+3)(x-3)^2$$

96. $16x^2-40x+25=(4x-5)(4x-5)$
$$=(4x-5)^2$$

97. $x^4-16=(x^2)^2-4^2$
$$=(x^2+4)(x^2-4)$$
$$=(x^2+4)(x+2)(x-2)$$

98. $y^3-8=y^3-2^3=(y-2)(y^2+2y+4)$

99. $x^3+64=x^3+4^3=(x+4)(x^2-4x+16)$

100. $3x^4-12x^2=3x^2(x^2-4)$
$$=3x^2(x-2)(x+2)$$

101. $27x^3-125=(3x)^3-5^3$
$$=(3x-5)[(3x)^2+(3x)(5)+5^2]$$
$$=(3x-5)(9x^2+15x+25)$$

102. $x^5-x=x(x^4-1)$
$$=x(x^2-1)(x^2+1)$$
$$=x(x-1)(x+1)(x^2+1)$$

103. $x^3+5x^2-2x-10=x^2(x+5)-2(x+5)$
$$=(x^2-2)(x+5)$$

104. $x^2+18x+81-y^2=\left(x^2+18x+81\right)-y^2$
$$=(x+9)^2-y^2$$
$$=(x+9-y)(x+9+y)$$

105. $16x^{-\frac{3}{4}}+32x^{\frac{1}{4}}=16x^{-\frac{3}{4}}\left(1+2x^{\frac{1}{4}-\left(-\frac{3}{4}\right)}\right)$
$$=16x^{-\frac{3}{4}}(1+2x)$$
$$=\frac{(1+2x)}{16x^{\frac{3}{4}}}$$

106. $\left(x^2-4\right)\left(x^2+3\right)^{\frac{1}{2}}-\left(x^2-4\right)^2\left(x^2+3\right)^{\frac{3}{2}}$
$$=\left(x^2-4\right)\left(x^2+3\right)^{\frac{1}{2}}\left[1-\left(x^2-4\right)\left(x^2+3\right)\right]$$
$$=(x-2)(x+2)\left(x^2+3\right)^{\frac{1}{2}}\left[1-(x-2)(x+2)\left(x^2+3\right)\right]$$
$$=(x-2)(x+2)(x^2+3)^{\frac{1}{2}}(-x^4+x^2+13)$$

107. $12x^{-\frac{1}{2}}+6x^{-\frac{3}{2}}=6x^{-\frac{3}{2}}(2x+1)=\frac{6(2x+1)}{x^{\frac{3}{2}}}$

108. $\dfrac{x^3+2x^2}{x+2}=\dfrac{x^2(x+2)}{x+2}=x^2,\,x\neq-2$

109. $\dfrac{x^2+3x-18}{x^2-36}=\dfrac{(x+6)(x-3)}{(x+6)(x-6)}=\dfrac{x-3}{x-6}$,
$$x\neq-6,6$$

110. $\dfrac{x^2+2x}{x^2+4x+4}=\dfrac{x(x+2)}{(x+2)^2}=\dfrac{x}{x+2}$,
$$x\neq-2$$

111. $\dfrac{x^2+6x+9}{x^2-4}\cdot\dfrac{x+3}{x-2}=\dfrac{(x+3)^2}{(x-2)(x+2)}\cdot\dfrac{x+3}{x-2}$

$\qquad\qquad\qquad = \dfrac{(x+3)^3}{(x-2)^2(x+2)}$,

$\qquad x\neq 2,-2$

112. $\dfrac{6x+2}{x^2-1}\div\dfrac{3x^2+x}{x-1}$

$\qquad = \dfrac{2(3x+1)}{(x-1)(x+1)}\div\dfrac{x(3x+1)}{x-1}$

$\qquad = \dfrac{2(3x+1)}{(x-1)(x+1)}\cdot\dfrac{x-1}{x(3x+1)}$

$\qquad = \dfrac{2}{x(x+1)}$,

$\qquad x\neq 0,1,-1,-\dfrac{1}{3}$

113. $\dfrac{x^2-5x-24}{x^2-x-12}\div\dfrac{x^2-10x+16}{x^2+x-6}$

$\qquad = \dfrac{(x-8)(x+3)}{(x-4)(x+3)}\div\dfrac{(x-2)(x-8)}{(x+3)(x-2)}$

$\qquad = \dfrac{x-8}{x-4}\cdot\dfrac{x+3}{x-8}$

$\qquad = \dfrac{x+3}{x-4}$,

$\qquad x\neq -3,4,2,8$

114. $\dfrac{2x-7}{x^2-9}-\dfrac{x-10}{x^2-9}=\dfrac{2x-7-(x-10)}{x^2-9}$

$\qquad\qquad\qquad = \dfrac{x+3}{(x+3)(x-3)}$

$\qquad\qquad\qquad = \dfrac{1}{x-3}$,

$\qquad\qquad\qquad x\neq 3,-3$

115. $\dfrac{3x}{x+2}+\dfrac{x}{x-2}=\dfrac{3x}{x+2}\cdot\dfrac{x-2}{x-2}+\dfrac{x}{x-2}\cdot\dfrac{x+2}{x+2}$

$\qquad = \dfrac{3x^2-6x+x^2+2x}{(x+2)(x-2)}$

$\qquad = \dfrac{4x^2-4x}{(x+2)(x-2)}$

$\qquad = \dfrac{4x(x-1)}{(x+2)(x-2)}$,

$\qquad x\neq 2,-2$

116. $\dfrac{x}{x^2-9}+\dfrac{x-1}{x^2-5x+6}$

$\qquad = \dfrac{x}{(x-3)(x+3)}+\dfrac{x-1}{(x-2)(x-3)}$

$\qquad = \dfrac{x}{(x-3)(x+3)}\cdot\dfrac{x-2}{x-2}+\dfrac{x-1}{(x-2)(x-3)}\cdot\dfrac{x+3}{x+3}$

$\qquad = \dfrac{x(x-2)+(x-1)(x+3)}{(x-3)(x+3)(x-2)}$

$\qquad = \dfrac{x^2-2x+x^2+2x-3}{(x-3)(x+3)(x-2)}$

$\qquad = \dfrac{2x^2-3}{(x-3)(x+3)(x-2)}$

$\qquad x\neq 3,-3,2$

117. $\dfrac{4x-1}{2x^2+5x-3}-\dfrac{x+3}{6x^2+x-2}$

$\qquad = \dfrac{4x-1}{(2x-1)(x+3)}-\dfrac{x+3}{(2x-1)(3x+2)}$

$\qquad = \dfrac{4x-1}{(2x-1)(x+3)}\cdot\dfrac{3x+2}{3x+2}$

$\qquad\quad -\dfrac{x+3}{(2x-1)(3x+2)}\cdot\dfrac{x+3}{x+3}$

$\qquad = \dfrac{12x^2+8x-3x-2-x^2-6x-9}{(2x-1)(x+3)(3x+2)}$

$\qquad = \dfrac{11x^2-x-11}{(2x-1)(x+3)(3x+2)}$,

$\qquad x\neq \dfrac{1}{2},-3,-\dfrac{2}{3}$

118. $\dfrac{\frac{1}{x}-\frac{1}{2}}{\frac{1}{3}-\frac{x}{6}}=\dfrac{\frac{1}{x}-\frac{1}{2}}{\frac{1}{3}-\frac{x}{6}}\cdot\dfrac{6x}{6x}$

$\qquad = \dfrac{6-3x}{2x-x^2}$

$\qquad = \dfrac{-3(x-2)}{-x(x-2)}$

$\qquad = \dfrac{3}{x}$,

$\qquad x\neq 0,2$

119. $\dfrac{3+\dfrac{12}{x}}{1-\dfrac{16}{x^2}} = \dfrac{3+\dfrac{12}{x}}{1-\dfrac{16}{x^2}} \cdot \dfrac{x^2}{x^2}$

$= \dfrac{3x^2 + 12x}{x^2 - 16}$

$= \dfrac{3x(x+4)}{(x+4)(x-4)}$

$= \dfrac{3x}{x-4}$,

$x \neq 0, 4, -4$

120. $\dfrac{3-\dfrac{1}{x+3}}{3+\dfrac{1}{x+3}} = \dfrac{3-\dfrac{1}{x+3}}{3+\dfrac{1}{x+3}} \cdot \dfrac{x+3}{x+3}$

$= \dfrac{3(x+3)-1}{3(x+3)+1}$

$= \dfrac{3x+9-1}{3x+9+1}$

$= \dfrac{3x+8}{3x+10}$,

$x \neq -3, -\dfrac{10}{3}$

Chapter P Test

1. $5(2x^2 - 6x) - (4x^2 - 3x) = 10x^2 - 30x - 4x^2 + 3x$
$= 6x^2 - 27x$

2. $7 + 2[3(x+1) - 2(3x-1)]$
$= 7 + 2[3x+3-6x+2]$
$= 7 + 2[-3x+5]$
$= 7 - 6x + 10$
$= -6x + 17$

3. $\{1,2,5\} \cap \{5,a\} = \{5\}$

4. $\{1,2,5\} \cup \{5,a\} = \{1,2,5,a\}$

5. $(2x^2 y^3 - xy + y^2) - (-4x^2 y^3 - 5xy - y^2)$
$= 2x^2 y^3 - xy + y^2 + 4x^2 y^3 + 5xy + y^2$
$= 2x^2 y^3 + 4x^2 y^3 - xy + 5xy + y^2 + y^2$
$= 6x^2 y^3 + 4xy + 2y^2$

6. $\dfrac{30x^3 y^4}{6x^9 y^{-4}} = 5x^{3-9} y^{4-(-4)} = 5x^{-6} y^8 = \dfrac{5y^8}{x^6}$

7. $\sqrt{6r} \cdot \sqrt{3r} = \sqrt{18r^2} = \sqrt{9r^2} \cdot \sqrt{2} = 3r\sqrt{2}$

8. $4\sqrt{50} - 3\sqrt{18} = 4\sqrt{25 \cdot 2} - 3\sqrt{9 \cdot 2}$
$= 4 \cdot 5\sqrt{2} - 3 \cdot 3\sqrt{2}$
$= 20\sqrt{2} - 9\sqrt{2}$
$= 11\sqrt{2}$

9. $\dfrac{3}{5+\sqrt{2}} = \dfrac{3}{5+\sqrt{2}} \cdot \dfrac{5-\sqrt{2}}{5-\sqrt{2}}$
$= \dfrac{3(5-\sqrt{2})}{25-2}$
$= \dfrac{3(5-\sqrt{2})}{23}$

10. $\sqrt[3]{16x^4} = \sqrt[3]{8x^3 \cdot 2x}$
$= \sqrt[3]{8x^3} \cdot \sqrt[3]{2x}$
$= 2x\sqrt[3]{2x}$

11. $\dfrac{x^2 + 2x - 3}{x^2 - 3x + 2} = \dfrac{(x+3)(x-1)}{(x-2)(x-1)} = \dfrac{x+3}{x-2}$,
$x \neq 2, 1$

12. $\dfrac{5 \times 10^{-6}}{20 \times 10^{-8}} = \dfrac{5}{20} \cdot \dfrac{10^{-6}}{10^{-8}} = 0.25 \times 10^2 = 2.5 \times 10^1$

13. $(2x-5)(x^2 - 4x + 3)$
$= 2x^3 - 8x^2 + 6x - 5x^2 + 20x - 15$
$= 2x^3 - 13x^2 + 26x - 15$

14. $(5x + 3y)^2 = (5x)^2 + 2(5x)(3y) + (3y)^2$
$= 25x^2 + 30xy + 9y^2$

15. $\dfrac{2x+8}{x-3} \div \dfrac{x^2 + 5x + 4}{x^2 - 9}$
$= \dfrac{2(x+4)}{x-3} \div \dfrac{(x+1)(x+4)}{(x-3)(x+3)}$
$= \dfrac{2(x+4)}{x-3} \cdot \dfrac{(x-3)(x+3)}{(x+1)(x+4)}$
$= \dfrac{2(x+3)}{x+1}$,
$x \neq 3, -1, -4, -3$

16. $\dfrac{x}{x+3}+\dfrac{5}{x-3}$

$=\dfrac{x}{x+3}\cdot\dfrac{x-3}{x-3}+\dfrac{5}{x-3}\cdot\dfrac{x+3}{x+3}$

$=\dfrac{x(x-3)+5(x+3)}{(x+3)(x-3)}$

$=\dfrac{x^2-3x+5x+15}{(x+3)(x-3)}$

$=\dfrac{x^2+2x+15}{(x+3)(x-3)}, x\neq 3,-3$

17. $\dfrac{2x+3}{x^2-7x+12}-\dfrac{2}{x-3}$

$=\dfrac{2x+3}{(x-3)(x-4)}-\dfrac{2}{x-3}$

$=\dfrac{2x+3}{(x-3)(x-4)}-\dfrac{2}{x-3}\cdot\dfrac{x-4}{x-4}$

$=\dfrac{2x+3-2(x-4)}{(x-3)(x-4)}$

$=\dfrac{2x+3-2(x-4)}{(x-3)(x-4)}$

$=\dfrac{2x+3-2x+8}{(x-3)(x-4)}$

$=\dfrac{11}{(x-3)(x-4)},$

$x\neq 3,4$

18. $\dfrac{\frac{1}{x}-\frac{1}{3}}{\frac{1}{x}}=\dfrac{\frac{1}{x}-\frac{1}{3}}{\frac{1}{x}}\cdot\dfrac{3x}{3x}=\dfrac{3-x}{3},$

$x\neq 0$

19. $x^2-9x+18=(x-3)(x-6)$

20. $x^3+2x^2+3x+6=x^2(x+2)+3(x+2)$
$\qquad\qquad\qquad\qquad =(x^2+3)(x+2)$

21. $25x^2-9=(5x)^2-3^2=(5x-3)(5x+3)$

22. $36x^2-84x+49=(6x)^2-2(6x)\cdot 7+7^2$
$\qquad\qquad\qquad\quad =(6x-7)^2$

23. $y^3-125=y^3-5^3=(y-5)(y^2+5y+25)$

24. $(x^2+10x+25)-9y^2$
$\quad =(x+5)^2-9y^2$
$\quad =(x+5-3y)(x+5+3y)$

25. $x(x+3)^{-\frac{3}{5}}+(x+3)^{\frac{2}{5}}$

$=(x+3)^{-\frac{3}{5}}\left[x+(x+3)\right]$

$=(x+3)^{-\frac{3}{5}}(2x+3)=\dfrac{2x+3}{(x+3)^{\frac{3}{5}}}$

26. $-7,-\dfrac{4}{5},0,0.25,\sqrt{4},\dfrac{22}{7}$ are rational numbers.

27. $3(2+5)=3(5+2);$
commutative property of addition

28. $6(7+4)=6\cdot 7+6\cdot 4$
distributive property of multiplication over addition

29. $0.00076=7.6\times 10^{-4}$

30. $27^{-\frac{5}{3}}=\dfrac{1}{27^{\frac{5}{3}}}=\dfrac{1}{\left(\sqrt[3]{27}\right)^5}=\dfrac{1}{(3)^5}=\dfrac{1}{243}$

31. $2\left(6.3\times 10^9\right)=12.6\times 10^9=1.26\times 10^{10}$

32. a. Model 2 describes data for men and Model 1 describes data for women.

b. $E=0.18t+65$
$E=0.18(50)+65$
$\quad =74$
The model predicts that the life expectancy for men in 2000 was 74 years. This fits the data in the graph fairly well.

Chapter 1

Section 1.1

Check Point Exercises

1.

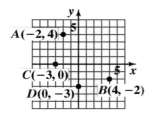

2.

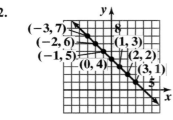

$$y = 4 - x$$

$x = -3, y = 7$

$x = -2, y = 6$

$x = -1, y = 5$

$x = 0, y = 4$

$x = 1, y = 3$

$x = 2, y = 2$

$x = 3, y = 1$

3.

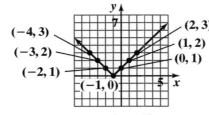

$$y = |x + 1|$$

$x = -4, y = 3$

$x = -3, y = 2$

$x = -2, y = 1$

$x = -1, y = 0$

$x = 0, y = 1$

$x = 1, y = 2$

$x = 2, y = 3$

4. The meaning of a
$[-100, 100, 50]$ by $[-100, 100, 10]$
viewing rectangle is as follows:

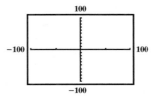

$$\begin{matrix} \text{minimum} & \text{maximum} & \text{distance between } x\text{-axis tick marks} \\ x\text{-value} & x\text{-value} & \\ [\overbrace{-100} & , \overbrace{100} & , \overbrace{50}\ ] \end{matrix}$$

by

$$\begin{matrix} \text{minimum} & \text{maximum} & \text{distance between } y\text{-axis tick marks} \\ y\text{-value} & y\text{-value} & \\ [\overbrace{-100} & , \overbrace{100} & , \overbrace{10}\ ] \end{matrix}$$

5. a. The graph crosses the x-axis at $(-3, 0)$.
Thus, the x-intercept is -3.
The graph crosses the y-axis at $(0, 5)$.
Thus, the y-intercept is 5.

   b. The graph does not cross the x-axis.
Thus, there is no x-intercept.
The graph crosses the y-axis at $(0, 4)$.
Thus, the y-intercept is 4.

   c. The graph crosses the x- and y-axes at
the origin $(0, 0)$.
Thus, the x-intercept is 0 and the
y-intercept is 0.

6. The number of federal prisoners sentenced for
drug offenses in 2003 is about 57% of 159,275.
This can be estimated by finding 60% of
160,000.

$N \approx 60\%$ of $160,000$

$= 0.60 \times 160,000$

$= 96,000$

Exercise Set 1.1

1.

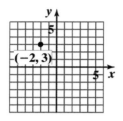

3.

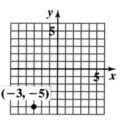

5.

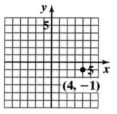

7.

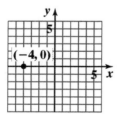

9.

11.

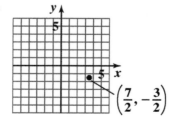

13.

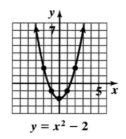

$$y = x^2 - 2$$

$x = -3, y = 7$

$x = -2, y = 2$

$x = -1, y = -1$

$x = 0, y = -2$

$x = 1, y = -1$

$x = 2, y = 2$

$x = 3, y = 7$

15.

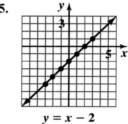

$$y = x - 2$$

$x = -3, y = -5$

$x = -2, y = -4$

$x = -1, y = -3$

$x = 0, y = -2$

$x = 1, y = -1$

$x = 2, y = 0$

$x = 3, y = 1$

44

17.

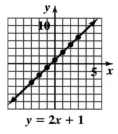

$y = 2x + 1$

$x = -3, y = -5$
$x = -2, y = -3$
$x = -1, y = -1$
$x = 0, y = 1$
$x = 1, y = 3$
$x = 2, y = 5$
$x = 3, y = 7$

21.

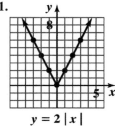

$y = 2\,|x|$

$x = -3, y = 6$
$x = -2, y = 4$
$x = -1, y = 2$
$x = 0, y = 0$
$x = 1, y = 2$
$x = 2, y = 4$
$x = 3, y = 6$

19.

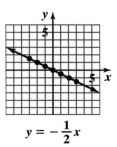

$y = -\dfrac{1}{2}x$

$x = -3, y = \dfrac{3}{2}$
$x = -2, y = 1$
$x = -1, y = \dfrac{1}{2}$
$x = 0, y = 0$
$x = 1, y = -\dfrac{1}{2}$
$x = 2, y = -1$
$x = 3, y = -\dfrac{3}{2}$

23.

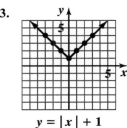

$y = |x| + 1$

$x = -3, y = 4$
$x = -2, y = 3$
$x = -1, y = 2$
$x = 0, y = 1$
$x = 1, y = 2$
$x = 2, y = 3$
$x = 3, y = 4$

25.

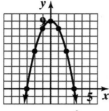

$$y = 9 - x^2$$

$x = -3, y = 0$
$x = -2, y = 5$
$x = -1, y = 8$
$x = 0, y = 9$
$x = 1, y = 8$
$x = 2, y = 5$
$x = 3, y = 0$

27.

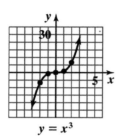

$$y = x^3$$

$x = -3, y = -27$
$x = -2, y = -8$
$x = -1, y = 1$
$x = 0, y = 0$
$x = 1, y = 1$
$x = 2, y = 8$
$x = 3, y = 27$

29. (c) *x*-axis tick marks $-5, -4, -3, -2, -1, 0, 1, 2,$
3, 4, 5; *y*-axis tick marks are the same.

31. (b); *x*-axis tick marks $-20, -10, 0, 10, 20, 30, 40,$
50, 60, 70, 80; *y*-axis tick marks $-30, -20, -10,$
0, 10, 20, 30, 40, 50, 60, 70

33. The equation that corresponds to Y_2 in the table
is (c), $y_2 = 2 - x$. We can tell because all of
the points $(-3, 5)$, $(-2, 4)$, $(-1, 3)$, $(0, 2)$, $(1, 1)$,
$(2, 0)$, and $(3, -1)$ are on the line $y = 2 - x$, but
all are not on any of the others.

35. No. It passes through the point $(0, 2)$.

37. $(2, 0)$

39. The graphs of Y_1 and Y_2 intersect at the points
$(-2, 4)$ and $(1, 1)$.

41. **a.** 2; The graph intersects the *x*-axis at (2, 0).

b. -4; The graph intersects the *y*-axis at $(0, -4)$.

43. **a.** 1, -2; The graph intersects the *x*-axis at (1, 0)
and $(-2, 0)$.

b. 2; The graph intersects the *y*-axis at (0, 2).

45. **a.** -1; The graph intersects the *x*-axis at $(-1, 0)$.

b. none; The graph does not intersect the *y*-axis.

47.

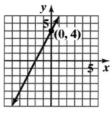

$$y = 2x + 4$$

49.

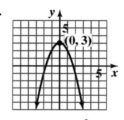

$$y = 3 - x^2$$

51.

x	(x, y)
-3	$(-3, 5)$
-2	$(-2, 5)$
-1	$(-1, 5)$
0	$(0, 5)$
1	$(1, 5)$
2	$(2, 5)$
3	$(3, 5)$

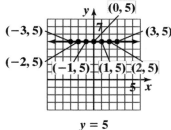

$$y = 5$$

53.

x	(x, y)
-2	$\left(-2, -\dfrac{1}{2}\right)$
-1	$(-1, -1)$
$-\dfrac{1}{2}$	$\left(-\dfrac{1}{2}, -2\right)$
$-\dfrac{1}{3}$	$\left(-\dfrac{1}{3}, -3\right)$
$\dfrac{1}{3}$	$\left(\dfrac{1}{3}, 3\right)$
$\dfrac{1}{2}$	$\left(\dfrac{1}{2}, 2\right)$
1	$(1, 1)$
2	$\left(2, \dfrac{1}{2}\right)$

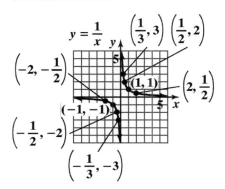

55. There were approximately 65 democracies in 1989.

57. The number of democracies increased at the greatest rate between 1989 and 1993.

59. There were 49 democracies in 1977.

61. $R = 165 - 0.75A; \quad A = 40$

$R - 165 - 0.75A = 165 - 0.75(40)$

$\qquad = 165 - 30 = 135$

The desirable heart rate during exercise for a 40-year old man is 135 beats per minute. This corresponds to the point (40, 135) on the blue graph.

63. a. At birth we have $x = 0$.

$y = 2.9\sqrt{x} + 36$

$\quad = 2.9\sqrt{0} + 36$

$\quad = 2.9(0) + 36$

$\quad = 36$

According to the model, the head circumference at birth is 36 cm.

b. At 9 months we have $x = 9$.

$y = 2.9\sqrt{x} + 36$

$\quad = 2.9\sqrt{9} + 36$

$\quad = 2.9(3) + 36$

$\quad = 44.7$

According to the model, the head circumference at 9 months is 44.7 cm.

c. At 14 months we have $x = 14$.

$y = 2.9\sqrt{x} + 36$

$\quad = 2.9\sqrt{14} + 36$

$\quad \approx 46.9$

According to the model, the head circumference at 14 months is roughly 46.9 cm.

d. The model describes healthy children.

47

71. $y = 45.48x^2 - 334.35x + 1237.9$

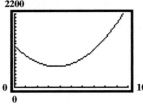

The discharges decreased from 1990 to 1994, but started to increase after 1994. The policy was not a success.

73. (a)

75. (b)

77. (b)

Section 1.2

Check Point Exercises

1.
$$4x + 5 = 29$$
$$4x + 5 - 5 = 29 - 5$$
$$4x = 24$$
$$\frac{4x}{4} = \frac{24}{4}$$
$$x = 6$$
Check:
$$4x + 5 = 29$$
$$4(6) + 5 = 29$$
$$24 + 5 = 29$$
$$29 = 29 \text{ true}$$
The solution set is $\{6\}$.

2.
$$4(2x + 1) - 29 = 3(2x - 5)$$
$$8x + 4 - 29 = 6x - 15$$
$$8x - 25 = 6x - 15$$
$$8x - 25 - 6x = 6x - 15 - 6x$$
$$2x - 25 = -15$$
$$2x - 25 + 25 = -15 + 25$$
$$2x = 10$$
$$\frac{2x}{2} = \frac{10}{2}$$
$$x = 5$$

Check:
$$4(2x + 1) - 29 = 3(2x - 5)$$
$$4[2(5) + 1] - 29 = 3[2(5) - 5]$$
$$4[10 + 1] - 29 = 3[10 - 5]$$
$$4[11] - 29 = 3[5]$$
$$44 - 29 = 15$$
$$15 = 15 \text{ true}$$
The solution set is $\{5\}$.

3.
$$\frac{x-3}{4} = \frac{5}{14} - \frac{x+5}{7}$$
$$28 \cdot \frac{x-3}{4} = 28\left(\frac{5}{14} - \frac{x+5}{7}\right)$$
$$7(x - 3) = 2(5) - 4(x + 5)$$
$$7x - 21 = 10 - 4x - 20$$
$$7x - 21 = -4x - 10$$
$$7x + 4x = -10 + 21$$
$$11x = 11$$
$$\frac{11x}{11} = \frac{11}{11}$$
$$x = 1$$
Check:
$$\frac{x-3}{4} = \frac{5}{14} - \frac{x+5}{7}$$
$$\frac{1-3}{4} = \frac{5}{14} - \frac{1+5}{7}$$
$$\frac{-2}{4} = \frac{5}{14} - \frac{6}{7}$$
$$-\frac{1}{2} = -\frac{1}{2}$$
The solution set is $\{1\}$.

4.
$$\frac{5}{2x} = \frac{17}{18} - \frac{1}{3x}, \ x \neq 0$$
$$18x \cdot \frac{5}{2x} = 18x\left(\frac{17}{18} - \frac{1}{3x}\right)$$
$$18 \cdot \frac{5}{2x} = 18x \cdot \frac{17}{18} - 18x \cdot \frac{1}{3x}$$
$$45 = 17x - 6$$
$$45 + 6 = 17x - 6 + 6$$
$$51 = 17x$$
$$\frac{51}{17} = \frac{17x}{17}$$
$$3 = x$$
The solution set is $\{3\}$.

48

5.
$$\frac{x}{x-2}=\frac{2}{x-2}-\frac{2}{3}, \quad x \neq 2$$

$$3(x-2)\cdot\frac{x}{x-2}=3(x-2)\left[\frac{2}{x-2}-\frac{2}{3}\right]$$

$$3(x-2)\cdot\frac{x}{x-2}=(3x-2)\cdot\frac{2}{x-2}-3(x-2)\cdot\frac{2}{3}$$

$$3x=6-(x-2)\cdot 2$$

$$3x=6-2(x-2)$$

$$3x=6-2x+4$$

$$3x=10-2x$$

$$3x+2x=10-2x+2x$$

$$5x=10$$

$$\frac{5x}{5}=\frac{10}{5}$$

$$x=2$$

The solution set is the empty set, $\varnothing$.

6. Set $y_1 = y_2$.

$$\frac{1}{x+4}+\frac{1}{x-4}=\frac{22}{x^2-16}$$

$$\frac{1}{x+4}+\frac{1}{x-4}=\frac{22}{(x+4)(x-4)}$$

$$\frac{(x+4)(x-4)}{x+4}+\frac{(x+4)(x-4)}{x-4}=\frac{22(x+4)(x-4)}{(x+4)(x-4)}$$

$$(x-4)+(x+4)=22$$

$$x-4+x+4=22$$

$$2x=22$$

$$x=11$$

Check:

$$\frac{1}{x+4}+\frac{1}{x-4}=\frac{22}{x^2-16}$$

$$\frac{1}{11+4}+\frac{1}{11-4}=\frac{22}{11^2-16}$$

$$\frac{1}{15}+\frac{1}{7}=\frac{22}{105}$$

$$\frac{22}{105}=\frac{22}{105} \quad \text{true}$$

7.
$$4x-7=4(x-1)+3$$
$$4x-7=4(x-1)+3$$
$$4x-7=4x-4+3$$
$$4x-7=4x-1$$
$$-7=-1$$

The original equation is equivalent to the statement $-7=-1$, which is false for every value of x. The solution set is the empty set, $\varnothing$. The equation is an inconsistent equation.

Exercise Set 1.2

1.
$$7x-5=72$$
$$7x=77$$
$$x=11$$
Check:
$$7x-5=72$$
$$7(11)-5=72$$
$$77-5=72$$
$$72=72$$
The solution set is $\{11\}$.

3.
$$11x-(6x-5)=40$$
$$11x-6x+5=40$$
$$5x+5=40$$
$$5x=35$$
$$x=7$$
The solution set is $\{7\}$.

Check:
$$11x-(6x-5)=40$$
$$11(7)-[6(7)-5]=40$$
$$77-(42-5)=40$$
$$77-(37)=40$$
$$40=40$$

5.
$$2x-7=6+x$$
$$x-7=6$$
$$x=13$$
The solution set is $\{13\}$.

Check:
$$2(13)-7=6+13$$
$$26-7=19$$
$$19=19$$

7.
$$7x+4=x+16$$
$$6x+4=16$$
$$6x=12$$
$$x=2$$
The solution set is $\{2\}$.

Check:
$$7(2)+4=2+16$$
$$14+4=18$$
$$18=18$$

9. $3(x-2) + 7 = 2(x+5)$
    $3x - 6 + 7 = 2x + 10$
    $3x + 1 = 2x + 10$

    $x + 1 = 10$
    $x = 9$
    The solution set is $\{9\}$.

    Check:
    $3(9-2)+7 = 2(9+5)$
    $3(7)+7 = 2(14)$
    $21+7 = 28$
    $28 = 28$

11. $3(x-4) - 4(x-3) = x + 3 - (x-2)$
    $3x - 12 - 4x + 12 = x + 3 - x + 2$
    $-x = 5$
    $x = -5$
    The solution set is $\{-5\}$.

    Check:
    $3(-5-4) - 4(-5-3) = -5+3-(-5-2)$
    $3(-9) - 4(-8) = -2 - (-7)$
    $-27 + 32 = -2 + 7$
    $5 = 5$

13. $16 = 3(x-1) - (x-7)$
    $16 = 3x - 3 - x + 7$
    $16 = 2x + 4$
    $12 = 2x$
    $6 = x$
    The solution set is $\{6\}$.

    Check:
    $16 = 3(6-1)-(6-7)$
    $16 = 3(5)-(-1)$
    $16 = 15+1$
    $16 = 16$

15. $25 - [2 + 5y - 3(y+2)] = -3(2y-5) - [5(y-1) - 3y + 3]$
    $25 - [2 + 5y - 3y - 6] = -6y + 15 - [5y - 5 - 3y + 3]$
    $25 - [2y - 4] = -6y + 15 - [2y - 2]$
    $25 - 2y + 4 = -6y + 15 - 2y + 2$
    $-2y + 29 = -8y + 17$
    $6y = -12$
    $y = -2$
    The solution set is $\{-2\}$.

    Check:
    $25 - [2 + 5y - 3(y+2) = -3(2y-5) - [5(y-1) - 3y + 3]$
    $25 - [2 + 5(-2) - 3(-2+2) = -3[2(-2) - 5] - [5(-2-1) - 3(-2) + 3]$
    $25 - [2 - 10 - 3(0)] = -3[-4 - 5] - [5(-3) + 6 + 3]$
    $25 - [-8] = -3(-9) - [-15 + 9]$
    $25 + 8 = 27 - (-6)$
    $33 = 27 + 6$
    $33 = 33$

17. $\dfrac{x}{3} = \dfrac{x}{2} - 2$

$6\left[\dfrac{x}{3} = \dfrac{x}{2} - 2\right]$

$2x = 3x - 12$

$12 = 3x - 2x$

$x = 12$

The solution set is $\{12\}$.

19. $20 - \dfrac{x}{3} = \dfrac{x}{2}$

$6\left[20 - \dfrac{x}{3} = \dfrac{x}{2}\right]$

$120 - 2x = 3x$

$120 = 3x + 2x$

$120 = 5x$

$x = \dfrac{120}{5}$

$x = 24$

The solution set is $\{24\}$.

21. $\dfrac{3x}{5} = \dfrac{2x}{3} + 1$

$15\left[\dfrac{3x}{5} = \dfrac{2x}{3} + 1\right]$

$9x = 10x + 15$

$9x - 10x = 15$

$-x = 15$

$x = -15$

The solution set is $\{-15\}$.

23. $\dfrac{3x}{5} - x = \dfrac{x}{10} - \dfrac{5}{2}$

$10\left[\dfrac{3x}{5} - x = \dfrac{x}{10} - \dfrac{5}{2}\right]$

$6x - 10x = x - 25$

$-4x - x = -25$

$-5x = -25$

$x = 5$

The solution set is $\{5\}$.

25. $\dfrac{x+3}{6} = \dfrac{3}{8} + \dfrac{x-5}{4}$

$24\left[\dfrac{x+3}{6} = \dfrac{3}{8} + \dfrac{x-5}{4}\right]$

$4x + 12 = 9 + 6x - 30$

$4x - 6x = -21 - 12$

$-2x = -33$

$x = \dfrac{33}{2}$

The solution set is $\left\{\dfrac{33}{2}\right\}$.

27. $\dfrac{x}{4} = 2 + \dfrac{x-3}{3}$

$12\left[\dfrac{x}{4} = 2 + \dfrac{x-3}{3}\right]$

$3x = 24 + 4x - 12$

$3x - 4x = 12$

$-x = 12$

$x = -12$

The solution set is $\{-12\}$.

29. $\dfrac{x+1}{3} = 5 - \dfrac{x+2}{7}$

$21\left[\dfrac{x+1}{3} = 5 - \dfrac{x+2}{7}\right]$

$7x + 7 = 105 - 3x - 6$

$7x + 3x = 99 - 7$

$10x = 92$

$x = \dfrac{92}{10}$

$x = \dfrac{46}{5}$

The solution set is $\left\{\dfrac{46}{5}\right\}$.

31. a. $\dfrac{4}{x} = \dfrac{5}{2x} + 3 \ (x \neq 0)$

b. $\dfrac{4}{x} = \dfrac{5}{2x} + 3$

$8 = 5 + 6x$

$3 = 6x$

$\dfrac{1}{2} = x$

The solution set is $\left\{\dfrac{1}{2}\right\}$.

33. a. $\dfrac{2}{x}+3=\dfrac{5}{2x}+\dfrac{13}{4}\ (x\neq 0)$

b. $\dfrac{2}{x}+3=\dfrac{5}{2x}+\dfrac{13}{4}$
$8+12x=10+13x$
$-x=2$
$x=-2$
The solution set is $\{-2\}$.

35. a. $\dfrac{2}{3x}+\dfrac{1}{4}=\dfrac{11}{6x}-\dfrac{1}{3}\ (x\neq 0)$

b. $\dfrac{2}{3x}+\dfrac{1}{4}=\dfrac{11}{6x}-\dfrac{1}{3}$
$8+3x=22-4x$
$7x=14$
$x=2$
The solution set is $\{2\}$.

37. a. $\dfrac{x-2}{2x}+1=\dfrac{x+1}{x}\quad (x\neq 0)$

b. $\dfrac{x-2}{2x}+1=\dfrac{x+1}{x}$
$x-2+2x=2x+2$
$x-2=2$
$x=4$
The solution set is $\{4\}$.

39. a. $\dfrac{1}{x-1}+5=\dfrac{11}{x-1}\ (x\neq 1)$

b. $\dfrac{1}{x-1}+5=\dfrac{11}{x-1}$
$1+5(x-1)=11$
$1+5x-5=11$
$5x-4=11$
$5x=15$
$x=3$
The solution set is $\{3\}$.

41. a. $\dfrac{8x}{x+1}=4-\dfrac{8}{x+1}\ (x\neq -1)$

b. $\dfrac{8x}{x+1}=4-\dfrac{8}{x+1}$
$8x=4(x+1)-8$
$8x=4x+4-8$
$4x=-4$
$x=-1\Rightarrow$ no solution
The solution set is the empty set, $\varnothing$.

43. a. $\dfrac{3}{2x-2}+\dfrac{1}{2}=\dfrac{2}{x-1}\ (x\neq 1)$

b. $\dfrac{3}{2x-2}+\dfrac{1}{2}=\dfrac{2}{x-1}$
$\dfrac{3}{2(x-1)}+\dfrac{1}{2}=\dfrac{2}{x-1}$
$3+1(x-1)=4$
$3+x-1=4$
$x=2$
The solution set is $\{2\}$.

45. a. $\dfrac{3}{x+2}+\dfrac{2}{x-2}=\dfrac{8}{(x+2)(x-2)};(x\neq -2,2)$

b. $\dfrac{3}{x+2}+\dfrac{2}{x-2}=\dfrac{8}{(x+2)(x-2)}$
$(x\neq 2, x\neq -2)$
$3(x-2)+2(x+2)=8$
$3x-6+2x+4=8$
$5x=10$
$x=2\Rightarrow$ no solution
The solution set is the empty set, $\varnothing$.

47. a. $\dfrac{2}{x+1}-\dfrac{1}{x-1}=\dfrac{2x}{x^2-1}\ (x\neq 1, x\neq -1)$

b. $\dfrac{2}{x+1}-\dfrac{1}{x-1}=\dfrac{2x}{x^2-1}$
$\dfrac{2}{x+1}-\dfrac{1}{x-1}=\dfrac{2x}{(x+1)(x-1)}$
$2(x-1)-1(x+1)=2x$
$2x-2-x-1=2x$
$-x=3$
$x=-3$
The solution set is $\{-3\}$.

49. a. $\dfrac{1}{x-4}-\dfrac{5}{x+2}=\dfrac{6}{(x-4)(x+2)};(x\neq-2,4)$

b.
$$\dfrac{1}{x-4}-\dfrac{5}{x+2}=\dfrac{6}{x^2-2x-8}$$
$$\dfrac{1}{x-4}-\dfrac{5}{x+2}=\dfrac{6}{(x-4)(x+2)}$$
$$(x\neq4,x\neq-2)$$
$$1(x+2)-5(x-4)=6$$
$$x+2-5x+20=6$$
$$-4x=-16$$
$$x=4\Rightarrow\text{ no solution}$$
The solution set is the empty set, $\varnothing$.

51. Set $y_1=y_2$.
$$5(2x-8)-2=5(x-3)+3$$
$$10x-40-2=5x-15+3$$
$$10x-42=5x-12$$
$$10x-5x=-12+42$$
$$5x=30$$
$$x=6$$
The solution set is $\{6\}$.

53. Set $y_1-y_2=1$.
$$\dfrac{x-3}{5}-\dfrac{x-5}{4}=1$$
$$20\cdot\dfrac{x-3}{5}-20\cdot\dfrac{x-5}{4}=20\cdot1$$
$$4(x-3)-5(x-5)=20$$
$$4x-12-5x+25=20$$
$$-x+13=20$$
$$-x=7$$
$$x=-7$$
The solution set is $\{-7\}$.

55. Set $y_1+y_2=y_3$.
$$\dfrac{5}{x+4}+\dfrac{3}{x+3}=\dfrac{12x+19}{x^2+7x+12}$$
$$\dfrac{5}{x+4}+\dfrac{3}{x+3}=\dfrac{12x+19}{(x+4)(x+3)}$$
$$(x+4)(x+3)\left(\dfrac{5}{x+4}+\dfrac{3}{x+3}\right)=(x+4)(x+3)\dfrac{12x+19}{(x+4)(x+3)}$$
$$5(x+3)+3(x+4)=12x+19$$
$$5x+15+3x+12=12x+19$$
$$8x+27=12x+19$$
$$-4x=-8$$
$$x=2$$
The solution set is $\{2\}$.

57.
$$0=4[x-(3-x)]-7(x+1)$$
$$0=4[x-3+x]-7x-7$$
$$0=4[2x-3]-7x-7$$
$$0=8x-12-7x-7$$
$$0=x-19$$
$$-x=-19$$
$$x=19$$
The solution set is $\{19\}$.

59.
$$0 = \frac{x+6}{3x-12} - \frac{5}{x-4} - \frac{2}{3}$$
$$0 = \frac{x+6}{3(x-4)} - \frac{5}{x-4} - \frac{2}{3}$$
$$3(x-4)\cdot 0 = 3(x-4)\left(\frac{x+6}{3(x-4)} - \frac{5}{x-4} - \frac{2}{3}\right)$$
$$0 = \frac{3(x-4)(x+6)}{3(x-4)} - \frac{5\cdot 3(x-4)}{x-4} - \frac{2\cdot 3(x-4)}{3}$$
$$0 = (x+6) - 15 - 2(x-4)$$
$$0 = x+6-15-2x+8$$
$$0 = -x-1$$
$$x = -1$$
The solution set is $\{-1\}$.

61. $4(x-7) = 4x - 28$
$4x - 28 = 4x - 28$
The given equation is an identity.

63. $2x + 3 = 2x - 3$
$3 = -3$
The given equation is an inconsistent equation.

65. $4x + 5x = 8x$
$9x = 8x$
$x = 0$
The given equation is a conditional equation.

67. $\dfrac{2x}{x-3} = \dfrac{6}{x-3} + 4$
$2x = 6 + 4(x-3)$
$2x = 6 + 4x - 12$
$-2x = -6$
$x = 3 \Rightarrow$ no solution
The given equation is an inconsistent equation.

69. $\dfrac{x+5}{2} - 4 = \dfrac{2x-1}{3}$
$3(x+5) - 24 = 2(2x-1)$
$3x + 15 - 24 = 4x - 2$
$-x = 7$
$x = -7$
The solution set is $\{-7\}$.
The given equation is a conditional equation.

71. $\dfrac{2}{x-2} = 3 + \dfrac{x}{x-2}$
$2 = 3(x-2) + x$
$2 = 3x - 6 + x$
$-4x = -8$
$x = 2 \Rightarrow$ no solution
The solution set is the empty set, $\varnothing$.
The given equation is an inconsistent equation.

73. $8x - (3x + 2) + 10 = 3x$
$8x - 3x - 2 + 10 = 3x$
$2x = -8$
$x = -4$
The solution set is $\{-4\}$.
The given equation is a conditional equation.

75. $\dfrac{2}{x} + \dfrac{1}{2} = \dfrac{3}{4}$
$8 + 2x = 3x$
$-x = -8$
$x = 8$
The solution set is $\{8\}$.
The given equation is a conditional equation.

77. $\dfrac{4}{x-2} + \dfrac{3}{x+5} = \dfrac{7}{(x+5)(x-2)}$
$4(x+5) + 3(x-2) = 7$
$4x + 20 + 3x - 6 = 7$
$7x = -7$
$x = -1$
The solution set is $\{-1\}$.
The given equation is a conditional equation.

79.
$$\frac{4x}{x+3} - \frac{12}{x-3} = \frac{4x^2+36}{x^2-9}; x \neq 3, -3$$
$$4x(x-3) - 12(x+3) = 4x^2 + 36$$
$$4x^2 - 12x - 12x - 36 = 4x^2 + 36$$
$$4x^2 - 24x - 36 = 4x^2 + 36$$
$$-24x - 36 = 36$$
$$-24x = 72$$
$$x = -3 \quad \text{No solution}$$

The solution set is { }.
The given equation is an inconsistent equation.

81. The equation is $3(x-4) = 3(2-2x)$, and the solution is $x = 2$.

83. The equation is $-3(x-3) = 5(2-x)$, and the solution is $x = 0.5$.

85. Solve: $4(x-2) + 2 = 4x - 2(2-x)$
$$4x - 8 + 2 = 4x - 4 + 2x$$
$$4x - 6 = 6x - 4$$
$$-2x - 6 = -4$$
$$-2x = 2$$
$$x = -1$$

Now, evaluate $x^2 - x$ for $x = -1$:
$$x^2 - x = (-1)^2 - (-1)$$
$$= 1 - (-1) = 1 + 1 = 2$$

87. Solve for x: $\dfrac{3(x+3)}{5} = 2x + 6$
$$3(x+3) = 5(2x+6)$$
$$3x + 9 = 10x + 30$$
$$-7x + 9 = 30$$
$$-7x = 21$$
$$x = -3$$

Solve for y: $-2y - 10 = 5y + 18$
$$-7y - 10 = 18$$
$$-7y = 28$$
$$y = -4$$

Now, evaluate $x^2 - (xy - y)$ for $x = -3$ and $y = -4$:
$$x^2 - (xy - y)$$
$$= (-3)^2 - [-3(-4) - (-4)]$$
$$= (-3)^2 - [12 - (-4)]$$
$$= 9 - (12 + 4) = 9 - 16 = -7$$

89.
$$\left[(3+6)^2 \div 3\right] \cdot 4 = -54x$$
$$(9^2 \div 3) \cdot 4 = -54x$$
$$(81 \div 3) \cdot 4 = -54x$$
$$27 \cdot 4 = -54x$$
$$108 = -54x$$
$$-2 = x$$

The solution set is $\{-2\}$.

91.
$$5 - 12x = 8 - 7x - \left[6 \div 3(2 + 5^3) + 5x\right]$$
$$5 - 12x = 8 - 7x - \left[6 \div 3(2 + 125) + 5x\right]$$
$$5 - 12x = 8 - 7x - \left[6 \div 3 \cdot 127 + 5x\right]$$
$$5 - 12x = 8 - 7x - \left[2 \cdot 127 + 5x\right]$$
$$5 - 12x = 8 - 7x - \left[254 + 5x\right]$$
$$5 - 12x = 8 - 7x - 254 - 5x$$
$$5 - 12x = -12x - 246$$
$$5 = -246$$

The final statement is a contradiction, so the equation has no solution. The solution set is $\varnothing$.

93. $0.7x + 0.4(20) = 0.5(x+20)$
$$0.7x + 8 = 0.5x + 10$$
$$0.2x + 8 = 10$$
$$0.2x = 2$$
$$x = 10$$

The solution set is $\{10\}$.

95. $4x + 13 - \left\{2x - \left[4(x-3) - 5\right]\right\} = 2(x-6)$
$$4x + 13 - \left\{2x - \left[4x - 12 - 5\right]\right\} = 2x - 12$$
$$4x + 13 - \left\{2x - \left[4x - 17\right]\right\} = 2x - 12$$
$$4x + 13 - \left\{2x - 4x + 17\right\} = 2x - 12$$
$$4x + 13 - \left\{-2x + 17\right\} = 2x - 12$$
$$4x + 13 + 2x - 17 = 2x - 12$$
$$6x - 4 = 2x - 12$$
$$4x - 4 = -12$$
$$4x = -8$$
$$x = -2$$

The solution set is $\{-2\}$.

97. Let T = 4421. Then

$$4421 = 165x + 2771$$

$$1650 = 165x$$

$$10 = x$$

Tuition will be $4421 ten years after 1996, which is the school year ending 2006.

99. $D = \frac{1}{9}N + \frac{26}{9}; \ D = \frac{7}{2}$

$$\frac{7}{2} = \frac{1}{9}N + \frac{26}{9}$$

$$18\left(\frac{7}{2}\right) = 18\left(\frac{1}{9}N + \frac{26}{9}\right)$$

$$63 = 2N + 52$$

$$11 = 2N$$

$$\frac{11}{2} = \frac{2N}{2}$$

$$5.5 = N$$

If the high-humor group averages a level of depression of 3.5 in response to a negative life event, the intensity of that event would be 5.5. The solution is the point along the horizontal axis where the graph for the high-humor group has a value of 3.5 on the vertical axis. This corresponds to the point $(5.5, 3.5)$ on the high-humor graph.

101. $C = \frac{DA}{A + 12}; C = 500, D = 1000$

$$500 = \frac{1000A}{A + 12}$$

$$(A + 12) \cdot 500 = (A + 12)\left(\frac{1000A}{A + 12}\right)$$

$$500A + 6000 = 1000A$$

$$6000 = 500A$$

$$12 = A$$

The child's age is 12 years old.

103. The solution is the point (12, 500) on the blue graph.

105. No, because the graphs cross, neither formula gives a consistently smaller dosage.

107. 11 learning trials; represented by the point $(11, 0.95)$ on the graph.

109.

$$C = \frac{x + 0.1(500)}{x + 500}$$

$$0.28 = \frac{x + 0.1(500)}{x + 500}$$

$$0.28(x + 500) = x + 0.1(500)$$

$$0.28x + 140 = x + 50$$

$$-0.72x = -90$$

$$\frac{-0.72x}{-0.72} = \frac{-90}{-0.72}$$

$$x = 125$$

125 liters of pure peroxide must be added.

120. $\{3\}$

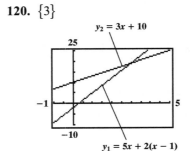

121. $\{5\}$

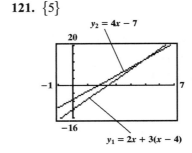

123. $\{-5\}$

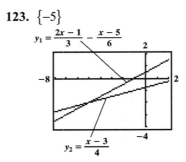

125. Answers may vary.

127. $\dfrac{4x-b}{x-5}=3$

$4x-b=3(x-5)$

The solution set will be $\varnothing$ if $x=5$.

$4(5)-b=3(5-5)$

$20-b=0$

$20=b$

$b=20$

Section 1.3

Check Point Exercises

1. Let x = the number of football injuries
Let $x+0.6$ = the number of basketball injuries
Let $x+0.3$ = the number of bicycling injuries

$x+(x+0.6)+(x+0.3)=3.9$

$x+x+0.6+x+0.3=3.9$

$3x+0.9=3.9$

$3x=3$

$x=1$

$x=1$

$x+0.6=1+0.6=1.6$

$x+0.3=1+0.3=1.3$

In 2004 there were 1 million football injuries, 1.6 million basketball injuries, and 1.3 million bicycling injuries.

2. Let x = the number of years after 2004 that it will take until Americans will purchase 79.9 million gallons of organic milk.

$40.7+5.6x=79.9$

$5.6x=79.9-40.7$

$5.6x=39.2$

$x=\dfrac{39.2}{5.6}$

$x=7$

Americans will purchase 79.9 million gallons of organic milk 7 years after 2004, or 2011.

3. Let x = the number of minutes at which the costs of the two plans are the same.

$$\overbrace{15+0.08x}^{\text{Plan A}}=\overbrace{3+0.12x}^{\text{Plan B}}$$

$15+0.08x-15=3+0.12x-15$

$0.08x=0.12x-12$

$0.08x-0.12x=0.12x-12-0.12x$

$-0.04x=-12$

$\dfrac{-0.04x}{-0.04}=\dfrac{-12}{-0.04}$

$x=300$

The two plans are the same at 300 minutes.

4. Let x = the computer's price before the reduction.

$x-0.30x=840$

$0.70x=840$

$x=\dfrac{840}{0.70}$

$x=1200$

Before the reduction the computer's price was $1200.

5. Let x = the amount invested at 9%.
Let $5000-x$ = the amount invested at 11%.

$0.09x+0.11(5000-x)=487$

$0.09x+550-0.11x=487$

$-0.02x+550=487$

$-0.02x=-63$

$x=\dfrac{-63}{-0.02}$

$x=3150$

$5000-x=1850$

$3150 was invested at 9% and $1850 was invested at 11%.

6. Let x = the width of the court.
Let $x + 44$ = the length of the court.
$$2l + 2w = P$$
$$2(x+44)+2x = 288$$
$$2x+88+2x = 288$$
$$4x+88 = 288$$
$$4x = 200$$
$$x = \frac{200}{4}$$
$$x = 50$$
$$x+44 = 94$$
The dimensions of the court are 50 by 94.

7.
$$2l + 2w = P$$
$$2l + 2w - 2l = P - 2l$$
$$2w = P - 2l$$
$$\frac{2w}{2} = \frac{P-2l}{2}$$
$$w = \frac{P-2l}{2}$$

8.
$$P = C + MC$$
$$P = C(1+M)$$
$$\frac{P}{1+M} = \frac{C(1+M)}{1+M}$$
$$\frac{P}{1+M} = C$$
$$C = \frac{P}{1+M}$$

Exercise Set 1.3

1. Let x = the number
$$5x - 4 = 26$$
$$5x = 30$$
$$x = 6$$
The number is 6.

3. Let x = the number
$$x - 0.20x = 20$$
$$0.80x = 20$$
$$x = 25$$
The number is 25.

5. Let x = the number
$$0.60x + x = 192$$
$$1.6x = 192$$
$$x = 120$$
The number is 120.

7. Let x = the number
$$0.70x = 224$$
$$x = 320$$
The number is 320.

9. Let x = the number
$x + 26$ = the other number
$$x + (x+26) = 64$$
$$x + x + 26 = 64$$
$$2x + 26 = 64$$
$$2x = 38$$
$$x = 19$$
If $x = 19$, then $x + 26 = 45$.
The numbers are 19 and 45.

11.
$$y_1 - y_2 = 2$$
$$(13x-4)-(5x+10) = 2$$
$$13x - 4 - 5x - 10 = 2$$
$$8x - 14 = 2$$
$$8x = 16$$
$$\frac{8x}{8} = \frac{16}{8}$$
$$x = 2$$

13.
$$y_1 = 8y_2 + 14$$
$$10(2x-1) = 8(2x+1)+14$$
$$20x - 10 = 16x + 8 + 14$$
$$20x - 10 = 16x + 22$$
$$4x = 32$$
$$\frac{4x}{4} = \frac{32}{4}$$
$$x = 8$$

15.
$$3y_1 - 5y_2 = y_3 - 22$$
$$3(2x+6)-5(x+8) = (x)-22$$
$$6x + 18 - 5x - 40 = x - 22$$
$$x - 22 = x - 22$$
$$x - x = -22 + 22$$
$$0 = 0$$
The solution set is the set of all real numbers.

17.
$$3y_1 + 4y_2 = 4y_3$$

$$3\left(\frac{1}{x}\right) + 4\left(\frac{1}{2x}\right) = 4\left(\frac{1}{x-1}\right)$$

$$\frac{3}{x} + \frac{2}{x} = \frac{4}{x-1}$$

$$\frac{5}{x} = \frac{4}{x-1}$$

$$\frac{5x(x-1)}{x} = \frac{4x(x-1)}{x-1}$$

$$5(x-1) = 4x$$

$$5x - 5 = 4x$$

$$x = 5$$

19. Let x = the number of births (in thousands)
Let $x - 229$ = the number of deaths (in thousands).

$$x + (x - 229) = 521$$

$$x + x - 229 = 521$$

$$2x - 229 = 521$$

$$2x - 229 + 229 = 521 + 229$$

$$2x = 750$$

$$\frac{2x}{2} = \frac{750}{2}$$

$$x = 375$$

There are 375 thousand births and
$375 - 229 = 146$ thousand deaths each day.

21. Let x = the number of Internet users in China.
$x + 10$ = the number of Internet users in Japan.
$x + 123$ = the number of Internet users in the United States.

$$x + (x + 10) + (x + 123) = 271$$

$$3x + 133 = 271$$

$$3x = 138$$

$$x = 46$$

If $x = 46$, then $x + 10 = 56$ and $x + 123 = 169$.
Thus, there are 46 million Internet users in China, 56 million Internet users in Japan, and 169 Internet users in the United States.

23. Let x = the percentage of Conservatives.
Let $2x + 4.4$ = the percentage of Liberals.

$$x + (2x + 4.4) = 57.2$$

$$x + 2x + 4.4 = 57.2$$

$$3x + 4.4 = 57.2$$

$$3x + 4.4 - 4.4 = 57.2 - 4.4$$

$$3x = 52.8$$

$$\frac{3x}{3} = \frac{52.8}{3}$$

$$x = 17.6$$

$$2x + 4.4 = 39.6$$

The percentage of Conservatives is 17.6% and the percentage of Liberals is 39.6%

25. Let L = the life expectancy of an American man.
y = the number of years after 1900.

$$L = 55 + 0.2y$$

$$85 = 55 + 0.2y$$

$$30 = 0.2y$$

$$150 = y$$

The life expectancy will be 85 years in the year $1900 + 150 = 2050$.

27. a. $y = 1.7x + 39.8$

b.
$$1.7x + 39.8 = 44.9 + 8.5$$

$$1.7x + 39.8 = 53.4$$

$$1.7x = 13.6$$

$$\frac{1.7x}{1.7} = \frac{13.6}{1.7}$$

$$x = 8$$

The number of Americans without health insurance will exceed 44.9 million by 8.5 million 8 years after 2000, or 2008.

c.

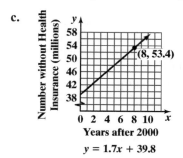

$$y = 1.7x + 39.8$$

29. Let v = the car's value.
y = the number of years (after 2003).
$$v = 80,500 - 8705y$$
$$19,565 = 80,500 - 8705y$$
$$-60,935 = -8705y$$
$$7 = y$$
The car's value will be $19,565 after 7 years.

31. Let x = the number of months.
The cost for Club A: $25x + 40$
The cost for Club B: $30x + 15$
$$25x + 40 = 30x + 15$$
$$-5x + 40 = 15$$
$$-5x = -25$$
$$x = 5$$
The total cost for the clubs will be the same at 5 months. The cost will be
$$25(5) + 40 = 30(5) + 15 = \$165$$

33. Let x = the number of uses.
Cost without coupon book: $1.25x$
Cost with coupon book: $15 + 0.75x$
$$1.25x = 15 + 0.75x$$
$$0.50x = 15$$
$$x = 30$$
The bus must be used 30 times in a month for the costs to be equal.

35. a. Let x = the number of years (after 2005).
College A's enrollment: $13,300 + 1000x$

College B's enrollment: $26,800 - 500x$
$$13,300 + 1000x = 26,800 - 500x$$
$$13,300 + 1500x = 26,800$$
$$1500x = 13,500$$
$$x = 9$$
The two colleges will have the same enrollment in the year $2005 + 9 = 2014$. That year the enrollments will be
$$13,300 + 1000(9)$$
$$= 26,800 - 500(9)$$
$$= 22,300 \text{ students}$$

b. Check points to determine that $y_1 = 13,300 + 1000x$ and $y_2 = 26,800 - 500x$.

37. Let x = the cost of the television set.
$$x - 0.20x = 336$$
$$0.80x = 336$$
$$x = 420$$
The television set's price is $420.

39. Let x = the nightly cost
$$x + 0.08x = 162$$
$$1.08x = 162$$
$$x = 150$$
The nightly cost is $150.

41. Let x = the annual salary for men whose highest educational attainment is a high school degree.
$$x + 0.22x = 44,000$$
$$1.22x = 44,000$$
$$x \approx 36,000$$
The annual salary for men whose highest educational attainment is a high school degree is about $36,000.

43. Let c = the dealer's cost
$$584 = c + 0.25c$$
$$584 = 1.25c$$
$$467.20 = c$$
The dealer's cost is $467.20.

45. Let x = the amount invested at 6%.
Let $7000 - x$ = the amount invested at 8%.
$$0.06x + 0.08(7000 - x) = 520$$
$$0.06x + 560 - 0.08x = 520$$
$$-0.02x + 560 = 520$$
$$-0.02x = -40$$
$$x = \frac{-40}{-0.02}$$
$$x = 2000$$
$$7000 - x = 5000$$
$2000 was invested at 6% and $5000 was invested at 8%.

47. Let x = amount invested at 12%
$8000 - x$ = amount invested at 5% loss
$$.12x - .05(8000 - x) = 620$$
$$.12x - 400 + .05x = 620$$
$$.17x = 1020$$
$$x = 6000$$
$$8000 - x = 2000$$
$6000 at 12%, $2000 at 5% loss

49. Let w = the width of the field
Let $2w$ = the length of the field
$$P = 2(\text{length}) + 2(\text{width})$$
$$300 = 2(2w) + 2(w)$$
$$300 = 4w + 2w$$
$$300 = 6w$$
$$50 = w$$
If $w = 50$, then $2w = 100$. Thus, the
dimensions are 50 yards by 100 yards.

51. Let w = the width of the field
Let $2w + 6$ = the length of the field
$$228 = 6w + 12$$
$$216 = 6w$$
$$36 = w$$
If $w = 36$, then $2w + 6 = 2(36) + 6 = 78$. Thus,
the dimensions are 36 feet by 78 feet.

53. Let x = the width of the frame.
Total length: $16 + 2x$
Total width: $12 + 2x$
$$P = 2(\text{length}) + 2(\text{width})$$
$$72 = 2(16 + 2x) + 2(12 + 2x)$$
$$72 = 32 + 4x + 24 + 4x$$
$$72 = 8x + 56$$
$$16 = 8x$$
$$2 = x$$
The width of the frame is 2 inches.

55. Let x = number of hours
$35x$ = labor cost
$$35x + 63 = 448$$
$$35x = 385$$
$$x = 11$$
It took 11 hours.

57. Let x = inches over 5 feet
$$100 + 5x = 135$$
$$5x = 35$$
$$x = 7$$
A height of 5 feet 7 inches corresponds to 135
pounds.

59. Let x = the weight of unpeeled bananas.
$\dfrac{7}{8}x$ = weight of peeled bananas
$$x = \frac{7}{8}x + \frac{7}{8}$$
$$\frac{1}{8}x = \frac{7}{8}$$
$$x = 7$$
The banana with peel weighs 7 ounces.

61. $A = lw$
$$w = \frac{A}{l}$$
area of rectangle

63. $A = \dfrac{1}{2}bh$
$$2A = bh$$
$$b = \frac{2A}{h};$$
area of triangle

65. $I = Prt$
$$P = \frac{I}{rt};$$
interest

67. $E = mc^2$
$$m = \frac{E}{c^2};$$
Einstein's equation

69. $$T = D + pm$$
$$T - D = pm$$
$$\frac{T - D}{m} = \frac{pm}{m}$$
$$\frac{T - D}{m} = p$$
total of payment

71. $$A = \frac{1}{2}h(a + b)$$
$$2A = h(a + b)$$
$$\frac{2A}{h} = a + b$$
$$\frac{2A}{h} - b = a$$
area of trapezoid

73. $S = P + Prt$
$S - P = Prt$
$\dfrac{S - P}{Pt} = r;$
interest

75. $B = \dfrac{F}{S - V}$
$B(S - V) = F$
$S - V = \dfrac{F}{B}$
$S = \dfrac{F}{B} + V$

77. $IR + Ir = E$
$I(R + r) = E$
$I = \dfrac{E}{R + r}$
electric current

79. $\dfrac{1}{p} + \dfrac{1}{q} = \dfrac{1}{f}$
$qf + pf = pq$
$f(q + p) = pq$
$f = \dfrac{pq}{p + q}$
thin lens equation

89. a. $F = 30 + 5x$
$F = 7.5x$

b.   120

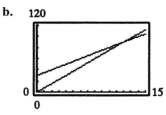

0   15
0

c.   Calculator shows the graphs to intersect at (12, 90); the two options both cost $90 when 12 hours court time is used per month.

d. $30 + 5x = 7.5x$
$30 = 2.5x$
$x = 12$
Rent the court 12 hours per month.

91.   Let x = original price
$x - 0.4x = 0.6x$ = price after first reduction
$0.6x - 0.4(0.6x)$ = price after second reduction
$0.6x - 0.24x = 72$
$0.36x = 72$
$x = 200$
The original price was $200.

93.   Let x = correct answers
$26 - x$ = incorrect answers
$8x - 5(26 - x) = 0$
$8x - 130 + 5x = 0$
$13x - 130 = 0$
$13x = 130$
$x = 10$
10 problems were solved correctly.

95.   Let x = the number of plants originally stolen
After passing the first security guard, the thief

has: $x - \left(\dfrac{1}{2}x + 2\right) = x - \dfrac{1}{2}x - 2 = \dfrac{1}{2}x - 2$

After passing the second security guard, the thief

has: $\dfrac{1}{2}x - 2 - \left(\dfrac{\dfrac{1}{2}x - 2}{2} + 2\right) = \dfrac{1}{4}x - 3$

After passing the third security guard, the thief

has: $\dfrac{1}{4}x - 3 - \left(\dfrac{\dfrac{1}{4}x - 3}{2} + 2\right) = \dfrac{1}{8}x - \dfrac{7}{2}$

Thus, $\dfrac{1}{8}x - \dfrac{7}{2} = 1$
$x - 28 = 8$
$x = 36$
The thief stole 36 plants.

62

Section 1.4

Check Point Exercises

1. a. $(5-2i)+(3+3i)$
        $=5-2i+3+3i$
        $=(5+3)+(-2+3)i$
        $=8+i$

    b. $(2+6i)-(12-i)$
        $=2+6i-12+i$
        $=(2-12)+(6+1)i$
        $=-10+7i$

2. a. $7i(2-9i)=7i(2)-7i(9i)$
        $=14i-63i^2$
        $=14i-63(-1)$
        $=63+14i$

    b. $(5+4i)(6-7i)=30-35i+24i-28i^2$
        $=30-35i+24i-28(-1)$
        $=30+28-35i+24i$
        $=58-11i$

3. $\dfrac{5+4i}{4-i}=\dfrac{5+4i}{4-i}\cdot\dfrac{4+i}{4+i}$
    $=\dfrac{20+5i+16i+4i^2}{16+4i-4i-i^2}$
    $=\dfrac{20+21i-4}{16+1}$
    $=\dfrac{16+21i}{17}$
    $=\dfrac{16}{17}+\dfrac{21}{17}i$

4. a. $\sqrt{-27}+\sqrt{-48}=i\sqrt{27}+i\sqrt{48}$
        $=i\sqrt{9\cdot3}+i\sqrt{16\cdot3}$
        $=3i\sqrt{3}+4i\sqrt{3}$
        $=7i\sqrt{3}$

    b. $(-2+\sqrt{-3})^2=(-2+i\sqrt{3})^2$
        $=(-2)^2+2(-2)(i\sqrt{3})+(i\sqrt{3})^2$
        $=4-4i\sqrt{3}+3i^2$
        $=4-4i\sqrt{3}+3(-1)$
        $=1-4i\sqrt{3}$

    c. $\dfrac{-14+\sqrt{-12}}{2}=\dfrac{-14+i\sqrt{12}}{2}$
        $=\dfrac{-14+2i\sqrt{3}}{2}$
        $=\dfrac{-14}{2}+\dfrac{2i\sqrt{3}}{2}$
        $=-7+i\sqrt{3}$

Exercise Set 1.4

1. $(7+2i)+(1-4i)=7+2i+1-4i$
    $=7+1+2i-4i$
    $=8-2i$

3. $(3+2i)-(5-7i)=3-5+2i+7i$
    $=3+2i-5+7i$
    $=-2+9i$

5. $6-(-5+4i)-(-13-i)=6+5-4i+13+i$
    $=24-3i$

7. $8i-(14-9i)=8i-14+9i$
    $=-14+8i+9i$
    $=-14+17i$

9. $-3i(7i-5)=-21i^2+15i$
    $=-21(-1)+15i$
    $=21+15i$

11. $(-5+4i)(3+i)=-15-5i+12i+4i^2$
     $=-15+7i-4$
     $=-19+7i$

13. $(7-5i)(-2-3i)=-14-21i+10i+15i^2$
     $=-14-15-11i$
     $=-29-11i$

15. $(3+5i)(3-5i)$

17. $(-5+i)(-5-i)=25+5i-5i-i^2$
     $=25+1$
     $=26$

19. $(2+3i)^2=4+12i+9i^2$
     $=4+12i-9$
     $=-5+12i$

21.
$$\frac{2}{3-i} = \frac{2}{3-i} \cdot \frac{3+i}{3+i}$$
$$= \frac{2(3+i)}{9+1}$$
$$= \frac{2(3+i)}{10}$$
$$= \frac{3+i}{5}$$
$$= \frac{3}{5} + \frac{1}{5}i$$

23.
$$\frac{2i}{1+i} = \frac{2i}{1+i} \cdot \frac{1-i}{1-i} = \frac{2i-2i^2}{1+1} = \frac{2+2i}{2} = 1+i$$

25.
$$\frac{8i}{4-3i} = \frac{8i}{4-3i} \cdot \frac{4+3i}{4+3i}$$
$$= \frac{32i+24i^2}{16+9}$$
$$= \frac{-24+32i}{25}$$
$$= -\frac{24}{25} + \frac{32}{25}i$$

27.
$$\frac{2+3i}{2+i} = \frac{2+3i}{2+i} \cdot \frac{2-i}{2-i}$$
$$= \frac{4+4i-3i^2}{4+1}$$
$$= \frac{7+4i}{5}$$
$$= \frac{7}{5} + \frac{4}{5}i$$

29.
$$\sqrt{-64} - \sqrt{-25} = i\sqrt{64} - i\sqrt{25}$$
$$= 8i - 5i = 3i$$

31.
$$5\sqrt{-16} + 3\sqrt{-81} = 5(4i) + 3(9i)$$
$$= 20i + 27i = 47i$$

33.
$$\left(-2+\sqrt{-4}\right)^2 = \left(-2+2i\right)^2$$
$$= 4 - 8i + 4i^2$$
$$= 4 - 8i - 4$$
$$= -8i$$

35.
$$\left(-3-\sqrt{-7}\right)^2 = \left(-3-i\sqrt{7}\right)^2$$
$$= 9 + 6i\sqrt{7} + i^2(7)$$
$$= 9 - 7 + 6i\sqrt{7}$$
$$= 2 + 6i\sqrt{7}$$

37.
$$\frac{-8+\sqrt{-32}}{24} = \frac{-8+i\sqrt{32}}{24}$$
$$= \frac{-8+i\sqrt{16\cdot2}}{24}$$
$$= \frac{-8+4i\sqrt{2}}{24}$$
$$= -\frac{1}{3} + \frac{\sqrt{2}}{6}i$$

39.
$$\frac{-6-\sqrt{-12}}{48} = \frac{-6-i\sqrt{12}}{48}$$
$$= \frac{-6-i\sqrt{4\cdot3}}{48}$$
$$= \frac{-6-2i\sqrt{3}}{48}$$
$$= -\frac{1}{8} - \frac{\sqrt{3}}{24}i$$

41.
$$\sqrt{-8}\left(\sqrt{-3}-\sqrt{5}\right) = i\sqrt{8}(i\sqrt{3}-\sqrt{5})$$
$$= 2i\sqrt{2}\left(i\sqrt{3}-\sqrt{5}\right)$$
$$= -2\sqrt{6} - 2i\sqrt{10}$$

43.
$$\left(3\sqrt{-5}\right)\left(-4\sqrt{-12}\right) = \left(3i\sqrt{5}\right)\left(-8i\sqrt{3}\right)$$
$$= -24i^2\sqrt{15}$$
$$= 24\sqrt{15}$$

45.
$$(2-3i)(1-i) - (3-i)(3+i)$$
$$= \left(2-2i-3i+3i^2\right) - \left(3^2-i^2\right)$$
$$= 2 - 5i + 3i^2 - 9 + i^2$$
$$= -7 - 5i + 4i^2$$
$$= -7 - 5i + 4(-1)$$
$$= -11 - 5i$$

47. $(2+i)^2 - (3-i)^2$

$= (4+4i+i^2) - (9-6i+i^2)$

$= 4+4i+i^2 - 9+6i-i^2$

$= -5+10i$

49. $5\sqrt{-16} + 3\sqrt{-81}$

$= 5\sqrt{16}\sqrt{-1} + 3\sqrt{81}\sqrt{-1}$

$= 5 \cdot 4i + 3 \cdot 9i$

$= 20i + 27i$

$= 47i$ or $0+47i$

51. $f(x) = x^2 - 2x + 2$

$f(1+i) = (1+i)^2 - 2(1+i) + 2$

$= 1+2i+i^2 - 2 - 2i + 2$

$= 1+i^2$

$= 1-1$

$= 0$

53. $f(x) = \dfrac{x^2+19}{2-x}$

$f(3i) = \dfrac{(3i)^2+19}{2-3i}$

$= \dfrac{9i^2+19}{2-3i}$

$= \dfrac{-9+19}{2-3i}$

$= \dfrac{10}{2-3i}$

$= \dfrac{10}{2-3i} \cdot \dfrac{2+3i}{2+3i}$

$= \dfrac{20+30i}{4-9i^2}$

$= \dfrac{20+30i}{4+9}$

$= \dfrac{20+30i}{13}$

$= \dfrac{20}{13} + \dfrac{30}{13}i$

55. $E = IR = (4-5i)(3+7i)$

$= 12+28i-15i-35i^2$

$= 12+13i-35(-1)$

$= 12+35+13i = 47+13i$

The voltage of the circuit is
$(47 + 13i)$ volts.

57. Sum:

$(5+i\sqrt{15}) + (5-i\sqrt{15})$

$= 5+i\sqrt{15} + 5 - i\sqrt{15}$

$= 5+5$

$= 10$

Product:

$(5+i\sqrt{15})(5-i\sqrt{15})$

$= 25 - 5i\sqrt{15} + 5i\sqrt{15} - 15i^2$

$= 25+15$

$= 40$

67. a. False; all irrational numbers are complex numbers.

b. False; $(3+7i)(3-7i) = 9 + 49 = 58$ is a real number.

c. False; $\dfrac{7+3i}{5+3i} = \dfrac{7+3i}{5+3i} \cdot \dfrac{5-3i}{5-3i}$

$= \dfrac{44-6i}{34} = \dfrac{22}{17} - \dfrac{3}{17}i$

d. True; $(x+yi)(x-yi) = x^2 - (yi)^2 = x^2 + y^2$

(d) is true.

69. $\dfrac{1+i}{1+2i} + \dfrac{1-i}{1-2i}$

$= \dfrac{(1+i)(1-2i)}{(1+2i)(1-2i)} + \dfrac{(1-i)(1+2i)}{(1+2i)(1-2i)}$

$= \dfrac{(1+i)(1-2i) + (1-i)(1+2i)}{(1+2i)(1-2i)}$

$= \dfrac{1-2i+i-2i^2 + 1+2i-i-2i^2}{1-4i^2}$

$= \dfrac{1-2i+i+2+1+2i-i+2}{1+4}$

$= \dfrac{6}{5}$

$= \dfrac{6}{5} + 0i$

Section 1.5

Check Point Exercises

1. **a.** $3x^2 - 9x = 0$

    $3x(x-3) = 0$

    $3x = 0$ or $x - 3 = 0$

    $x = 0$ $x = 3$

    The solution set is $\{0, 3\}$.

    b. $2x^2 + x = 1$

    $2x^2 + x - 1 = 0$

    $(2x-1)(x+1) = 0$

    $2x - 1 = 0$ or $x + 1 = 0$

    $2x = 1$ $x = -1$

    $x = \dfrac{1}{2}$

    The solution set is $\left\{-1, \dfrac{1}{2}\right\}$.

2. **a.** $3x^2 = 21$

    $\dfrac{3x^2}{3} = \dfrac{21}{3}$

    $x^2 = 7$

    $x = \pm\sqrt{7}$

    The solution set is $\left\{-\sqrt{7}, \sqrt{7}\right\}$.

    b. $5x^2 + 45 = 0$

    $5x^2 = -45$

    $x^2 = -9$

    $x = \pm\sqrt{-9}$

    $x = \pm 3i$

    c. $(x+5)^2 = 11$

    $x + 5 = \pm\sqrt{11}$

    $x = -5 \pm \sqrt{11}$

    The solution set is $\left\{-5+\sqrt{11}, -5-\sqrt{11}\right\}$.

3. **a.** The coefficient of the x-term is 6. Half of 6 is 3, and 3^2 is 9.
    9 should be added to the binomial.
    $x^2 + 6x + 9 = (x+3)^2$

b. The coefficient of the x-term is -5. Half of

-5 is $-\dfrac{5}{2}$, and $\left(-\dfrac{5}{2}\right)^2$ is $\dfrac{25}{4}$.

$\dfrac{25}{4}$ should be added to the binomial.

$x^2 - 5x + \dfrac{25}{4} = \left(x - \dfrac{5}{2}\right)^2$

c. The coefficient of the x-term is $\dfrac{2}{3}$. Half of

$\dfrac{2}{3}$ is $\dfrac{1}{3}$, and $\left(\dfrac{1}{3}\right)^2$ is $\dfrac{1}{9}$.

$\dfrac{1}{9}$ should be added to the binomial.

$x^2 + \dfrac{2}{3}x + \dfrac{1}{9} = \left(x + \dfrac{1}{3}\right)^2$

4. $x^2 + 4x - 1 = 0$

    $x^2 + 4x = 1$

    $x^2 + 4x + 4 = 1 + 4$

    $(x+2)^2 = 5$

    $x + 2 = \pm\sqrt{5}$

    $x = -2 \pm \sqrt{5}$

5. $2x^2 + 3x - 4 = 0$

    $x^2 + \dfrac{3}{2}x - 2 = 0$

    $x^2 + \dfrac{3}{2}x = 2$

    $x^2 + \dfrac{3}{2}x + \dfrac{9}{16} = 2 + \dfrac{9}{16}$

    $\left(x + \dfrac{3}{4}\right)^2 = \dfrac{41}{16}$

    $x + \dfrac{3}{4} = \pm\sqrt{\dfrac{41}{16}}$

    $x + \dfrac{3}{4} = \pm\dfrac{\sqrt{41}}{4}$

    $x = -\dfrac{3}{4} \pm \dfrac{\sqrt{41}}{4}$

    $x = \dfrac{-3 \pm \sqrt{41}}{4}$

6. $2x^2 + 2x - 1 = 0$

$a = 2, b = 2, c = -1$

$x = \dfrac{-b \pm \sqrt{b^2 - 4ac}}{2a}$

$= \dfrac{-2 \pm \sqrt{2^2 - 4(2)(-1)}}{2(2)}$

$= \dfrac{-2 \pm \sqrt{4 + 8}}{4}$

$= \dfrac{-2 \pm \sqrt{12}}{4}$

$= \dfrac{-2 \pm 2\sqrt{3}}{4}$

$= \dfrac{2(-1 \pm \sqrt{3})}{4}$

$= \dfrac{-1 \pm \sqrt{3}}{2}$

The solution set is $\left\{ \dfrac{-1 + \sqrt{3}}{2}, \dfrac{-1 - \sqrt{3}}{2} \right\}$.

7. $x^2 - 2x + 2 = 0$

$a = 1, b = -2, c = 2$

$x = \dfrac{-b \pm \sqrt{b^2 - 4ac}}{2a}$

$x = \dfrac{-(-2) \pm \sqrt{(-2)^2 - 4(1)(2)}}{2(1)}$

$x = \dfrac{2 \pm \sqrt{4 - 8}}{2}$

$x = \dfrac{2 \pm \sqrt{-4}}{2}$

$x = \dfrac{2 \pm 2i}{2}$

$x = 1 \pm i$

The solution set is $\{1 + i, 1 - i\}$.

8.   **a.** $a = 1, \quad b = 6, \quad c = 9$

$b^2 - 4ac = (6)^2 - 4(1)(9)$

$= 36 - 36$

$= 0$

Since $b^2 - 4ac = 0$, the equation has one real solution.

b. $a = 2, \quad b = -7, \quad c = -4$

$b^2 - 4ac = (-7)^2 - 4(2)(-4)$

$= 49 + 32$

$= 81$

Since $b^2 - 4ac > 0$, the equation has two real solutions. Since 81 is a perfect square, the two solutions are rational.

c. $a = 3, \quad b = -2, \quad c = 4$

$b^2 - 4ac = (-2)^2 - 4(3)(4)$

$= 4 - 48$

$= -44$

Since $b^2 - 4ac < 0$, the equation has two imaginary solutions that are complex conjugates.

9. $P = 0.01A^2 + 0.05A + 107$

$115 = 0.01A^2 + 0.05A + 107$

$0 = 0.01A^2 + 0.05A - 8$

$a = 0.01, \quad b = 0.05, \quad c = -8$

$A = \dfrac{-b \pm \sqrt{b^2 - 4ac}}{2a}$

$A = \dfrac{-(0.05) \pm \sqrt{(0.05)^2 - 4(0.01)(-8)}}{2(0.01)}$

$A = \dfrac{-0.05 \pm \sqrt{0.3225}}{0.02}$

$A \approx \dfrac{-0.05 + \sqrt{0.3225}}{0.02} \qquad A \approx \dfrac{-0.05 - \sqrt{0.3225}}{0.02}$

$A \approx 26 \qquad\qquad\qquad A \approx -31$

Age cannot be negative, reject the negative answer.

Thus, a woman whose normal systolic blood pressure is 115 mm Hg is 26 years old.

10. $w^2 + 9^2 = 15^2$

$w^2 + 81 = 225$

$w^2 = 144$

$w = \pm\sqrt{144}$

$w = \pm 12$

The width of the television is 12 inches.

Exercise Set 1.5

1. $x^2 - 3x - 10 = 0$
    $(x+2)(x-5) = 0$
    $x+2 = 0$ or $x-5 = 0$
    $x = -2$ or $x = 5$
    The solution set is $\{-2, 5\}$.

3. $x^2 = 8x - 15$
    $x^2 - 8x + 15 = 0$
    $(x-3)(x-5) = 0$
    $x-3 = 0$ or $x-5 = 0$
    $x = 3$ or $x = 5$
    The solution set is $\{3, 5\}$.

5. $6x^2 + 11x - 10 = 0$
    $(2x+5)(3x-2) = 0$
    $2x+5 = 0$ or $3x-2 = 0$
    $2x = -5$ $3x = 2$
    $x = -\dfrac{5}{2}$ or $x = \dfrac{2}{3}$
    The solution set is $\left\{-\dfrac{5}{2}, \dfrac{2}{3}\right\}$.

7. $3x^2 - 2x = 8$
    $3x^2 - 2x - 8 = 0$
    $(3x+4)(x-2) = 0$
    $3x+4 = 0$ or $x-2 = 0$
    $3x = -4$
    $x = -\dfrac{4}{3}$ or $x = 2$
    The solution set is $\left\{-\dfrac{4}{3}, 2\right\}$.

9. $3x^2 + 12x = 0$
    $3x(x+4) = 0$
    $3x = 0$ or $x+4 = 0$
    $x = 0$ or $x = -4$
    The solution set is $\{-4, 0\}$.

11. $2x(x-3) = 5x^2 - 7x$
    $2x^2 - 6x - 5x^2 + 7x = 0$
    $-3x^2 + x = 0$
    $x(-3x+1) = 0$
    $x = 0$ or $-3x+1 = 0$
                    $-3x = -1$
                    $x = \dfrac{1}{3}$
    The solution set is $\left\{0, \dfrac{1}{3}\right\}$.

13. $7 - 7x = (3x+2)(x-1)$
    $7 - 7x = 3x^2 - x - 2$
    $7 - 7x - 3x^2 + x + 2 = 0$
    $-3x^2 - 6x + 9 = 0$
    $-3(x+3)(x-1) = 0$
    $x+3 = 0$ or $x-1 = 0$
    $x = -3$ or $x = 1$
    The solution set is $\{-3, 1\}$.

15. $3x^2 = 27$
    $x^2 = 9$
    $x = \pm\sqrt{9} = \pm 3$
    The solution set is $\{-3, 3\}$.

17. $5x^2 + 1 = 51$
    $5x^2 = 50$
    $x^2 = 10$
    $x = \pm\sqrt{10}$
    The solution set is $\left\{-\sqrt{10}, \sqrt{10}\right\}$.

19. $2x^2 - 5 = -55$
    $2x^2 = -50$
    $x^2 = -25$
    $x = \pm\sqrt{-25} = \pm 5i$
    The solution set is $\{5i, -5i\}$.

21. $(x+2)^2 = 25$
    $x+2 = \pm\sqrt{25}$
    $x+2 = \pm 5$
    $x = -2 \pm 5$
    $x = -2+5$ or $x = -2-5$
    $x = 3$ $x = -7$
    The solution set is $\{-7, 3\}$.

23. $3(x-4)^2 = 15$

$(x-4)^2 = 5$

$x-4 = \pm\sqrt{5}$

$x = 4 \pm \sqrt{5}$

The solution set is $\left\{4+\sqrt{5}, 4-\sqrt{5}\right\}$.

25. $(x+3)^2 = -16$

$x+3 = \pm\sqrt{-16}$

$x+3 = \pm 4i$

$x = -3 \pm 4i$

The solution set is $\left\{-3+4i, -3-4i\right\}$.

27. $(x-3)^2 = -5$

$x-3 = \pm\sqrt{-5}$

$x-3 = \pm i\sqrt{5}$

$x = 3 \pm i\sqrt{5}$

The solution set is $\left\{3+i\sqrt{5}, 3-i\sqrt{5}\right\}$.

29. $(3x+2)^2 = 9$

$3x+2 = \pm\sqrt{9} = \pm 3$

$3x+2 = -3$ or $3x+2 = 3$

$3x = -5$ $3x = 1$

$x = -\dfrac{5}{3}$ or $x = \dfrac{1}{3}$

The solution set is $\left\{-\dfrac{5}{3}, \dfrac{1}{3}\right\}$.

31. $(5x-1)^2 = 7$

$5x-1 = \pm\sqrt{7}$

$5x = 1 \pm \sqrt{7}$

$x = \dfrac{1 \pm \sqrt{7}}{5}$

The solution set is $\left\{\dfrac{1-\sqrt{7}}{5}, \dfrac{1+\sqrt{7}}{5}\right\}$.

33. $(3x-4)^2 = 8$

$3x-4 = \pm\sqrt{8} = \pm 2\sqrt{2}$

$3x = 4 \pm 2\sqrt{2}$

$x = \dfrac{4 \pm 2\sqrt{2}}{3}$

The solution set is $\left\{\dfrac{4-2\sqrt{2}}{3}, \dfrac{4+2\sqrt{2}}{3}\right\}$.

35. $x^2 + 12x$

$\left(\dfrac{12}{2}\right)^2 = 6^2 = 36$

$x^2 + 12x + 36 = (x+6)^2$

37. $x^2 - 10x$

$\left(\dfrac{10}{2}\right)^2 = 5^2 = 25$

$x^2 - 10x + 25 = (x-5)^2$

39. $x^2 + 3x$

$\left(\dfrac{3}{2}\right)^2 = \dfrac{9}{4}$

$x^2 + 3x + \dfrac{9}{4} = \left(x + \dfrac{3}{2}\right)^2$

41. $x^2 - 7x$

$\left(\dfrac{7}{2}\right)^2 = \dfrac{49}{4}$

$x^2 - 7x + \dfrac{49}{4} = \left(x - \dfrac{7}{2}\right)^2$

43. $x^2 - \dfrac{2}{3}x$

$\left(\dfrac{\frac{2}{3}}{2}\right)^2 = \left(\dfrac{1}{3}\right)^2 = \dfrac{1}{9}$

$x^2 - \dfrac{2}{3}x + \dfrac{1}{9} = \left(x - \dfrac{1}{3}\right)^2$

45. $x^2 - \dfrac{1}{3}x$

$\left(\dfrac{\frac{1}{3}}{2}\right)^2 = \left(\dfrac{1}{6}\right)^2 = \dfrac{1}{36}$

$x^2 - \dfrac{1}{3}x + \dfrac{1}{36} = \left(x - \dfrac{1}{6}\right)^2$

47.
$$x^2 + 6x = 7$$
$$x^2 + 6x + 9 = 7 + 9$$
$$(x+3)^2 = 16$$
$$x + 3 = \pm 4$$
$$x = -3 \pm 4$$
The solution set is $\{-7, 1\}$.

49.
$$x^2 - 2x = 2$$
$$x^2 - 2x + 1 = 2 + 1$$
$$(x-1)^2 = 3$$
$$x - 1 = \pm\sqrt{3}$$
$$x = 1 \pm \sqrt{3}$$
The solution set is $\left\{1+\sqrt{3}, 1-\sqrt{3}\right\}$.

51.
$$x^2 - 6x - 11 = 0$$
$$x^2 - 6x = 11$$
$$x^2 - 6x + 9 = 11 + 9$$
$$(x-3)^2 = 20$$
$$x - 3 = \pm\sqrt{20}$$
$$x = 3 \pm 2\sqrt{5}$$
The solution set is $\left\{3+2\sqrt{5}, 3-2\sqrt{5}\right\}$.

53.
$$x^2 + 4x + 1 = 0$$
$$x^2 + 4x = -1$$
$$x^2 + 4x + 4 = -1 + 4$$
$$(x+2)^2 = 3$$
$$x + 2 = \pm\sqrt{3}$$
$$x = -2 \pm \sqrt{3}$$
The solution set is $\left\{-2+\sqrt{3}, -2-\sqrt{3}\right\}$.

55.
$$x^2 - 5x + 6 = 0$$
$$x^2 - 5x = -6$$
$$x^2 - 5x + \frac{25}{4} = -6 + \frac{25}{4}$$
$$\left(x - \frac{5}{2}\right)^2 = \frac{1}{4}$$
$$x - \frac{5}{2} = \pm\sqrt{\frac{1}{4}}$$
$$x - \frac{5}{2} = \pm\frac{1}{2}$$
$$x = \frac{5}{2} \pm \frac{1}{2}$$
$$x = \frac{5}{2} + \frac{1}{2} \quad \text{or} \quad x = \frac{5}{2} - \frac{1}{2}$$
$$x = 3 \qquad\qquad x = 2$$
The solution set is $\{2, 3\}$.

57.
$$x^2 + 3x - 1 = 0$$
$$x^2 + 3x = 1$$
$$x^2 + 3x + \frac{9}{4} = 1 + \frac{9}{4}$$
$$\left(x + \frac{3}{2}\right)^2 = \frac{13}{4}$$
$$x + \frac{3}{2} = \pm\frac{\sqrt{13}}{2}$$
$$x = \frac{-3 \pm \sqrt{13}}{2}$$
The solution set is $\left\{\dfrac{-3+\sqrt{13}}{2}, \dfrac{-3-\sqrt{13}}{2}\right\}$.

59. $2x^2 - 7x + 3 = 0$

$$x^2 - \frac{7}{2}x + \frac{3}{2} = 0$$

$$x^2 - \frac{7}{2}x = \frac{-3}{2}$$

$$x^2 - \frac{7}{2}x + \frac{49}{16} = -\frac{3}{2} + \frac{49}{16}$$

$$\left(x - \frac{7}{4}\right)^2 = \frac{25}{16}$$

$$x - \frac{7}{4} = \pm\frac{5}{4}$$

$$x = \frac{7}{4} \pm \frac{5}{4}$$

The solution set is $\left\{\frac{1}{2}, 3\right\}$.

61. $4x^2 - 4x - 1 = 0$

$$4x^2 - 4x - 1 = 0$$

$$x^2 - x - \frac{1}{4} = 0$$

$$x^2 - x = \frac{1}{4}$$

$$x^2 - x + \frac{1}{4} = \frac{1}{4} + \frac{1}{4}$$

$$\left(x - \frac{1}{2}\right)^2 = \frac{2}{4}$$

$$x - \frac{1}{2} = \frac{\pm\sqrt{2}}{2}$$

$$x = \frac{1 \pm \sqrt{2}}{2}$$

The solution set is $\left\{\frac{1+\sqrt{2}}{2}, \frac{1-\sqrt{2}}{2}\right\}$.

63. $3x^2 - 2x - 2 = 0$

$$x^2 - \frac{2}{3}x - \frac{2}{3} = 0$$

$$x^2 - \frac{2}{3}x = \frac{2}{3}$$

$$x^2 - \frac{2}{3}x + \frac{1}{9} = \frac{2}{3} + \frac{1}{9}$$

$$\left(x - \frac{1}{3}\right)^2 = \frac{7}{9}$$

$$x - \frac{1}{3} = \frac{\pm\sqrt{7}}{3}$$

$$x = \frac{1 \pm \sqrt{7}}{3}$$

The solution set is $\left\{\frac{1+\sqrt{7}}{3}, \frac{1-\sqrt{7}}{3}\right\}$.

65. $x^2 + 8x + 15 = 0$

$$x = \frac{-8 \pm \sqrt{8^2 - 4(1)(15)}}{2(1)}$$

$$x = \frac{-8 \pm \sqrt{64 - 60}}{2}$$

$$x = \frac{-8 \pm \sqrt{4}}{2}$$

$$x = \frac{-8 \pm 2}{2}$$

The solution set is $\{-5, -3\}$.

67. $x^2 + 5x + 3 = 0$

$$x = \frac{-5 \pm \sqrt{5^2 - 4(1)(3)}}{2(1)}$$

$$x = \frac{-5 \pm \sqrt{25 - 12}}{2}$$

$$x = \frac{-5 \pm \sqrt{13}}{2}$$

The solution set is $\left\{\frac{-5+\sqrt{13}}{2}, \frac{-5-\sqrt{13}}{2}\right\}$.

69. $3x^2 - 3x - 4 = 0$

$$x = \frac{3 \pm \sqrt{(-3)^2 - 4(3)(-4)}}{2(3)}$$

$$x = \frac{3 \pm \sqrt{9 + 48}}{6}$$

$$x = \frac{3 \pm \sqrt{57}}{6}$$

The solution set is $\left\{ \dfrac{3 + \sqrt{57}}{6}, \dfrac{3 - \sqrt{57}}{6} \right\}$

71.
$$4x^2 = 2x + 7$$
$$4x^2 - 2x - 7 = 0$$

$$x = \frac{2 \pm \sqrt{(-2)^2 - 4(4)(-7)}}{2(4)}$$

$$x = \frac{2 \pm \sqrt{4 + 112}}{8}$$

$$x = \frac{2 \pm \sqrt{116}}{8}$$

$$x = \frac{2 \pm 2\sqrt{29}}{8}$$

$$x = \frac{1 \pm \sqrt{29}}{4}$$

The solution set is $\left\{ \dfrac{1 + \sqrt{29}}{4}, \dfrac{1 - \sqrt{29}}{4} \right\}$.

73. $x^2 - 6x + 10 = 0$

$$x = \frac{6 \pm \sqrt{(-6)^2 - 4(1)(10)}}{2(1)}$$

$$x = \frac{6 \pm \sqrt{36 - 40}}{2}$$

$$x = \frac{6 \pm \sqrt{-4}}{2}$$

$$x = \frac{6 \pm 2i}{2}$$

$$x = 3 \pm i$$

The solution set is $\{3 + i, 3 - i\}$.

75. $x^2 - 4x - 5 = 0$

$(-4)^2 - 4(1)(-5)$

$= 16 + 20$

$= 36$; 2 unequal real solutions

77. $2x^2 - 11x + 3 = 0$

$(-11)^2 - 4(2)(3)$

$= 121 - 24$

$= 97$; 2 unequal real solutions

79. $x^2 - 2x + 1 = 0$

$(-2)^2 - 4(1)(1)$

$= 4 - 4$

$= 0$; 1 real solution

81. $x^2 - 3x - 7 = 0$

$(-3)^2 - 4(1)(-7)$

$= 9 + 28$

$= 37$; 2 unequal real solutions

83.
$$2x^2 - x = 1$$
$$2x^2 - x - 1 = 0$$
$$(2x + 1)(x - 1) = 0$$
$$2x + 1 = 0 \text{ or } x - 1 = 0$$
$$2x = -1$$
$$x = -\frac{1}{2} \text{ or } x = 1$$

The solution set is $\left\{ -\dfrac{1}{2}, 1 \right\}$.

85.
$$5x^2 + 2 = 11x$$
$$5x^2 - 11x + 2 = 0$$
$$(5x - 1)(x - 2) = 0$$
$$5x - 1 = 0 \text{ or } x - 2 = 0$$
$$5x = 1$$
$$x = \frac{1}{5} \text{ or } x = 2$$

The solution set is $\left\{ \dfrac{1}{5}, 2 \right\}$.

87. $3x^2 = 60$

$$x^2 = 20$$

$$x = \pm\sqrt{20}$$

$$x = \pm 2\sqrt{5}$$

The solution set is $\left\{ -2\sqrt{5}, 2\sqrt{5} \right\}$.

89.
$$x^2 - 2x = 1$$
$$x^2 - 2x + 1 = 1 + 1$$
$$(x-1)^2 = 2$$
$$x - 1 = \pm\sqrt{2}$$
$$x = 1 \pm \sqrt{2}$$
The solution set is $\left\{1+\sqrt{2}, 1-\sqrt{2}\right\}$.

91.
$$(2x+3)(x+4) = 1$$
$$2x^2 + 8x + 3x + 12 = 1$$
$$2x^2 + 11x + 11 = 0$$
$$x = \frac{-11 \pm \sqrt{11^2 - 4(2)(11)}}{2(2)}$$
$$x = \frac{-11 \pm \sqrt{121 - 88}}{4}$$
$$x = \frac{-11 \pm \sqrt{33}}{4}$$
The solution set is $\left\{\dfrac{-11+\sqrt{33}}{4}, \dfrac{-11-\sqrt{33}}{4}\right\}$.

93.
$$(3x-4)^2 = 16$$
$$3x - 4 = \pm\sqrt{16}$$
$$3x - 4 = \pm 4$$
$$3x = 4 \pm 4$$
$$3x = 8 \text{ or } 3x = 0$$
$$x = \frac{8}{3} \text{ or } x = 0$$
The solution set is $\left\{0, \dfrac{8}{3}\right\}$.

95.
$$3x^2 - 12x + 12 = 0$$
$$x^2 - 4x + 4 = 0$$
$$(x-2)(x-2) = 0$$
$$x - 2 = 0$$
$$x = 2$$
The solution set is $\{2\}$.

97.
$$4x^2 - 16 = 0$$
$$4x^2 = 16$$
$$x^2 = 4$$
$$x = \pm 2$$
The solution set is $\{-2, 2\}$.

99.
$$x^2 - 6x + 13 = 0$$
$$x^2 - 6x = -13$$
$$x^2 - 6x + 9 = -13 + 9$$
$$(x-3)^2 = -4$$
$$x - 3 = \pm 2i$$
$$x = 3 \pm 2i$$
The solution set is $\{3+2i, 3-2i\}$.

101.
$$x^2 = 4x - 7$$
$$x^2 - 4x = -7$$
$$x^2 - 4x + 4 = -7 + 4$$
$$(x-2)^2 = -3$$
$$x - 2 = \pm i\sqrt{3}$$
$$x = 2 \pm i\sqrt{3}$$
The solution set is $\left\{2+i\sqrt{3}, 2-i\sqrt{3}\right\}$.

103.
$$2x^2 - 7x = 0$$
$$x(2x-7) = 0$$
$$x = 0 \text{ or } 2x - 7 = 0$$
$$2x = 7$$
$$x = 0 \text{ or } x = \frac{7}{2}$$
The solution set is $\left\{0, \dfrac{7}{2}\right\}$.

105.　$\dfrac{1}{x} + \dfrac{1}{x+2} = \dfrac{1}{3}; x \neq 0, -2$

$$3x + 6 + 3x = x^2 + 2x$$

$$0 = x^2 - 4x - 6$$

$$x = \dfrac{-(-4) \pm \sqrt{(-4)^2 - 4(1)(-6)}}{2(1)}$$

$$x = \dfrac{4 \pm \sqrt{16 + 24}}{2}$$

$$x = \dfrac{4 \pm \sqrt{40}}{2}$$

$$x = \dfrac{4 \pm 2\sqrt{10}}{2}$$

$$x = 2 \pm \sqrt{10}$$

The solution set is $\{2 + \sqrt{10},\ 2 - \sqrt{10}\}$.

107.　$\dfrac{2x}{x-3} + \dfrac{6}{x+3} = \dfrac{-28}{x^2 - 9}; x \neq 3, -3$

$$2x(x+3) + 6(x-3) = -28$$

$$2x^2 + 6x + 6x - 18 = -28$$

$$2x^2 + 12x + 10 = 0$$

$$x^2 + 6x + 5 = 0$$

$$(x+1)(x+5) = 0$$

The solution set is $\{-5,\ -1\}$.

109.　$x^2 - 4x - 5 = 0$

$$(x+1)(x-5) = 0$$

$$x + 1 = 0 \quad \text{or} \quad x - 5 = 0$$
$$x = -1 \qquad\qquad x = 5$$

This equation matches graph (d).

111.　$0 = -(x+1)^2 + 4$

$$(x+1)^2 = 4$$

$$x + 1 = \pm 2$$

$$x = -1 \pm 2$$

$$x = -3, \quad x = 1$$

This equation matches graph (f).

113.　$x^2 - 2x + 2 = 0$

$$a = 1, \quad b = -2, \quad c = 2$$

$$x = \dfrac{-b \pm \sqrt{b^2 - 4ac}}{2a}$$

$$x = \dfrac{-(-2) \pm \sqrt{(-2)^2 - 4(1)(2)}}{2(1)}$$

$$x = \dfrac{2 \pm \sqrt{-4}}{2}$$

$$x = \dfrac{2 \pm 2i}{2}$$

$$x = 1 \pm i$$

This equation has no real roots. Thus, its equation has no x-intercepts. This equation matches graph (b).

115.　$y = 2x^2 - 3x$

$$2 = 2x^2 - 3x$$

$$0 = 2x^2 - 3x - 2$$

$$0 = (2x+1)(x-2)$$

$$x = -\dfrac{1}{2}, \quad x = 2$$

117.　$\qquad y_1 y_2 = 14$

$$(x-1)(x+4) = 14$$

$$x^2 + 3x - 4 = 14$$

$$x^2 + 3x - 18 = 0$$

$$(x+6)(x-3) = 0$$

$$x = -6, \quad x = 3$$

119.

$$y_1 + y_2 = 1$$

$$\frac{2x}{x+2} + \frac{3}{x+4} = 1$$

$$(x+2)(x+4)\left(\frac{2x}{x+2} + \frac{3}{x+4}\right) = 1(x+2)(x+4)$$

$$\frac{2x(x+2)(x+4)}{x+2} + \frac{3(x+2)(x+4)}{x+4} = (x+2)(x+4)$$

$$2x(x+4) + 3(x+2) = (x+2)(x+4)$$

$$2x^2 + 8x + 3x + 6 = x^2 + 6x + 8$$

$$x^2 + 5x - 2 = 0$$

$$x = \frac{-b \pm \sqrt{b^2 - 4ac}}{2a}$$

$$x = \frac{-(5) \pm \sqrt{(5)^2 - 4(1)(-2)}}{2(1)}$$

$$x = \frac{-5 \pm \sqrt{33}}{2}$$

The solution set is $\left\{\dfrac{-5 + \sqrt{33}}{2}, \dfrac{-5 - \sqrt{33}}{2}\right\}$.

121.

$$y_1 - y_2 = 0$$

$$(2x^2 + 5x - 4) - (-x^2 + 15x - 10) = 0$$

$$2x^2 + 5x - 4 + x^2 - 15x + 10 = 0$$

$$3x^2 - 10x + 6 = 0$$

$$x = \frac{-b \pm \sqrt{b^2 - 4ac}}{2a}$$

$$x = \frac{-(-10) \pm \sqrt{(-10)^2 - 4(3)(6)}}{2(3)}$$

$$x = \frac{10 \pm \sqrt{28}}{6}$$

$$x = \frac{10 \pm 2\sqrt{7}}{6}$$

$$x = \frac{5 \pm \sqrt{7}}{3}$$

The solution set is $\left\{\dfrac{5 + \sqrt{7}}{3}, \dfrac{5 - \sqrt{7}}{3}\right\}$.

123. Values that make the denominator zero must be excluded.

$$2x^2 + 4x - 9 = 0$$

$$x = \frac{-b \pm \sqrt{b^2 - 4ac}}{2a}$$

$$x = \frac{-(4) \pm \sqrt{(4)^2 - 4(2)(-9)}}{2(2)}$$

$$x = \frac{-4 \pm \sqrt{88}}{4}$$

$$x = \frac{-4 \pm 2\sqrt{22}}{4}$$

$$x = \frac{-2 \pm \sqrt{22}}{2}$$

125. $x^2 - (6 + 2x) = 0$

$x^2 - 2x - 6 = 0$

Apply the quadratic formula.

$a = 1 \quad b = -2 \quad c = -6$

$x = \dfrac{-(-2) \pm \sqrt{(-2)^2 - 4(1)(-6)}}{2(1)}$

$= \dfrac{2 \pm \sqrt{4 - (-24)}}{2}$

$= \dfrac{2 \pm \sqrt{28}}{2}$

$= \dfrac{2 \pm \sqrt{4 \cdot 7}}{2} = \dfrac{2 \pm 2\sqrt{7}}{2} = 1 \pm \sqrt{7}$

We disregard $1 - \sqrt{7}$ because it is negative, and we are looking for a positive number.

Thus, the number is $1 + \sqrt{7}$.

127.

$\dfrac{1}{x^2 - 3x + 2} = \dfrac{1}{x + 2} + \dfrac{5}{x^2 - 4}$

$\dfrac{1}{(x-1)(x-2)} = \dfrac{1}{x+2} + \dfrac{5}{(x+2)(x-2)}$

Multiply both sides of the equation by the least common denominator, $(x-1)(x-2)(x+2)$. This results in the following:

$x + 2 = (x-1)(x-2) + 5(x-1)$

$x + 2 = x^2 - 2x - x + 2 + 5x - 5$

$x + 2 = x^2 + 2x - 3$

$0 = x^2 + x - 5$

Apply the quadratic formula:

$a = 1 \quad b = 1 \quad c = -5$.

$x = \dfrac{-1 \pm \sqrt{1^2 - 4(1)(-5)}}{2(1)} = \dfrac{-1 \pm \sqrt{1 - (-20)}}{2}$

$= \dfrac{-1 \pm \sqrt{21}}{2}$

The solutions are $\dfrac{-1 \pm \sqrt{21}}{2}$, and the solution set is

$\left\{ \dfrac{-1 \pm \sqrt{21}}{2} \right\}$.

129. $\sqrt{2}x^2 + 3x - 2\sqrt{2} = 0$

Apply the quadratic formula:

$a = \sqrt{2} \quad b = 3 \quad c = -2\sqrt{2}$

$x = \dfrac{-3 \pm \sqrt{3^2 - 4(\sqrt{2})(-2\sqrt{2})}}{2(\sqrt{2})}$

$= \dfrac{-3 \pm \sqrt{9 - (-16)}}{2\sqrt{2}}$

$= \dfrac{-3 \pm \sqrt{25}}{2\sqrt{2}} = \dfrac{-3 \pm 5}{2\sqrt{2}}$

Evaluate the expression to obtain two solutions.

$x = \dfrac{-3 - 5}{2\sqrt{2}} \quad$ or $\quad x = \dfrac{-3 + 5}{2\sqrt{2}}$

$= \dfrac{-8}{2\sqrt{2}} \cdot \dfrac{\sqrt{2}}{\sqrt{2}} \qquad = \dfrac{2}{2\sqrt{2}} \cdot \dfrac{\sqrt{2}}{\sqrt{2}}$

$= \dfrac{-8\sqrt{2}}{4} \qquad\qquad = \dfrac{2\sqrt{2}}{4}$

$= -2\sqrt{2} \qquad\qquad = \dfrac{\sqrt{2}}{2}$

The solutions are $-2\sqrt{2}$ and $\dfrac{\sqrt{2}}{2}$, and the solution

set is $\left\{ -2\sqrt{2}, \dfrac{\sqrt{2}}{2} \right\}$.

131. $f(x) = 0.013x^2 - 1.19x + 28.24$

$3 = 0.013x^2 - 1.19x + 28.24$

$0 = 0.013x^2 - 1.19x + 25.24$

Apply the quadratic formula:

$a = 0.013 \quad b = -1.19 \quad c = 25.24$

$x = \dfrac{-(-1.19) \pm \sqrt{(-1.19)^2 - 4(0.013)(25.24)}}{2(0.013)}$

$= \dfrac{1.19 \pm \sqrt{1.4161 - 1.31248}}{0.026}$

$= \dfrac{1.19 \pm \sqrt{0.10362}}{0.026}$

$\approx \dfrac{1.19 \pm 0.32190}{0.026}$

≈ 58.15 or 33.39

The solutions are approximately 33.39 and 58.15. Thus, 33 year olds and 58 year olds are expected to be in 3 fatal crashes per 100 million miles driven. The function models the actual data well.

133. Let $y_1 = -0.01x^2 + 0.7x + 6.1$

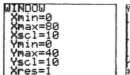 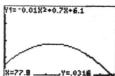

Using the TRACE feature, we find that the height of the shot put is approximately 0 feet when the distance is 77.8 feet. Graph (b) shows the shot' path.

135. Ignoring the thickness of the panel, we essentially need to find the diameter of the rectangular opening.

$$a^2 + b^2 = c^2$$

$$4^2 + 8^2 = c^2$$

$$16 + 64 = c^2$$

$$80 = c^2$$

$$c = \pm\sqrt{80} = \pm 4\sqrt{5}$$

Since we are looking for a length, we discard the negative solution. The solution is $4\sqrt{5} \approx 8.9$ and we conclude that a panel that is about 8.9 feet long is the longest that can be taken through the door diagonally.

137. $15^2 + x^2 = 20^2$

$$225 + x^2 = 400$$

$$x^2 = 175$$

$$x \approx \pm 13.23$$

13.23

The ladder reaches 13.23 feet up.

139. Let w = the width

Let $w + 3$ = the length

Area $= lw$

$$54 = (w + 3)w$$

$$54 = w^2 + 3w$$

$$0 = w^2 + 3w - 54$$

$$0 = (w + 9)(w - 6)$$

Apply the zero product principle.

$$w + 9 = 0 \qquad w - 6 = 0$$

$$w = -9 \qquad w = 6$$

The solution set is $\{-9, 6\}$. Disregard -9 because we can't have a negative length measurement. The width is 6 feet and the length is $6 + 3 = 9$ feet.

141. Let x = the length of the side of the original square

Let $x + 3$ = the length of the side of the new, larger square

$$(x + 3)^2 = 64$$

$$x^2 + 6x + 9 = 64$$

$$x^2 + 6x - 55 = 0$$

$$(x + 11)(x - 5) = 0$$

Apply the zero product principle.

$$x + 11 = 0 \qquad x - 5 = 0$$

$$x = -11 \qquad x = 5$$

The solution set is $\{-11, 5\}$. Disregard -11 because we can't have a negative length measurement. This means that x, the length of the side of the original square, is 5 inches.

143. Let x = the width of the path

$$(20 + 2x)(10 + 2x) = 600$$

$$200 + 40x + 20x + 4x^2 = 600$$

$$200 + 60x + 4x^2 = 600$$

$$4x^2 + 60x + 200 = 600$$

$$4x^2 + 60x - 400 = 0$$

$$4(x^2 + 15x - 100) = 0$$

$$4(x + 20)(x - 5) = 0$$

Apply the zero product principle.

$$4(x + 20) = 0 \qquad x - 5 = 0$$

$$x + 20 = 0 \qquad x = 5$$

$$x = -20$$

The solution set is $\{-20, 5\}$. Disregard -20 because we can't have a negative width measurement. The width of the path is 5 meters.

145. $x(x)(2) = 200$

$$2x^2 = 200$$

$$x^2 = 100$$

$$x = \pm 10$$

The length and width are 10 inches.

147.
$$x(20 - 2x) = 13$$
$$20x - 2x^2 = 13$$
$$0 = 2x^2 - 20x + 13$$
$$x = \frac{-(-20) \pm \sqrt{(-20)^2 - 4(2)(13)}}{2(2)}$$
$$x = \frac{20 \pm \sqrt{296}}{4}$$
$$x = \frac{10 \pm 17.2}{4}$$
$$x = 9.3, 0.7$$

9.3 in and 0.7 in

161.
$$(x + 3)(x - 5) = 0$$
$$x^2 - 5x + 3x - 15 = 0$$
$$x^2 - 2x - 15 = 0$$

163. The dimensions of the pool are 12 meters by 8 meters. With the tile, the dimensions will be 12 + 2x meters by 8 + 2x meters. If we take the area of the pool with the tile and subtract the area of the pool without the tile, we are left with the area of the tile only.
$$(12 + 2x)(8 + 2x) - 12(8) = 120$$
$$\cancel{96} + 24x + 16x + 4x^2 - \cancel{96} = 120$$
$$4x^2 + 40x - 120 = 0$$
$$x^2 + 10x - 30 = 0$$
$$a = 1 \quad b = 10 \quad c = -30$$
$$x = \frac{-10 \pm \sqrt{10^2 - 4(1)(-30)}}{2(1)}$$
$$= \frac{-10 \pm \sqrt{100 + 120}}{2}$$
$$= \frac{-10 \pm \sqrt{220}}{2} \approx \frac{-10 \pm 14.8}{2}$$

Evaluate the expression to obtain two solutions.
$$x = \frac{-10 + 14.8}{2} \quad \text{or} \quad x = \frac{-10 - 14.8}{2}$$
$$x = \frac{4.8}{2} \qquad\qquad x = \frac{-24.8}{2}$$
$$x = 2.4 \qquad\qquad x = -12.4$$

We disregard −12.4 because we can't have a negative width measurement. The solution is 2.4 and we conclude that the width of the uniform tile border is 2.4 meters. This is more than the 2-meter requirement, so the tile meets the zoning laws.

Mid-Chapter 1 Check Point

1.
$$-5 + 3(x + 5) = 2(3x - 4)$$
$$-5 + 3x + 15 = 6x - 8$$
$$3x + 10 = 6x - 8$$
$$-3x = -18$$
$$\frac{-3x}{-3} = \frac{-18}{-3}$$
$$x = 6$$

The solution set is $\{6\}$.

2.
$$5x^2 - 2x = 7$$
$$5x^2 - 2x - 7 = 0$$
$$(5x - 7)(x + 1) = 0$$
$$5x - 7 = 0 \quad \text{or} \quad x + 1 = 0$$
$$5x = 7 \qquad\qquad x = -1$$
$$x = \frac{7}{5}$$

The solution set is $\left\{-1, \dfrac{7}{5}\right\}$.

3.
$$\frac{x - 3}{5} - 1 = \frac{x - 5}{4}$$
$$20\left(\frac{x - 3}{5} - 1\right) = 20\left(\frac{x - 5}{4}\right)$$
$$\frac{20(x - 3)}{5} - 20(1) = \frac{20(x - 5)}{4}$$
$$4(x - 3) - 20 = 5(x - 5)$$
$$4x - 12 - 20 = 5x - 25$$
$$4x - 32 = 5x - 25$$
$$-x = 7$$
$$x = -7$$

The solution set is $\{-7\}$.

4. $3x^2 - 6x - 2 = 0$

$x = \dfrac{-b \pm \sqrt{b^2 - 4ac}}{2a}$

$x = \dfrac{-(-6) \pm \sqrt{(-6)^2 - 4(3)(-2)}}{2(3)}$

$x = \dfrac{6 \pm \sqrt{60}}{6}$

$x = \dfrac{6 \pm 2\sqrt{15}}{6}$

$x = \dfrac{3 \pm \sqrt{15}}{3}$

The solution set is $\left\{ \dfrac{3 + \sqrt{15}}{3}, \dfrac{3 - \sqrt{15}}{3} \right\}$.

5. $4x - 2(1 - x) = 3(2x + 1) - 5$

$4x - 2(1 - x) = 3(2x + 1) - 5$

$4x - 2 + 2x = 6x + 3 - 5$

$6x - 2 = 6x - 2$

$0 = 0$

The solution set is all real numbers.

6. $5x^2 + 1 = 37$

$5x^2 = 36$

$\dfrac{5x^2}{5} = \dfrac{36}{5}$

$x^2 = \dfrac{36}{5}$

$x = \pm\sqrt{\dfrac{36}{5}}$

$x = \pm\dfrac{6}{\sqrt{5}}$

$x = \pm\dfrac{6}{\sqrt{5}} \cdot \dfrac{\sqrt{5}}{\sqrt{5}}$

$x = \pm\dfrac{6\sqrt{5}}{5}$

The solution set is $\left\{ -\dfrac{6\sqrt{5}}{5}, \dfrac{6\sqrt{5}}{5} \right\}$.

7. $x(2x - 3) = -4$

$2x^2 - 3x = -4$

$2x^2 - 3x + 4 = 0$

$x = \dfrac{-b \pm \sqrt{b^2 - 4ac}}{2a}$

$x = \dfrac{-(-3) \pm \sqrt{(-3)^2 - 4(2)(4)}}{2(2)}$

$x = \dfrac{3 \pm \sqrt{-23}}{4}$

$x = \dfrac{3 \pm i\sqrt{23}}{4}$

The solution set is $\left\{ \dfrac{3 + i\sqrt{23}}{4}, \dfrac{3 - i\sqrt{23}}{4} \right\}$.

8. $\dfrac{3x}{4} - \dfrac{x}{3} + 1 = \dfrac{4x}{5} - \dfrac{3}{20}$

$\dfrac{3x}{4} - \dfrac{x}{3} + 1 = \dfrac{4x}{5} - \dfrac{3}{20}$

$60\left(\dfrac{3x}{4} - \dfrac{x}{3} + 1 \right) = 60\left(\dfrac{4x}{5} - \dfrac{3}{20} \right)$

$\dfrac{60(3x)}{4} - \dfrac{60x}{3} + 60(1) = \dfrac{60(4x)}{5} - \dfrac{60(3)}{20}$

$45x - 20x + 60 = 48x - 9$

$25x + 60 = 48x - 9$

$-23x = -69$

$\dfrac{-23x}{-23} = \dfrac{-69}{-23}$

$x = 3$

The solution set is $\{3\}$.

9. $(x + 3)^2 = 24$

$x + 3 = \pm\sqrt{24}$

$x = -3 \pm 2\sqrt{6}$

The solution set is $\left\{ -3 + 2\sqrt{6}, -3 - 2\sqrt{6} \right\}$.

10.
$$\frac{1}{x^2} - \frac{4}{x} + 1 = 0$$

$$x^2\left(\frac{1}{x^2} - \frac{4}{x} + 1\right) = x^2(0)$$

$$\frac{x^2}{x^2} - \frac{4x^2}{x} + x^2 = 0$$

$$1 - 4x + x^2 = 0$$

$$x^2 - 4x + 1 = 0$$

$$x = \frac{-b \pm \sqrt{b^2 - 4ac}}{2a}$$

$$x = \frac{-(-4) \pm \sqrt{(-4)^2 - 4(1)(1)}}{2(1)}$$

$$x = \frac{4 \pm \sqrt{12}}{2}$$

$$x = \frac{4 \pm 2\sqrt{3}}{2}$$

$$x = 2 \pm \sqrt{3}$$

The solution set is $\left\{2 + \sqrt{3}, 2 - \sqrt{3}\right\}$.

11. $3x + 1 - (x - 5) = 2x - 4$
$$2x + 6 = 2x - 4$$
$$6 = -4$$
The solution set is $\varnothing$.

12.
$$\frac{2x}{x^2 + 6x + 8} = \frac{x}{x+4} - \frac{2}{x+2}, \quad x \neq -2, x \neq -4$$

$$\frac{2x}{(x+4)(x+2)} = \frac{x}{x+4} - \frac{2}{x+2}$$

$$\frac{2x(x+4)(x+2)}{(x+4)(x+2)} = (x+4)(x+2)\left(\frac{x}{x+4} - \frac{2}{x+2}\right)$$

$$2x = \frac{x(x+4)(x+2)}{x+4} - \frac{2(x+4)(x+2)}{x+2}$$

$$2x = x(x+2) - 2(x+4)$$

$$2x = x^2 + 2x - 2x - 8$$

$$0 = x^2 - 2x - 8$$

$$0 = (x+2)(x-4)$$

$$x + 2 = 0 \quad \text{or} \quad x - 4 = 0$$
$$x = -2 \quad\quad\quad x = 4$$
-2 must be rejected.
The solution set is $\{4\}$.

13. Let $y = 0$.
$$0 = x^2 + 6x + 2$$

$$x = \frac{-b \pm \sqrt{b^2 - 4ac}}{2a}$$

$$x = \frac{-(6) \pm \sqrt{(6)^2 - 4(1)(2)}}{2(1)}$$

$$x = \frac{-6 \pm \sqrt{28}}{2}$$

$$x = \frac{-6 \pm 2\sqrt{7}}{2}$$

$$x = -3 \pm \sqrt{7}$$

x-intercepts: $-3 + \sqrt{7}$ and $-3 - \sqrt{7}$.

14. Let $y = 0$.
$$0 = 4(x+1) - 3x - (6 - x)$$
$$0 = 4x + 4 - 3x - 6 + x$$
$$0 = 2x - 2$$
$$-2x = -2$$
$$x = 1$$
x-intercept: 1.

15. Let $y = 0$.
$$0 = 2x^2 + 26$$
$$-2x^2 = 26$$
$$x^2 = -13$$
$$x = \pm\sqrt{-13}$$
$$x = \pm i\sqrt{13}$$
There are no x-intercepts.

16. Let $y = 0$.
$$0 = \frac{x^2}{3} + \frac{x}{2} - \frac{2}{3}$$

$$6(0) = 6\left(\frac{x^2}{3} + \frac{x}{2} - \frac{2}{3}\right)$$

$$0 = \frac{6 \cdot x^2}{3} + \frac{6 \cdot x}{2} - \frac{6 \cdot 2}{3}$$

$$0 = 2x^2 + 3x - 4$$

$$x = \frac{-b \pm \sqrt{b^2 - 4ac}}{2a}$$

$$x = \frac{-(3) \pm \sqrt{(3)^2 - 4(2)(-4)}}{2(2)}$$

$$x = \frac{-3 \pm \sqrt{41}}{4}$$

x-intercepts: $\dfrac{-3 + \sqrt{41}}{4}$ and $\dfrac{-3 - \sqrt{41}}{4}$.

17. Let $y = 0$.

$$0 = x^2 - 5x + 8$$

$$x = \frac{-b \pm \sqrt{b^2 - 4ac}}{2a}$$

$$x = \frac{-(-5) \pm \sqrt{(-5)^2 - 4(1)(8)}}{2(1)}$$

$$x = \frac{5 \pm \sqrt{-7}}{2}$$

$$x = \frac{5 \pm i\sqrt{7}}{2}$$

There are no *x*-intercepts.

18.
$$y_1 = y_2$$
$$3(2x - 5) - 2(4x + 1) = -5(x + 3) - 2$$
$$6x - 15 - 8x - 2 = -5x - 15 - 2$$
$$-2x - 17 = -5x - 17$$
$$3x = 0$$
$$x = 0$$

The solution set is $\{0\}$.

19.
$$y_1 y_2 = 10$$
$$(2x + 3)(x + 2) = 10$$
$$2x^2 + 7x + 6 = 10$$
$$2x^2 + 7x - 4 = 0$$
$$(2x - 1)(x + 4) = 0$$
$$2x - 1 = 0 \quad \text{or} \quad x + 4 = 0$$
$$x = \frac{1}{2} \qquad\qquad x = -4$$

The solution set is $\left\{-4, \frac{1}{2}\right\}$.

20. $x^2 + 10x - 3 = 0$

$x^2 + 10x = 3$

Since $b = 10$, we add $\left(\frac{10}{2}\right)^2 = 5^2 = 25$.

$$x^2 + 10x + 25 = 3 + 25$$
$$(x + 5)^2 = 28$$

Apply the square root principle:

$$x + 5 = \pm\sqrt{28}$$
$$x + 5 = \pm\sqrt{4 \cdot 7} = \pm 2\sqrt{7}$$
$$x = -5 \pm 2\sqrt{7}$$

The solutions are $-5 \pm 2\sqrt{7}$, and the solution set is $\left\{-5 \pm 2\sqrt{7}\right\}$.

21. $2x^2 + 5x + 4 = 0$

$a = 2 \quad b = 5 \quad c = 4$

$$b^2 - 4ac = 5^2 - 4(2)(4)$$
$$= 25 - 32 = -7$$

Since the discriminant is negative, there are no real solutions. There are two imaginary solutions that are complex conjugates.

22. $10x(x + 4) = 15x - 15$

$10x^2 + 40x = 15x - 15$

$10x^2 - 25x + 15 = 0$

$a = 10 \quad b = -25 \quad c = 15$

$$b^2 - 4ac = (-25)^2 - 4(10)(15)$$
$$= 625 - 600 = 25$$

Since the discriminant is positive and a perfect square, there are two rational solutions.

23.

x	(x, y)
-2	-5
-1	-3
0	-1
1	1
2	3

$y = 2x - 1$

24.

x	(x, y)
-3	-2
-2	-1
-1	0
0	1
1	0
2	-1
3	-2

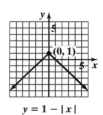

$y = 1 - |x|$

25.

x	(x, y)
-2	6
-1	3
0	2
1	3
2	6

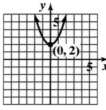

$(0, 2)$

$$y = x^2 + 2$$

26.
$$L = a + (n-1)d$$
$$L = a + dn - d$$
$$-dn = a - d - L$$
$$\frac{-dn}{-d} = \frac{a}{-d} - \frac{d}{-d} - \frac{L}{-d}$$
$$n = -\frac{a}{d} + 1 + \frac{L}{d}$$
$$n = \frac{L}{d} - \frac{a}{d} + 1$$
$$n = \frac{L-a}{d} + 1$$

27.
$$A = 2lw + 2lh + 2wh$$
$$-2lw - 2lh = 2wh - A$$
$$l(-2w - 2h) = 2wh - A$$
$$l = \frac{2wh - A}{-2w - 2h}$$
$$l = \frac{A - 2wh}{2w + 2h}$$

28.
$$f = \frac{f_1 f_2}{f_1 + f_2}$$
$$(f_1 + f_2)(f) = (f_1 + f_2)\frac{f_1 f_2}{f_1 + f_2}$$
$$f_1 f + f_2 f = f_1 f_2$$
$$f_1 f - f_1 f_2 = -f_2 f$$
$$f_1(f - f_2) = -f_2 f$$
$$f_1 = \frac{-f_2 f}{f - f_2}$$
$$f_1 = \frac{f f_2}{f - f_2}$$

29. Let x = the defense budget of Japan in billions
Let $x + 4$ = the defense budget of Russia in billions
Let $x + 251$ = the defense budget of U.S. in billions
$$x + (x+4) + (x+251) = 375$$
$$3x + 255 = 375$$
$$3x = 120$$
$$x = 40$$
$$x + 4 = 44$$
$$x + 251 = 291$$
The defense budget of Japan is \$40 billion, of Russia \$44 billion, and of the U.S. \$291 billion.

30. Let x = the number of months it takes for the average female infant to weigh 16 pounds
$$7 + 1.5x = 16$$
$$1.5x = 9$$
$$\frac{1.5x}{1.5} = \frac{9}{1.5}$$
$$x = 6$$
It takes 6 months for the average female infant to weigh 16 pounds.

31. Let x = the amount invested at 8%.
Let $25,000 - x$ = the amount invested at 9%.
$$0.08x + 0.09(25,000 - x) = 2135$$
$$0.08x + 2250 - 0.09x = 2135$$
$$-0.01x + 2250 = 2135$$
$$-0.01x = -115$$
$$x = \frac{-115}{-0.01}$$
$$x = 11,500$$
$$25,000 - x = 13,500$$
\$11,500 was invested at 8% and \$13,500 was invested at 9%.

32. Let x = the number of prints.
Photo Shop A: $0.11x + 1.60$
Photo Shop B: $0.13x + 1.20$
$$0.13x + 1.20 = 0.11x + 1.60$$
$$0.02x + 1.20 = 1.60$$
$$0.02x = 0.40$$
$$x = 20$$
The cost will be the same for 20 prints.
That common price is
$$0.11(20) + 1.60 = 0.13(20) + 1.20$$
$$= \$3.80$$

33. Let x = the average weight for an American woman aged 20 through 29 in 1960.
$$x + 0.22x = 157$$
$$1.22x = 157$$
$$\frac{1.22x}{1.22} = \frac{157}{1.22}$$
$$x \approx 129$$
The average weight for an American woman aged 20 through 29 in 1960 was 129 pounds.

34. Let x = the amount invested at 4%.
Let $4000 - x$ = the amount invested that lost 3%.
$$0.04x - 0.03(4000 - x) = 55$$
$$0.04x - 120 + 0.03x = 55$$
$$0.07x - 120 = 55$$
$$0.07x = 175$$
$$x = \frac{175}{0.07}$$
$$x = 2500$$
$$4000 - x = 1500$$
$2500 was invested at 4% and $1500 lost 3%.

35. Let x = the width of the rectangle
Let $2x + 5$ = the length of the rectangle
$$2l + 2w = P$$
$$2(2x + 5) + 2x = 46$$
$$4x + 10 + 2x = 46$$
$$6x + 10 = 46$$
$$6x = 36$$
$$\frac{6x}{6} = \frac{36}{6}$$
$$x = 6$$
$$2x + 5 = 17$$
The dimensions of the rectangle are 6 by 17.

36. Let x = the width of the rectangle
Let $2x - 1$ = the length of the rectangle
$$lw = A$$
$$(2x - 1)x = 28$$
$$2x^2 - x = 28$$
$$2x^2 - x - 28 = 0$$
$$(2x + 7)(x - 4) = 0$$
$$2x + 7 = 0 \quad \text{or} \quad x - 4 = 0$$
$$2x = -7 \qquad\qquad x = 4$$
$$x = -\frac{7}{2}$$
$-\frac{7}{2}$ must be rejected.
If $x = 4$, then $2x - 1 = 7$
The dimensions of the rectangle are 4 by 7.

37. Let x = the height up the pole at which the wires are attached.
$$x^2 + 5^2 = 13^2$$
$$x^2 + 25 = 169$$
$$x^2 = 144$$
$$x = \pm 12$$
-12 must be rejected.
The wires are attached 12 feet up the pole.

38. $N = 62.2x^2 + 7000$
$$62.2x^2 + 7000 = N$$
$$62.2x^2 + 7000 = 46,000$$
$$62.2x^2 = 39,000$$
$$\frac{62.2x^2}{62.2} = \frac{39,000}{62.2}$$
$$x^2 \approx 627$$
$$x \approx \pm\sqrt{627}$$
$$x \approx \pm 25$$
-25 must be rejected.
The equation predicts that there were 46,000 multinational corporations 25 years after 1970, or 1995. The model describes the actual data shown in the graph quite well.

39. $P = 0.0049x^2 - 0.359x + 11.78$

$15 = 0.0049x^2 - 0.359x + 11.78$

$0 = 0.0049x^2 - 0.359x - 3.22$

$0 = 0.0049x^2 - 0.359x - 3.22$

$$x = \frac{-b \pm \sqrt{b^2 - 4ac}}{2a}$$

$$x = \frac{-(-0.359) \pm \sqrt{(-0.359)^2 - 4(0.0049)(-3.22)}}{2(0.0049)}$$

$$x = \frac{0.359 \pm \sqrt{0.191993}}{0.0098}$$

$x \approx 81, \quad x \approx -8$ (rejected)

The percentage of foreign born Americans will be 15% about 81 years after 1930, or 2011.

40. $(6 - 2i) - (7 - i) = 6 - 2i - 7 + i = -1 - i$

41. $3i(2 + i) = 6i + 3i^2 = -3 + 6i$

42. $(1 + i)(4 - 3i) = 4 - 3i + 4i - 3i^2$

$\qquad = 4 + i + 3$

$\qquad = 7 + i$

43. $\dfrac{1+i}{1-i} = \dfrac{1+i}{1-i} \cdot \dfrac{1+i}{1+i}$

$\qquad = \dfrac{1 + i + i + i^2}{1 - i^2}$

$\qquad = \dfrac{1 + 2i - 1}{1 + 1}$

$\qquad = \dfrac{2i}{2}$

$\qquad = i$

44. $\sqrt{-75} - \sqrt{-12} = 5i\sqrt{3} - 2i\sqrt{3} = 3i\sqrt{3}$

45. $\left(2 - \sqrt{-3}\right)^2 = \left(2 - i\sqrt{3}\right)^2$

$\qquad = 4 - 4i\sqrt{3} + 3i^2$

$\qquad = 4 - 4i\sqrt{3} - 3$

$\qquad = 1 - 4i\sqrt{3}$

Section 1.6

Check Point Exercises

1. $\qquad 4x^4 = 12x^2$

$4x^4 - 12x^2 = 0$

$4x^2(x^2 - 3) = 0$

$4x^2 = 0 \quad$ or $\quad x^2 - 3 = 0$

$x^2 = 0 \qquad\qquad x^2 = 3$

$x = \pm\sqrt{0} \qquad\qquad x = \pm\sqrt{3}$

$x = 0 \qquad\qquad x = \pm\sqrt{3}$

The solution set is $\left\{-\sqrt{3}, 0, \sqrt{3}\right\}$.

2. $2x^3 + 3x^2 = 8x + 12$

$x^2(2x + 3) - 4(2x + 3) = 10$

$(2x + 3)(x^2 - 4) = 0$

$2x + 3 = 0 \quad$ or $\quad x^2 - 4 = 0$

$2x = -3 \qquad\qquad x^2 = 4$

$x = -\dfrac{3}{2} \qquad\qquad x = \pm 2$

The solution set is $\left\{-2, -\dfrac{3}{2}, 2\right\}$.

3. $\sqrt{x+3}+3=x$

$\sqrt{x+3}=x-3$

$\left(\sqrt{x+3}\right)^2=(x-3)^2$

$x+3=x^2-6x+9$

$0=x^2-7x+6$

$0=(x-6)(x-1)$

$x-6=0$ or $x-1=0$

$x=6$ $x=1$

1 does not check and must be rejected.
The solution set is $\{6\}$.

4. $\sqrt{x+5}-\sqrt{x-3}=2$

$\sqrt{x+5}=2+\sqrt{x-3}$

$\left(\sqrt{x+5}\right)^2=\left(2+\sqrt{x-3}\right)^2$

$x+5=(2)^2+2(2)\left(\sqrt{x-3}\right)+\left(\sqrt{x-3}\right)^2$

$x+5=4+4\sqrt{x-3}+x-3$

$4=4\sqrt{x-3}$

$\dfrac{4}{4}=\dfrac{4\sqrt{x-3}}{4}$

$1=\sqrt{x-3}$

$(1)^2=\left(\sqrt{x-3}\right)^2$

$1=x-3$

$4=x$

The check indicates that 4 is a solution.
The solution set is $\{4\}$.

5. a. $5x^{3/2}-25=0$

$5x^{3/2}=25$

$x^{3/2}=5$

$\left(x^{3/2}\right)^{2/3}=(5)^{2/3}$

$x=5^{2/3}$ or $\sqrt[3]{25}$

Check:

$5\left(5^{2/3}\right)^{3/2}-25=0$

$5(5)-25=0$

$25-25=0$

$0=0$

The solution set is $\left\{5^{2/3}\right\}$ or $\left\{\sqrt[3]{25}\right\}$.

b. $x^{\tfrac{2}{3}}-8=-4$

$x^{2/3}=4$

$\left(x^{2/3}\right)^{3/2}=4^{3/2}$ or

$x=\left(2^2\right)^{3/2}$

$x=2^3$ $x=(-2)^3$

$x=8$ $x=-8$

The solution set is $\{-8,\,8\}$.

6. $x^4-5x^2+6=0$

$\left(x^2\right)^2-5x^2+6=0$

Let $t=x^2$.

$t^2-5t+6=0$

$(t-3)(t-2)=0$

$t-3=0$ or $t-2=0$

$t=3$ or $t=2$

$x^2=3$ or $x^2=2$

$x=\pm\sqrt{3}$ or $x=\pm\sqrt{2}$

The solution set is $\left\{-\sqrt{3},\sqrt{3},-\sqrt{2},\sqrt{2}\right\}$.

7. $3x^{2/3}-11x^{1/3}-4=0$

Let $t=x^{1/3}$.

$3t^2-11t-4=0$

$(3t+1)(t-4)=0$

$3t+1=0$ or $t-4=0$

$3t=-1$

$t=-\dfrac{1}{3}$ $t=4$

$x^{1/3}=-\dfrac{1}{3}$ $x^{1/3}=4$

$x=\left(-\dfrac{1}{3}\right)^3$ $x=4^3$

$x=-\dfrac{1}{27}$ $x=64$

The solution set is $\left\{-\dfrac{1}{27},64\right\}$.

8. $|2x-1|=5$

$2x-1=5$ or $2x-1=-5$

$2x=6$ $2x=-4$

$x=3$ $x=-2$

The solution set is $\{-2,\,3\}$.

85

9. $4|1-2x|-20=0$

$$4|1-2x|=20$$
$$|1-2x|=5$$
$$1-2x=5 \quad \text{or} \quad 1-2x=-5$$
$$-2x=4 \qquad\qquad -2x=-6$$
$$x=-2 \qquad\qquad x=3$$

The solution set is $\{-2, 3\}$.

Exercise Set 1.6

1. $3x^4-48x^2=0$

$$3x^2(x^2-16)=0$$
$$3x^2(x+4)(x-4)=0$$
$$3x^2=0 \quad x+4=0 \quad x-4=0$$
$$x^2=0 \qquad x=-4 \qquad x=4$$
$$x=0$$

The solution set is $\{-4, 0, 4\}$.

3. $3x^3+2x^2=12x+8$

$$3x^3+2x^2-12x-8=0$$
$$x^2(3x+2)-4(3x+2)=0$$
$$(3x+2)(x^2-4)=0$$
$$3x+2=0 \qquad x^2-4=0$$
$$3x=-2 \qquad\quad x^2=4$$
$$x=-\frac{2}{3} \qquad\quad x=\pm 2$$

The solution set is $\left\{-2, -\frac{2}{3}, 2\right\}$.

5. $2x-3=8x^3-12x^2$

$$8x^3-12x^2-2x+3=0$$
$$4x^2(2x-3)-(2x-3)=0$$
$$(2x-3)(4x^2-1)=0$$
$$2x-3=0 \quad 4x^2-1=0$$
$$2x=3 \qquad\quad 4x^2=1$$
$$x^2=\frac{1}{4}$$
$$x=\frac{3}{2} \qquad\quad x=\pm\frac{1}{2}$$

The solution set is $\left\{\frac{3}{2}, \frac{1}{2}, -\frac{1}{2}\right\}$.

7. $4y^3-2=y-8y^2$

$$4y^3+8y^2-y-2=0$$
$$4y^2(y+2)-(y+2)=0$$
$$(y+2)(4y^2-1)=0$$
$$y+2=0 \quad 4y^2-1=0$$
$$4y^2=1$$
$$y^2=\frac{1}{4}$$
$$y=-2 \qquad y=\pm\frac{1}{2}$$

The solution set is $\left\{-2, \frac{1}{2}, -\frac{1}{2}\right\}$.

9. $2x^4=16x$

$$2x^4-16x=0$$
$$2x\left(x^3-8\right)=0$$
$$2x=0 \qquad\qquad x^3-8=0$$
$$x=0 \qquad (x-2)(x^2+2x+2)=0$$
$$x-2=0 \quad x^2+2x+4=0$$
$$x=2 \quad x=\frac{-2\pm\sqrt{2^2-4(1)(4)}}{2(1)}$$
$$x=\frac{-2\pm\sqrt{-12}}{2}$$
$$x=\frac{-2\pm 2i\sqrt{3}}{2}$$
$$x=-1\pm i\sqrt{3}$$

The solution set is $\left\{0, 2, -1\pm i\sqrt{3}\right\}$.

11. $\sqrt{3x+18}=x$

$$3x+18=x^2$$
$$x^2-3x-18=0$$
$$(x+3)(x-6)=0$$
$$x+3=0 \quad x-6=0$$
$$x=-3 \qquad x=6$$
$$\sqrt{3(-3)+18}=-3 \quad \sqrt{3(6)+18}=6$$
$$\sqrt{-9+18}=-3 \qquad \sqrt{18+18}=6$$
$$\sqrt{9}=-3 \ \text{False} \ \sqrt{36}=6$$

The solution set is $\{6\}$.

13.
$$\sqrt{x+3} = x-3$$
$$x+3 = x^2 - 6x + 9$$
$$x^2 - 7x + 6 = 0$$
$$(x-1)(x-6) = 0$$
$$x-1 = 0 \quad x-6 = 0$$
$$x = 1 \qquad x = 6$$
$$\sqrt{1+3} = 1-3 \qquad \sqrt{6+3} = 6-3$$
$$\sqrt{4} = -2 \quad \text{False} \quad \sqrt{9} = 3$$
The solution set is $\{6\}$.

15.
$$\sqrt{2x+13} = x+7$$
$$2x+13 = (x+7)^2$$
$$2x+13 = x^2 + 14x + 49$$
$$x^2 + 12x + 36 = 0$$
$$(x+6)^2 = 0$$
$$x+6 = 0$$
$$x = -6$$
$$\sqrt{2(-6)+13} = -6+7$$
$$\sqrt{-12+13} = 1$$
$$\sqrt{1} = 1$$
The solution set is $\{-6\}$.

17.
$$x - \sqrt{2x+5} = 5$$
$$x-5 = \sqrt{2x+5}$$
$$(x-5)^2 = 2x+5$$
$$x^2 - 10x + 25 = 2x+5$$
$$x^2 - 12x + 20 = 0$$
$$(x-2)(x-10) = 0$$
$$x-2 = 0 \quad x-10 = 0$$
$$x = 2 \qquad x = 10$$
$$2 - \sqrt{2(2)+5} = 5 \quad 10 - \sqrt{2(10)+5} = 5$$
$$2 - \sqrt{9} = 5 \qquad 10 - \sqrt{25} = 5$$
$$2 - 3 = 5 \quad \text{False} \quad 10 - 5 = 5$$
The solution set is $\{10\}$.

19.
$$\sqrt{2x+19} - 8 = x$$
$$\sqrt{2x+19} = x+8$$
$$\left(\sqrt{2x+19}\right)^2 = (x+8)^2$$
$$2x+19 = x^2 + 16x + 64$$
$$0 = x^2 + 14x + 45$$
$$0 = (x+9)(x+5)$$
$$x+9 = 0 \quad \text{or} \quad x+5 = 0$$
$$x = -9 \qquad x = -5$$
-9 does not check and must be rejected.
The solution set is $\{-5\}$.

21.
$$\sqrt{3x} + 10 = x+4$$
$$\sqrt{3x} = x-6$$
$$3x = (x-6)^2$$
$$3x = x^2 - 12x + 36$$
$$x^2 - 15x + 36 = 0$$
$$(x-12)(x-3) = 0$$
$$x-12 = 0 \quad x-3 = 0$$
$$x = 12 \qquad x = 3$$
$$\sqrt{3(12)} + 10 = 12+4 \quad \sqrt{3(3)} + 10 = 3+4$$
$$\sqrt{36} + 10 = 16 \qquad \sqrt{9} + 10 = 7$$
$$6 + 10 = 16 \qquad 3 + 10 = 7 \text{ False}$$
The solution set is $\{12\}$.

23.
$$\sqrt{x+8} - \sqrt{x-4} = 2$$
$$\sqrt{x+8} = \sqrt{x-4} + 2$$
$$x+8 = (\sqrt{x-4}+2)^2$$
$$x+8 = x-4 + 4\sqrt{x-4} + 4$$
$$x+8 = x + 4\sqrt{x-4}$$
$$8 = 4\sqrt{x-4}$$
$$2 = \sqrt{x-4}$$
$$4 = x-4$$
$$x = 8$$
$$\sqrt{8+8} - \sqrt{8-4} = 2$$
$$\sqrt{16} - \sqrt{4} = 2$$
$$4 - 2 = 2$$
The solution set is $\{8\}$.

25.
$$\sqrt{x-5} - \sqrt{x-8} = 3$$
$$\sqrt{x-5} = \sqrt{x-8} + 3$$
$$x-5 = (\sqrt{x-8}+3)^2$$
$$x-5 = x-8+6\sqrt{x-8}+9$$
$$x-5 = x+1+6\sqrt{x-8}$$
$$-6 = 6\sqrt{x-8}$$
$$-1 = \sqrt{x-8}$$
$$1 = x-8$$
$$x = 9$$
$$\sqrt{9-5} - \sqrt{9-8} = 3$$
$$\sqrt{4} - \sqrt{1} = 3$$
$$2-1 = 3 \text{ False}$$
The solution set is the empty set, $\varnothing$.

27.
$$\sqrt{2x+3} + \sqrt{x-2} = 2$$
$$\sqrt{2x+3} = 2 - \sqrt{x-2}$$
$$2x+3 = (2-\sqrt{x-2})^2$$
$$2x+3 = 4 - 4\sqrt{x-2} + x - 2$$
$$x+1 = -4\sqrt{x-2}$$
$$(x+1)^2 = 16(x-2)$$
$$x^2 + 2x + 1 = 16x - 32$$
$$x^2 - 14x + 33 = 0$$
$$(x-11)(x-3) = 0$$
$$x-11 = 0 \quad x-3 = 0$$
$$x = 11 \qquad x = 3$$
$$\sqrt{2(11)+3} + \sqrt{11-2} = 2$$
$$\sqrt{22+3} + \sqrt{9} = 2$$
$$5+3 = 2 \text{ False}$$
$$\sqrt{2(3)+3} + \sqrt{3-2} = 2$$
$$\sqrt{6+3} + \sqrt{1} = 2$$
$$3+1 = 2 \text{ False}$$
The solution set is the empty set, $\varnothing$.

29.
$$\sqrt{3\sqrt{x+1}} = \sqrt{3x-5}$$
$$3\sqrt{x+1} = 3x-5$$
$$9(x+1) = 9x^2 - 30x + 25$$
$$9x^2 - 39x + 16 = 0$$
$$x = \frac{39 \pm \sqrt{945}}{18} = \frac{13 \pm \sqrt{105}}{6}$$
Check proposed solutions.
The solution set is $\left\{ \dfrac{13+\sqrt{105}}{6} \right\}$.

31.
$$x^{3/2} = 8$$
$$(x^{3/2})^{2/3} = 8^{2/3}$$
$$x = \sqrt[3]{8}^2$$
$$x = 2^2$$
$$x = 4$$
$$4^{3/2} = 8$$
$$\sqrt{4}^3 = 8$$
$$2^3 = 8$$
The solution set is $\{4\}$.

33.
$$(x-4)^{3/2} = 27$$
$$((x-4)^{3/2})^{2/3} = 27^{2/3}$$
$$x-4 = \sqrt[3]{27}^2$$
$$x-4 = 3^2$$
$$x-4 = 9$$
$$x = 13$$
$$(13-4)^{3/2} = 27$$
$$9^{3/2} = 27$$
$$\sqrt{9}^3 = 27$$
$$3^3 = 27$$
The solution set is $\{13\}$.

35. $6x^{5/2} - 12 = 0$

$$6x^{5/2} = 12$$

$$x^{5/2} = 2$$

$$(x^{5/2})^{2/5} = 2^{2/5}$$

$$x = \sqrt[5]{2^2}$$

$$x = \sqrt[5]{4}$$

$$6(\sqrt[5]{4})^{5/2} - 12 = 0$$

$$6(4^{1/5})^{5/2} - 12 = 0$$

$$6(4^{1/2}) - 12 = 0$$

$$6(2) - 12 = 0$$

The solution set is $\left\{ \sqrt[5]{4} \right\}$.

37.

$$\left(x-4\right)^{2/3} = 16$$

$$\left[\left(x-4\right)^{2/3} \right]^{3/2} = (16)^{3/2}$$

$$x - 4 = \left(2^4\right)^{3/2}$$

$$x - 4 = 4^3 \qquad x - 4 = (-4)^3$$

$$x - 4 = 64 \qquad x - 4 = -64$$

$$x = 68 \qquad x = -60$$

The solution set is $\{-60, 68\}$.

39. $(x^2 - x - 4)^{3/4} - 2 = 6$

$$(x^2 - x - 4)^{3/4} = 8$$

$$((x^2 - x - 4)^{3/4})^{4/3} = 8^{4/3}$$

$$x^2 - x - 4 = \sqrt[3]{8}^4$$

$$x^2 - x - 4 = 2^4$$

$$x^2 - x - 4 = 16$$

$$x^2 - x - 20 = 0$$

$$(x-5)(x+4) = 0$$

$$x - 5 = 0 \quad x + 4 = 0$$

$$x = 5 \qquad x = -4$$

$$(5^2 - 5 - 4)^{3/4} - 2 = 6$$

$$(25-9)^{3/4} - 2 = 6$$

$$16^{3/4} - 2 = 6$$

$$\sqrt[4]{16}^3 - 2 = 6$$

$$2^3 - 2 = 6$$

$$8 - 2 = 6$$

$$((-4)^2 - (-4) - 4)^{3/4} - 2 = 6$$

$$(16 + 4 - 4)^{3/4} - 2 = 6$$

$$16^{3/4} - 2 = 6$$

$$\sqrt[4]{16}^3 - 2 = 6$$

$$2^3 - 2 = 6$$

$$8 - 2 = 6$$

The solution set is $\{5, -4\}$.

41. $x^4 - 5x^2 + 4 = 0$ let $t = x^2$

$$t^2 - 5t + 4 = 0$$

$$(t-1)(t-4) = 0$$

$$t - 1 = 0 \quad t - 4 = 0$$

$$t = 1 \qquad t = 4$$

$$x^2 = 1 \qquad x^2 = 4$$

$$x = \pm 1 \qquad x = \pm 2$$

The solution set is $\{1, -1, 2, -2\}$.

43. $9x^4 = 25x^2 - 16$

$9x^4 - 25x^2 + 16 = 0$ let $t = x^2$

$9t^2 - 25t + 16 = 0$

$(9t - 16)(t - 1) = 0$

$9t - 16 = 0 \qquad t - 1 = 0$

$9t = 16 \qquad\quad t = 1$

$t = \dfrac{16}{9} \qquad x^2 = 1$

$\qquad\qquad\quad x = \pm 1$

$x^2 = \dfrac{16}{9}$

$x = \pm\dfrac{4}{3}$

The solution set is $\left\{1, -1, \dfrac{4}{3}, -\dfrac{4}{3}\right\}$.

45. $x - 13\sqrt{x} + 40 = 0 \quad$ Let $t = \sqrt{x}$.

$t^2 - 13t + 40 = 0$

$(t - 8)(t - 5) = 0$

$t - 8 = 0 \qquad t - 5 = 0$

$t = 8 \qquad\quad t = 5$

$\sqrt{x} = 8 \qquad \sqrt{x} = 5$

$x = 64 \qquad\quad x = 25$

The solution set is $\{25, 64\}$.

47. $x^{-2} - x^{-1} - 20 = 0 \quad$ Let $t = x^{-1}$

$t^2 - t - 20 = 0$

$(t - 5)(t + 4) = 0$

$t - 5 = 0 \quad t + 4 = 0$

$t = 5 \qquad t = -4$

$x^{-1} = 5 \quad x^{-1} = -4$

$\dfrac{1}{x} = 5 \qquad \dfrac{1}{x} = -4$

$1 = 5x \qquad 1 = -4x$

$\dfrac{1}{5} = x \qquad -\dfrac{1}{4} = x$

The solution set is $\left\{-\dfrac{1}{4}, \dfrac{1}{5}\right\}$.

49. $x^{2/3} - x^{1/3} - 6 = 0$ let $t = x^{1/3}$

$t^2 - t - 6 = 0$

$(t - 3)(t + 2) = 0$

$t - 3 = 0 \qquad t + 2 = 0$

$t = 3 \qquad\quad t = -2$

$x^{1/3} = 3 \qquad x^{1/3} = -2$

$x = 3^3 \qquad\quad x = (-2)^3$

$x = 27 \qquad\quad x = -8$

The solution set is $\{27, -8\}$.

51. $x^{3/2} - 2x^{3/4} + 1 = 0$ let $t = x^{3/4}$

$t^2 - 2t + 1 = 0$

$(t - 1)(t - 1) = 0$

$t - 1 = 0$

$t = 1$

$x^{3/4} = 1$

$x = 1^{4/3}$

$x = 1$

The solution set is $\{1\}$.

53. $2x - 3x^{1/2} + 1 = 0$ let $t = x^{1/2}$

$2t^2 - 3t + 1 = 0$

$(2t - 1)(t - 1) = 0$

$2t - 1 = 0 \qquad t - 1 = 0$

$2t = 1$

$t = \dfrac{1}{2} \qquad\qquad t = 1$

$x^{1/2} = \dfrac{1}{2} \qquad x^{1/2} = 1$

$x = \left(\dfrac{1}{2}\right)^2 \qquad x = 1^2$

$x = \dfrac{1}{4} \qquad\qquad x = 1$

The solution set is $\left\{\dfrac{1}{4}, 1\right\}$.

55. $(x - 5)^2 - 4(x - 5) - 21 = 0$ let $t = x - 5$

$t^2 - 4t - 21 = 0$

$(t + 3)(t - 7) = 0$

$t + 3 = 0 \qquad t - 7 = 0$

$t = -3 \qquad\quad t = 7$

$x - 5 = -3 \quad x - 5 = 7$

$x = 2 \qquad\quad x = 12$

The solution set is $\{2, 12\}$.

57. $\left(x^2-x\right)^2-14\left(x^2-x\right)+24=0$

Let $t=x^2-x$.
$t^2-14t+24=0$
$(t-2)(t-12)=0$
$t=2$ or $t=12$
$x^2-x=2$ or $x^2-x=12$
$x^2-x-2=0$ $x^2-x-12=0$
$(x-2)(x+1)=0$ $(x-4)(x+3)=0$
The solution set is $\{-3,-1,2,4\}$.

59. $\left(y-\dfrac{8}{y}\right)^2+5\left(y-\dfrac{8}{y}\right)-14=0$

Let $t=y-\dfrac{8}{y}$.

$t^2+5t-14=0$
$(t+7)(t-2)=0$
$t=-7$ or $t=2$

$y-\dfrac{8}{y}=-7$ or $y-\dfrac{8}{y}=2$
$y^2+7y-8=0$ $y^2-2y-8=0$
$(y+8)(y-1)=0$ $(y-4)(y+2)=0$
The solution set is $\{-8,-2,1,4\}$.

61. $|x|=8$
$x=8,\ x=-8$
The solution set is $\{8,-8\}$.

63. $|x-2|=7$
$x-2=7$ $x-2=-7$
   $x=9$ $x=-5$
The solution set is $\{9,-5\}$.

65. $|2x-1|=5$
$2x-1=5$ $2x-1=-5$
  $2x=6$ $2x=-4$
   $x=3$ $x=-2$
The solution set is $\{3,-2\}$.

67. $2|3x-2|=14$

$|3x-2|=7$
$3x-2=7$ $3x-2=-7$
  $3x=9$ $3x=-5$
   $x=3$ $x=-5/3$
The solution set is $\{3,-5/3\}$

69. $7|5x|+2=16$
  $7|5x|=14$
   $|5x|=2$
    $5x=2$ $5x=-2$
     $x=2/5$ $x=-2/5$
The solution set is $\left\{\dfrac{2}{5},-\dfrac{2}{5}\right\}$.

71. $2\left|4-\dfrac{5}{2}x\right|+6=18$

$2\left|4-\dfrac{5}{2}x\right|=12$

$\left|4-\dfrac{5}{2}x\right|=6$

$4-\dfrac{5}{2}x=6$ or $4-\dfrac{5}{2}x=-6$

$-\dfrac{5}{2}x=2$ $-\dfrac{5}{2}x=-10$

$-\dfrac{2}{5}\left(-\dfrac{5}{2}\right)x=-\dfrac{2}{5}(2)$ $-\dfrac{2}{5}\left(-\dfrac{5}{2}\right)x=-\dfrac{2}{5}(-10)$

$x=-\dfrac{4}{5}$ $x=4$

The solution set is $\left\{-\dfrac{4}{5},4\right\}$.

73. $|x + 1| + 5 = 3$
$|x + 1| = -2$
No solution
The solution set is $\{\ \}$.

75. $|2x - 1| + 3 = 3$
$|2x - 1| = 0$
$2x - 1 = 0$
$2x = 1$
$x = 1/2$
The solution set is $\{1/2\}$.

77. $|3x - 1| = |x + 5|$

$3x - 1 = x + 5 \qquad 3x - 1 = -x - 5$
$2x - 1 = 5 \qquad\qquad 4x - 1 = -5$
$2x = 6 \qquad\qquad\quad 4x = -4$
$x = 3 \qquad\qquad\quad\ x = -1$

The solution set is $\{3, -1\}$.

79. Set $y = 0$ to find the x-intercept(s).
$$0 = \sqrt{x+2} + \sqrt{x-1} - 3$$
$$-\sqrt{x+2} = \sqrt{x-1} - 3$$
$$\left(-\sqrt{x+2}\right)^2 = \left(\sqrt{x-1} - 3\right)^2$$
$$x + 2 = \left(\sqrt{x-1}\right)^2 - 2\left(\sqrt{x-1}\right)(3) + (3)^2$$
$$x + 2 = x - 1 - 6\sqrt{x-1} + 9$$
$$x + 2 = x - 1 - 6\sqrt{x-1} + 9$$
$$2 = 8 - 6\sqrt{x-1}$$
$$-6 = -6\sqrt{x-1}$$
$$\frac{-6}{-6} = \frac{-6\sqrt{x-1}}{-6}$$
$$1 = \sqrt{x-1}$$
$$(1)^2 = \left(\sqrt{x-1}\right)^2$$
$$1 = x - 1$$
$$2 = x$$
The x-intercept is 2.
The corresponding graph is graph (c).

81. Set $y = 0$ to find the x-intercept(s).
$$0 = x^{\frac{1}{3}} + 2x^{\frac{1}{6}} - 3$$
Let $t = x^{\frac{1}{6}}$.
$$x^{\frac{1}{3}} + 2x^{\frac{1}{6}} - 3 = 0$$
$$\left(x^{\frac{1}{6}}\right)^2 + 2x^{\frac{1}{6}} - 3 = 0$$
$$t^2 + 2t - 3 = 0$$
$$(t + 3)(t - 1) = 0$$
$$t + 3 = 0 \quad \text{or} \quad t - 1 = 0$$
$$t = -3 \qquad\qquad t = 1$$
Substitute $x^{\frac{1}{6}}$ for t.
$$x^{\frac{1}{6}} = -3 \quad \text{or} \quad x^{\frac{1}{6}} = 1$$
$$\left(x^{\frac{1}{6}}\right)^6 = (-3)^6 \qquad \left(x^{\frac{1}{6}}\right)^6 = (1)^6$$
$$x = 729 \qquad\qquad x = 1$$
729 does not check and must be rejected.
The x-intercept is 1.
The corresponding graph is graph (e).

83. Set $y = 0$ to find the x-intercept(s).
$$(x + 2)^2 - 9(x + 2) + 20 = 0$$
Let $t = x + 2$.
$$(x + 2)^2 - 9(x + 2) + 20 = 0$$
$$t^2 - 9t + 20 = 0$$
$$(t - 5)(t - 4) = 0$$
$$t - 5 = 0 \quad \text{or} \quad t - 4 = 0$$
$$t = 5 \qquad\qquad t = 4$$
Substitute $x + 2$ for t.
$$x + 2 = 5 \quad \text{or} \quad x + 2 = 4$$
$$x = 3 \qquad\qquad x = 2$$
The x-intercepts are 2 and 3.
The corresponding graph is graph (f).

85. $|5-4x| = 11$

$$5-4x = 11 \qquad 5-4x = -11$$
$$-4x = 6 \quad \text{or} \quad -4x = -16$$
$$x = -\frac{3}{2} \qquad\qquad x = 4$$

The solution set is $\left\{-\frac{3}{2}, 4\right\}$.

87. $x + \sqrt{x+5} = 7$

$$\sqrt{x+5} = 7 - x$$
$$\left(\sqrt{x+5}\right)^2 = (7-x)^2$$
$$x+5 = 49 - 14x + x^2$$
$$0 = x^2 - 15x + 44$$
$$0 = (x-4)(x-11)$$
$$x - 4 = 0 \quad \text{or} \quad x - 11 = 0$$
$$x = 4 \qquad\qquad x = 11$$

11 does not check and must be rejected.
The solution set is $\{4\}$.

89.

$$2x^3 + x^2 - 8x + 2 = 6$$
$$2x^3 + x^2 - 8x - 4 = 0$$
$$x^2(2x+1) - 4(2x+1) = 0$$
$$(2x+1)(x^2-4) = 0$$
$$(2x+1)(x+2)(x-2) = 0$$
$$2x+1 = 0 \quad \text{or} \quad x+2 = 0 \quad \text{or} \quad x-2 = 0$$
$$x = -\frac{1}{2} \qquad\qquad x = -2 \qquad\qquad x = 2$$

The solution set is $\left\{-\frac{1}{2}, -2, 2\right\}$.

91. $(x+4)^{\frac{3}{2}} = 8$

$$\left((x+4)^{\frac{3}{2}}\right)^{\frac{2}{3}} = (8)^{\frac{2}{3}}$$
$$x+4 = \left(\sqrt[3]{8}\right)^2$$
$$x+4 = (2)^2$$
$$x+4 = 4$$
$$x = 0$$

The solution set is $\{0\}$.

93.

$$y_1 = y_2 + 3$$
$$\left(x^2-1\right)^2 = 2\left(x^2-1\right) + 3$$
$$\left(x^2-1\right)^2 - 2\left(x^2-1\right) - 3 = 0$$

Let $t = x^2 - 1$ and substitute.

$$t^2 - 2t - 3 = 0$$
$$(t+1)(t-3) = 0$$
$$t+1 = 0 \quad \text{or} \quad t-3 = 0$$
$$t = -1 \qquad\qquad t = 3$$

Substitute $x^2 - 1$ for t.

$$x^2 - 1 = -1 \quad \text{or} \quad x^2 - 1 = 3$$
$$x^2 = 0 \qquad\qquad x^2 = 4$$
$$x = 0 \qquad\qquad x = \pm 2$$

The solution set is $\{-2, 0, 2\}$.

95. $|x^2 + 2x - 36| = 12$

$$x^2 + 2x - 36 = 12 \qquad x^2 + 2x - 36 = -12$$
$$x^2 + 2x - 48 = 0 \quad \text{or} \quad x^2 + 2x - 24 = 0$$
$$(x+8)(x-6) = 0 \qquad (x+6)(x-4) = 0$$

Setting each of the factors above equal to zero gives $x = -8$, $x = 6$, $x = -6$, and $x = 4$.
The solution set is $\{-8, -6, 4, 6\}$.

97. $x(x+1)^3 - 42(x+1)^2 = 0$

$$(x+1)^2 \left(x(x+1) - 42\right) = 0$$
$$(x+1)^2 \left(x^2 + x - 42\right) = 0$$
$$(x+1)^2 (x+7)(x-6) = 0$$

Setting each of the factors above equal to zero gives $x = -7$, $x = -1$, and $x = 6$.
The solution set is $\{-7, -1, 6\}$.

99. Let x = the number.

$$\sqrt{5x-4} = x-2$$
$$\left(\sqrt{5x-4}\right)^2 = (x-2)^2$$
$$5x-4 = x^2 - 4x + 4$$
$$0 = x^2 - 9x + 8$$
$$0 = (x-8)(x-1)$$
$$x-8 = 0 \quad \text{or} \quad x-1 = 0$$
$$x = 8 \qquad\qquad x = 1$$

Check $x = 8$: $\sqrt{5(8)-4} = 8-2$
$$\sqrt{40-4} = 6$$
$$\sqrt{36} = 6$$
$$6 = 6$$

Check $x = 1$: $\sqrt{5(1)-4} = 1-2$
$$\sqrt{5-4} = -1$$
$$\sqrt{-1} \neq -1$$

Discard $x = 1$. The number is 8.

101.

$$r = \sqrt{\frac{3V}{\pi h}}$$
$$r^2 = \left(\sqrt{\frac{3V}{\pi h}}\right)^2$$
$$r^2 = \frac{3V}{\pi h}$$
$$\pi r^2 h = 3V$$
$$\frac{\pi r^2 h}{3} = V$$
$$V = \frac{\pi r^2 h}{3} \quad \text{or} \quad V = \frac{1}{3}\pi r^2 h$$

103. Exclude any value that causes the denominator to equal zero.

$$|x+2| - 14 = 0$$
$$|x+2| = 14$$
$$x+2 = 14 \qquad x+2 = -14$$
$$\qquad\qquad \text{or}$$
$$x = 12 \qquad\qquad x = -16$$

−16 and 12 must be excluded from the domain.

105. Let $P = 192$.

$$P = 28\sqrt{t} + 80$$
$$192 = 28\sqrt{t} + 80$$
$$112 = 28\sqrt{t}$$
$$\frac{112}{28} = \frac{28\sqrt{t}}{28}$$
$$4 = \sqrt{t}$$
$$(4)^2 = \left(\sqrt{t}\right)^2$$
$$16 = t$$

192 million computers will be sold 16 years after 1996, or 2012.

107. For the year 2100, we use $x = 98$.

$$H = 0.083(98) + 57.9$$
$$= 66.034$$
$$L = 0.36\sqrt{98} + 57.9$$
$$\approx 61.464$$

In the year 2100, the projected high end temperature is about $66°$ and the projected low end temperature is about $61.5°$.

109. Using H:

$$0.083x + 57.9 = 57.9 + 1$$
$$0.083x = 1$$
$$x = \frac{1}{0.083}$$
$$x \approx 12$$

The projected global temperature will exceed the 2002 average by 1 degree in 2014 (12 years after 2002).

Using L:

$$0.36\sqrt{x} + 57.9 = 1 + 57.9$$
$$0.36\sqrt{x} = 1$$
$$\sqrt{x} = \frac{1}{0.36}$$
$$\left(\sqrt{x}\right)^2 = \left(\frac{1}{0.36}\right)^2$$
$$x \approx 8$$

The projected global temperature will exceed the 2002 average by 1 degree in 2010 (8 years after 2002).

111.
$$y = 5000\sqrt{100 - x}$$
$$40000 = 5000\sqrt{100 - x}$$
$$\frac{40000}{5000} = \frac{5000\sqrt{100 - x}}{5000}$$
$$8 = \sqrt{100 - x}$$
$$8^2 = \left(\sqrt{100 - x}\right)^2$$
$$64 = 100 - x$$
$$-36 = -x$$
$$36 = x$$
40,000 people in the group will survive to age 36. This is shown on the graph as the point $(36, \ 40000)$.

113.
$$365 = 0.2x^{3/2}$$
$$\frac{365}{0.2} = \frac{0.2x^{3/2}}{0.2}$$
$$1825 = x^{3/2}$$
$$1825^2 = \left(x^{3/2}\right)^2$$
$$3,330,625 = x^3$$
$$\sqrt[3]{3,330,625} = \sqrt[3]{x^3}$$
$$149.34 \approx x$$
The average distance of the Earth from the sun is approximately 149 million kilometers.

115.
$$\sqrt{6^2 + x^2} + \sqrt{8^2 + (10 - x)^2} = 18$$
$$\sqrt{36 + x^2} = 18 - \sqrt{64 + 100 - 20x + x^2}$$
$$36 + x^2 = 324 - 36\sqrt{x^2 - 20x + 164} + x^2 - 20x + 164$$
$$36\sqrt{x^2 - 20x + 164} = -20x + 452$$
$$9\sqrt{x^2 - 20x + 164} = -5x + 113$$
$$81(x^2 - 20x + 164) = 25x^2 - 1130x + 12769$$
$$81x^2 - 1620x + 13284 = 25x^2 - 1130x + 12769$$
$$56x^2 - 490x + 515 = 0$$
$$x = \frac{490 \pm \sqrt{(-490)^2 - 4(56)(515)}}{2(56)}$$
$$x = \frac{490 \pm 353.19}{112}$$
$$x \approx 1.2 \qquad x \approx 7.5$$
The point should be located approximately either 1.2 feet or 7.5 feet from the base of the 6-foot pole.

125. $x^3 + 3x^2 - x - 3 = 0$
The solution set is $\{-3, -1, 1\}$.
$$(-3)^3 + 3(-3)^2 - (-3) - 3 = 0$$
$$-27 + 27 + 3 - 3 = 0$$
$$(-1)^3 + 3(-1)^2 - (-1) - 3 = 0$$
$$-1 + 3 + 1 - 3 = 0$$
$$1^3 + 3(1)^2 - (1) - 3 = 0$$
$$1 + 3 - 1 - 3 = 0$$

127. $\sqrt{2x + 13} - x - 5 = 0$
The solution set is $\{-2\}$.
$$\sqrt{2(-2) + 13} - (-2) - 5 = 0$$
$$\sqrt{-4 + 13} + 2 - 5 = 0$$
$$\sqrt{9} - 3 = 0$$
$$3 - 3 = 0$$

129. a. False; $\left(\sqrt{y+4}+\sqrt{y-1}\right)^2 \neq y+4+y-1$

b. False; if $t = (x^2 - 2x)^3$, the original
equation can be written as $t^3 - 5t + 6 = 0$,
not a quadratic form.

c. False; the other value may be a solution.

d. True

(d) is true

131. $5 - \dfrac{2}{x} = \sqrt{5 - \dfrac{2}{x}}$

or

$5 - \dfrac{2}{x} = 0 \qquad 5 - \dfrac{2}{x} = 1$

$5 = \dfrac{2}{x} \qquad\quad -\dfrac{2}{x} = -4$

$5x = 2 \qquad\quad -4x = -2$

$x = \dfrac{2}{5} \qquad\quad x = \dfrac{1}{2}$

The solution set is $\left\{\dfrac{2}{5}, \dfrac{1}{2}\right\}$.

133. $x^{5/6} + x^{2/3} - 2x^{1/2} = 0$

$x^{1/2}(x^{2/6} + x^{1/6} - 2) = 0$ let $t = x^{1/6}$

$x^{1/2}(t^2 + t - 2) = 0$

$x^{1/2} = 0 \quad t^2 + t - 2 = 0$

$(t - 1)(t + 2) = 0$

$t - 1 = 0 \qquad t + 2 = 0$

$t = 1 \qquad\qquad t = -2$

$x^{1/6} = 1 \qquad x^{1/6} = -2$

$x = 1^6 \qquad\quad x = (-2)^6$

$x = 0 \quad x = 1 \qquad x = 64$

64 does not check and must be rejected.
The solution set is $\{0, 1\}$.

Section 1.7

Check Point Exercises

1. a. $[-2, 5) = \left\{x\mid -2 \le x < 5\right\}$

b. $[1, 3.5] = \left\{x\mid 1 \le x \le 3.5\right\}$

c. $[-\infty, -1) = \left\{x\mid x < -1\right\}$

2. a. Graph $[1, 3]$:

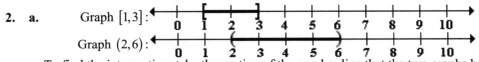

To find the intersection, take the portion of the number line that the two graphs have in common.
Numbers in both $[1, 3]$ and $(2, 6)$:

Thus, $[1, 3] \cap (2, 6) = (2, 3]$.

b. Graph $[1, 3]$:

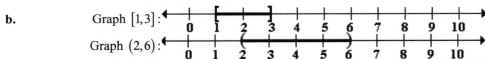

To find the union, take the portion of the number line representing the total collection of numbers in the two graphs.
Numbers in either $[1, 3]$ or $(2, 6)$ or both:

Thus, $[1, 3] \cup (2, 6) = [1, 6)$.

3. $2 - 3x \le 5$

   $-3x \le 3$

   $x \ge -1$

   The solution set is $\{x | x \ge -1\}$ or $[-1, \infty)$.

<!-- number line with point at -1 -->

4. $3x + 1 > 7x - 15$

   $-4x > -16$

   $\dfrac{-4x}{-4} < \dfrac{-16}{-4}$

   $x < 4$

   The solution set is $\{x | x < 4\}$ or $(-\infty, 4]$.

<!-- number line with point at 4 -->

5.   a. $3(x + 1) > 3x + 2$

   $3x + 3 > 3x + 2$

   $3 > 2$

   $3 > 2$ is true for all values of x.

   The solution set is $\{x | x$ is a real number$\}$.

b. $x + 1 \le x - 1$

   $1 \le -1$

   $1 \le -1$ is false for all values of x.

   The solution set is $\varnothing$.

6. $1 \le 2x + 3 < 11$

   $-2 \le 2x < 8$

   $-1 \le x < 4$

   The solution set is $\{x | -1 \le x < 4\}$ or $[-1, 4)$.

<!-- number line with points at -1 and 4 -->

7. $|x - 2| < 5$

   $-5 < x - 2 < 5$

   $-3 < x < 7$

   The solution set is $\{x | -3 < x < 7\}$ or $(-3, 7)$.

<!-- number line with points at -3 and 7 -->

8. $-3|5x - 2| + 20 \ge -19$

   $-3|5x - 2| \ge -39$

   $\dfrac{-3|5x - 2|}{-3} \le \dfrac{-39}{-3}$

   $|5x - 2| \le 13$

   $-13 \le 5x - 2 \le 13$

   $-11 \le 5x \le 15$

   $\dfrac{-11}{5} \le \dfrac{5x}{5} \le \dfrac{15}{5}$

   $-\dfrac{11}{5} \le x \le 3$

   The solution set is

   $\left\{ x \left| -\dfrac{11}{5} \le x \le 3 \right. \right\}$ or $\left[-\dfrac{11}{5}, 3 \right]$.

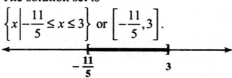

9. $18 < |6 - 3x|$

   $\begin{array}{lcl} 6 - 3x < -18 & & 6 - 3x > 18 \\ & \text{or} & \\ -3x < -24 & & -3x > 12 \\ \dfrac{-3x}{-3} > \dfrac{-24}{-3} & & \dfrac{-3x}{-3} < \dfrac{12}{-3} \\ x > 8 & & x < -4 \end{array}$

   The solution set is $\{x | x < -4 \text{ or } x > 8\}$

   or $(-\infty, -4) \cup (8, \infty)$.

<!-- number line with points at -4 and 8 -->

10.   Let x = the number of miles driven in a week.

   $260 < 80 + 0.25x$

   $180 < 0.25x$

   $720 < x$

   Driving more than 720 miles in a week makes Basic the better deal.

Exercise Set 1.7

1. $1 < x \le 6$

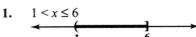

3. $-5 \le x < 2$

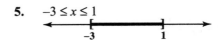

5. $-3 \le x \le 1$

7. $x > 2$

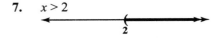

9. $x \ge -3$

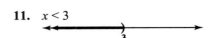

11. $x < 3$

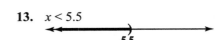

13. $x < 5.5$

15. Graph $(-3,0)$:

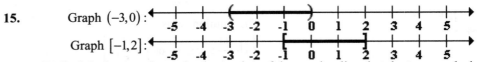

Graph $[-1,2]$:

To find the intersection, take the portion of the number line that the two graphs have in common.

Numbers in both
$(-3,0)$ and $[-1,2]$:

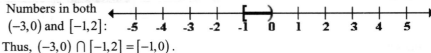

Thus, $(-3,0) \cap [-1,2] = [-1,0)$.

17. Graph $(-3,0)$:

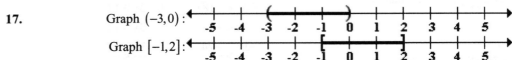

Graph $[-1,2]$:

To find the union, take the portion of the number line representing the total collection of numbers in the two graphs.

Numbers in either $(-3,0)$
or $[-1,2]$ or both:

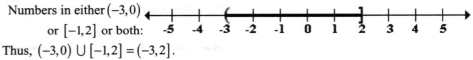

Thus, $(-3,0) \cup [-1,2] = (-3,2]$.

19. Graph $(-\infty,5)$:

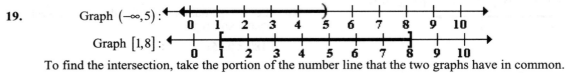

Graph $[1,8]$:

To find the intersection, take the portion of the number line that the two graphs have in common.

Numbers in both
$(-\infty,5)$ and $[1,8]$:

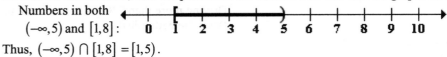

Thus, $(-\infty,5) \cap [1,8] = [1,5)$.

21. Graph $(-\infty,5)$:

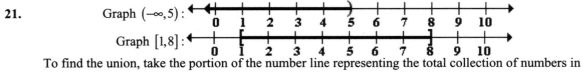

Graph $[1,8]$:

To find the union, take the portion of the number line representing the total collection of numbers in the two graphs.

Numbers in either $(-\infty,5)$
or $[1,8]$ or both:

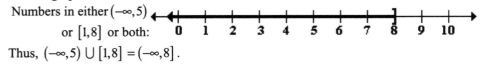

Thus, $(-\infty,5) \cup [1,8] = (-\infty,8]$.

23.   Graph $[3, \infty)$: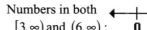

     Graph $(6, \infty)$: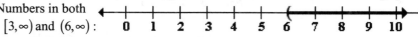

To find the intersection, take the portion of the number line that the two graphs have in common.

Numbers in both
$[3, \infty)$ and $(6, \infty)$: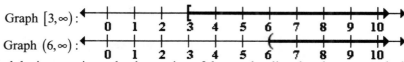

Thus, $[3, \infty) \cap (6, \infty) = (6, \infty)$.

25.   Graph $[3, \infty)$: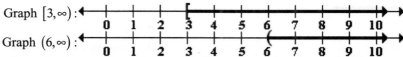

     Graph $(6, \infty)$:

To find the union, take the portion of the number line representing the total collection of numbers in the two graphs.

Numbers in either $[3, \infty)$
or $(6, \infty)$ or both: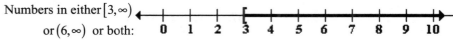

Thus, $[3, \infty) \cup (6, \infty) = [3, \infty)$.

27. $5x + 11 < 26$
$5x < 15$
$x < 3$
The solution set is $\{x \mid x < 3\}$, or $(-\infty, 3)$.

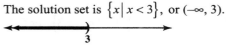

29. $3x - 7 \geq 13$
$3x \geq 20$
$x \geq \dfrac{20}{3}$
The solution set is $\left\{x \mid x > \dfrac{20}{3}\right\}$, or $\left[\dfrac{20}{3}, \infty\right)$.

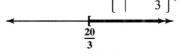

31. $-9x \geq 36$
$x \leq -4$
The solution set is $\{x \mid x \leq -4\}$, or $(-\infty, -4]$.

33. $8x - 11 \leq 3x - 13$
$8x - 3x \leq -13 + 11$
$5x \leq -2$
$x \leq -\dfrac{2}{5}$

The solution set is $\left\{x \mid x \leq -\dfrac{2}{5}\right\}$, or $\left(-\infty, -\dfrac{2}{5}\right]$.

35. $4(x + 1) + 2 \geq 3x + 6$
$4x + 4 + 2 \geq 3x + 6$
$4x + 6 \geq 3x + 6$
$4x - 3x \geq 6 - 6$
$x \geq 0$
The solution set is $\{x \mid x > 0\}$, or $[0, \infty)$.

37. $2x - 11 < -3(x + 2)$
$2x - 11 < -3x - 6$
$5x < 5$
$x < 1$
The solution set is $\{x \mid x < 1\}$, or $(-\infty, 1)$.

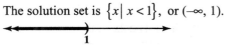

39. $1 - (x + 3) \geq 4 - 2x$
$1 - x - 3 \geq 4 - 2x$
$-x - 2 \geq 4 - 2x$
$x \geq 6$
The solution set is $\{x \mid x \geq 6\}$, or $[6, \infty)$.

41. $\dfrac{x}{4} - \dfrac{3}{2} \le \dfrac{x}{2} + 1$

$\dfrac{4x}{4} - \dfrac{4 \cdot 3}{2} \le \dfrac{4 \cdot x}{2} + 4 \cdot 1$

$x - 6 \le 2x + 4$

$-x \le 10$

$x \ge -10$

The solution set is $\{x \mid x \ge -10\}$, or $[-10, \infty)$.

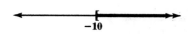

43. $1 - \dfrac{x}{2} > 4$

$-\dfrac{x}{2} > 3$

$x < -6$

The solution set is $\{x \mid x, -6\}$, or $(-\infty, -6)$.

45. $\dfrac{x-4}{6} \ge \dfrac{x-2}{9} + \dfrac{5}{18}$

$3(x-4) \ge 2(x-2) + 5$

$3x - 12 \ge 2x - 4 + 5$

$x \ge 13$

The solution set is $\{x \mid x \ge 13\}$, or $[13, \infty)$.

47. $4(3x - 2) - 3x < 3(1 + 3x) - 7$

$12x - 8 - 3x < 3 + 9x - 7$

$9x - 8 < -4 + 9x$

$-8 < -4$

True for all x

The solution set is $\{x \mid x \text{ is any real number}\}$, or

$(-\infty, \infty)$.

49. $5(x - 2) - 3(x + 4) \ge 2x - 20$

$5x - 10 - 3x - 12 \ge 2x - 20$

$2x - 22 \ge 2x - 20$

$-22 \ge -20$

Not true for any x.

The solution set is the empty set, $\varnothing$.

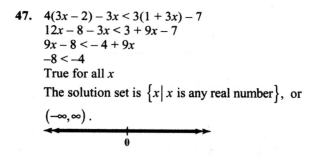

51. $6 < x + 3 < 8$

$6 - 3 < x + 3 - 3 < 8 - 3$

$3 < x < 5$

The solution set is $\{x \mid 3 < x < 5\}$, or $(3, 5)$.

53. $-3 \le x - 2 < 1$

$-1 \le x < 3$

The solution set is $\{x \mid -1 \le x < 3\}$, or $[-1, 3)$.

55. $-11 < 2x - 1 \le -5$

$-10 < 2x \le -4$

$-5 < x \le -2$

The solution set is $\{x \mid -5 < x \le -2\}$, or

$(-5, -2]$.

57. $-3 \le \dfrac{2}{3}x - 5 < -1$

$2 \le \dfrac{2}{3}x < 4$

$3 \le x < 6$

The solution set is $\{x \mid 3 \le x < 6\}$, or $[3, 6)$.

59. $|x| < 3$

$-3 < x < 3$

The solution set is $\{x \mid -3 < x < 3\}$, or $(-3, 3)$.

61. $|x - 1| \le 2$

$-2 \le x - 1 \le 2$

$-1 \le x \le 3$

The solution set is $\{x \mid -1 \le x \le 3\}$, or $[-1, 3]$.

62. $|x + 3| \le 4$

$-4 \le x + 3 \le 4$

$-7 \le x \le 1$

The solution set is $\{x \mid -7 \le x \le 1\}$ or $[-7, 1]$.

63. $|2x - 6| < 8$

$-8 < 2x - 6 < 8$

$-2 < 2x < 14$

$-1 < x < 7$

The solution set is $\{x \mid -1 < x < 7\}$, or $(-1, 7)$.

65. $|2(x - 1) + 4| \le 8$

$-8 \le 2(x - 1) + 4 \le 8$

$-8 \le 2x - 2 + 4 \le 8$

$-8 \le 2x + 2 \le 8$

$-10 \le 2x \le 6$

$-5 \le x \le 3$

The solution set is $\{x \mid -5 \le x \le 3\}$, or

$[-5, 3]$.

67. $\left|\dfrac{2y+6}{3}\right| < 2$

$-2 < \dfrac{2y+6}{3} < 2$

$-6 < 2y + 6 < 6$

$-12 < 2y < 0$

$-6 < y < 0$

The solution set is $\{x \mid -6 < y < 0\}$, or $(-6, 0)$.

69. $|x| > 3$

$x > 3$ or $x < -3$

The solution set is $\{x \mid x > 3 \text{ or } x < -3\}$, that is,

$(-\infty, -3)$ or $(3, \infty)$.

71. $|x - 1| \geq 2$

$x - 1 \geq 2$ or $x - 1 \leq -2$

$x \geq 3$ $x \leq -1$

The solution set is $\{x \mid x \leq -1 \text{ or } x \geq 3\}$, that is,

$(-\infty, -1]$ or $[3, \infty)$.

73. $|3x - 8| > 7$

$3x - 8 > 7$ or $3x - 8 < -7$

$3x > 15$ $3x < 1$

$x > 5$ $x < \dfrac{1}{3}$

The solution set is $\left\{x \mid x < \dfrac{1}{3} \text{ or } x > 5\right\}$, that is,

$\left(-\infty, \dfrac{1}{3}\right)$ or $(5, \infty)$.

75. $\left|\dfrac{2x+2}{4}\right| \geq 2$

$\dfrac{2x+2}{4} \geq 2$ or $\dfrac{2x+2}{4} \leq -2$

$2x + 2 \geq 8$ $2x + 2 \leq -8$

$2x \geq 6$ $2x \leq -10$

$x \geq 3$ $x \leq -5$

The solution set is $\{x \mid x \leq -5 \text{ or } x \geq 3\}$, that is,

$(-\infty, -5]$ or $[3, \infty)$.

77. $\left|3 - \dfrac{2}{3}x\right| > 5$

$3 - \dfrac{2}{3}x > 5$ or $3 - \dfrac{2}{3}x < -5$

$-\dfrac{2}{3}x > 2$ $-\dfrac{2}{3}x < -8$

$x < -3$ $x > 12$

The solution set is $\{x \mid x < -3 \text{ or } x > 12\}$, that is,

$(-\infty, -3)$ or $(12, \infty)$.

79. $3|x - 1| + 2 \geq 8$

$3|x - 1| \geq 6$

$|x - 1| \geq 2$

$x - 1 \geq 2$ or $x - 1 \leq -2$

$x \geq 3$ $x \leq -1$

The solution set is $\{x \mid x \leq 1 \text{ or } x \geq 3\}$, that is,

$(-\infty, -1]$ or $[3, \infty)$.

81. $-2|x - 4| \geq -4$

$\dfrac{-2|x-4|}{-2} \leq \dfrac{-4}{-2}$

$|x - 4| \leq 2$

$-2 \leq x - 4 \leq 2$

$2 \leq x \leq 6$

The solution set is $\{x \mid 2 \leq x \leq 6\}$.

83. $-4|1 - x| < -16$

$\dfrac{-4|1-x|}{-4} > \dfrac{-16}{-4}$

$|1 - x| > 4$

$1 - x > 4$ $1 - x < -4$

$-x > 3$ or $-x < -5$

$x < -3$ $x > 5$

The solution set is $\{x \mid x < -3 \text{ or } x > 5\}$.

85. $3 \leq |2x - 1|$

$2x - 1 \geq 3$ $2x - 1 \leq -3$

$2x \geq 4$ or $2x \leq -2$

$x \geq 2$ $x \leq -1$

The solution set is $\{x \mid x \leq -1 \text{ or } x \geq 2\}$.

87. $5 > |4 - x|$ is equivalent to $|4 - x| < 5$.

$$-5 < 4 - x < 5$$
$$-9 < -x < 1$$
$$\frac{-9}{-1} > \frac{-x}{-1} > \frac{1}{-1}$$
$$9 > x > -1$$
$$-1 < x < 9$$

The solution set is $\{x | -1 < x < 9\}$.

89. $1 < |2 - 3x|$ is equivalent to $|2 - 3x| > 1$.

$$\begin{array}{ccc} 2 - 3x > 1 & & 2 - 3x < -1 \\ -3x > -1 & & -3x < -3 \\ \frac{-3x}{-3} < \frac{-1}{-3} \quad \text{or} & & \frac{-3x}{-3} > \frac{-3}{-3} \\ x < \frac{1}{3} & & x > 1 \end{array}$$

The solution set is $\left\{ x \,\middle|\, x < \frac{1}{3} \text{ or } x > 1 \right\}$.

91. $12 < \left| -2x + \frac{6}{7} \right| + \frac{3}{7}$

$$\frac{81}{7} < \left| -2x + \frac{6}{7} \right|$$

$$-2x + \frac{6}{7} > \frac{81}{7} \quad \text{or} \quad -2x + \frac{6}{7} < -\frac{81}{7}$$

$$-2x > \frac{75}{7} \qquad\qquad -2x < -\frac{87}{7}$$

$$x < -\frac{75}{14} \qquad\qquad x > \frac{87}{14}$$

The solution set is $\left\{ x \,\middle|\, x < -\frac{75}{14} \text{ or } x > \frac{87}{14} \right\}$,

that is, $\left(-\infty, -\frac{75}{14} \right)$ or $\left(\frac{87}{14}, \infty \right)$.

93. $4 + \left| 3 - \frac{x}{3} \right| \geq 9$

$$\left| 3 - \frac{x}{3} \right| \geq 5$$

$$3 - \frac{x}{3} \geq 5 \quad \text{or} \quad 3 - \frac{x}{3} \leq -5$$

$$-\frac{x}{3} \geq 2 \qquad\qquad -\frac{x}{3} \leq -8$$

$$x \leq -6 \qquad\qquad x \geq 24$$

The solution set is $\{x | x \leq -6 \text{ or } x \geq 24\}$, that is,

$(-\infty, -6]$ or $[24, \infty)$.

95.

$$y_1 \leq y_2$$
$$\frac{x}{2} + 3 \leq \frac{x}{3} + \frac{5}{2}$$
$$6\left(\frac{x}{2} + 3 \right) \leq 6\left(\frac{x}{3} + \frac{5}{2} \right)$$
$$\frac{6x}{2} + 6(3) \leq \frac{6x}{3} + \frac{6(5)}{2}$$
$$3x + 18 \leq 2x + 15$$
$$x \leq -3$$

The solution set is $(-\infty, -3]$.

97.

$$y \geq 4$$
$$1 - (x + 3) + 2x \geq 4$$
$$1 - x - 3 + 2x \geq 4$$
$$x - 2 \geq 4$$
$$x \geq 6$$

The solution set is $[6, \infty)$.

99.

$$y < 8$$
$$|3x - 4| + 2 < 8$$
$$|3x - 4| < 6$$
$$-6 < 3x - 4 < 6$$
$$-2 < 3x < 10$$
$$\frac{-2}{3} < \frac{3x}{3} < \frac{10}{3}$$
$$\frac{-2}{3} < x < \frac{10}{3}$$

The solution set is $\left(\frac{-2}{3}, \frac{10}{3} \right)$.

101.

$$y \leq 4$$
$$7 - \left| \frac{x}{2} + 2 \right| \leq 4$$
$$-\left| \frac{x}{2} + 2 \right| \leq -3$$
$$\left| \frac{x}{2} + 2 \right| \geq 3$$

$$\frac{x}{2} + 2 \geq 3 \quad \text{or} \quad \frac{x}{2} + 2 \leq -3$$
$$x + 4 \geq 6 \qquad\qquad x + 4 \leq -6$$
$$x \geq 2 \qquad\qquad x \leq -10$$

The solution set is $(-\infty, -10] \cup [2, \infty)$.

103. The graph's height is below 5 on the interval $(-1, 9)$.

105. The solution set is $\{x \mid -1 \le x < 2\}$ or $[-1, 2)$.

107. Let x be the number.
$$|4 - 3x| \ge 5 \quad \text{or} \quad |3x - 4| \ge 5$$

$$\begin{array}{ll} 3x - 4 \ge 5 & 3x - 4 \le -5 \\ 3x \ge 9 \quad \text{or} & 3x \le -1 \\ x \ge 3 & x \le -\dfrac{1}{3} \end{array}$$

The solution set is $\left\{x \mid x \le -\dfrac{1}{3} \text{ or } x \ge 3\right\}$ or $\left(-\infty, -\dfrac{1}{3}\right] \cup [3, \infty)$.

109. $(0, 4)$

111. passion $\le$ intimacy or intimacy $\ge$ passion

113. passion<commitment or commitment > passion

115. 9, after 3 years

117. $3.1x + 25.8 > 63$
$3.1x > 37.2$
$x > 12$
Since x is the number of years after 1994, we calculate 1994+12=2006. 63% of voters will use electronic systems after 2006.

119. $28 \le 20 + 0.40(x - 60) \le 40$
$28 \le 20 + 0.40x - 24 \le 40$
$28 \le 0.40x - 4 \le 40$
$32 \le 0.40x \le 44$
$80 \le x \le 110$
Between 80 and 110 ten minutes, inclusive.

121. $\left|\dfrac{h - 50}{5}\right| \ge 1.645$

$$\dfrac{h - 50}{5} \ge 1.645 \quad \text{or} \quad \dfrac{h - 50}{5} \le -1.645$$

$$\begin{array}{ll} h - 50 \ge 8.225 & h - 50 \le -8.225 \\ h \ge 58.225 & h \le 41.775 \end{array}$$

The number of outcomes would be 59 or more, or 41 or less.

123. $15 + 0.08x < 3 + .12x$
$12 < 0.04x$
$300 < x$
Plan A is a better deal when driving more than 300 miles a month.

125. $2 + 0.08x < 8 + 0.05x$
$0.03x < 6$
$x < 200$
The credit union is a better deal when writing less than 200 checks.

127. $3000 + 3x < 5.5x$
$3000 < 2.5x$
$1200 < x$
More then 1200 packets of stationary need to be sold each week to make a profit.

129. $245 + 95x \le 3000$
$95x \le 2755$
$x \le 29$
29 bags or less can be lifted safely.

131. a. $\dfrac{86 + 88 + x}{3} \ge 90$
$\dfrac{174 + x}{3} \ge 90$
$174 + x \ge 270$
$x \ge 96$
You must get at least a 96.

b. $\dfrac{86 + 88 + x}{3} < 80$
$\dfrac{174 + x}{3} < 80$
$174 + x < 240$
$x < 66$
This will happen if you get a grade less than 66.

133. Let x = the number of times the bridge is crossed per three month period
The cost with the 3-month pass is
$C_3 = 7.50 + 0.50x$.

The cost with the 6-month pass is $C_6 = 30$.

Because we need to buy two 3-month passes per 6-month pass, we multiply the cost with the 3-month pass by 2.
$$2(7.50 + 0.50x) < 30$$
$$15 + x < 30$$
$$x < 15$$
We also must consider the cost without purchasing a pass. We need this cost to be less than the cost with a 3-month pass.
$$3x > 7.50 + 0.50x$$
$$2.50x > 7.50$$
$$x > 3$$
The 3-month pass is the best deal when making more than 3 but less than 15 crossings per 3-month period.

143.

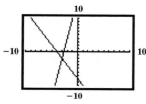

$x < -3$

145 a. The cost of Plan A is $4 + 0.10x$;
The cost of Plan B is $2 + 0.15x$.

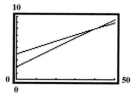

c. 41 or more checks make Plan A better.

d. $4 + 0.10x < 2 + 0.15x$
$$2 < 0.05x$$
$$x > 40$$
The solution set is $\{x \mid x > 40\}$ or $(40, \infty)$.

147. Because $x > y$, $y - x$ represents a negative number. When both sides are multiplied by $(y - x)$ the inequality must be reversed.

149. Model 1:
$$|T - 57| < 7$$
$$-7 < T - 57 < 7$$
$$50 < T < 64$$
Model 2:
$$|T - 50| < 22$$
$$-22 < T - 50 < 22$$
$$28 < T < 72$$

Model 1 describes a city with monthly temperature averages ranging from 50 degrees to 64 degrees Fahrenheit. Model 2 describes a city with monthly temperature averages ranging from 28 degrees to 72 degrees Fahrenheit.

Model 1 describes San Francisco and model 2 describes Albany.

Chapter 1 Review Exercises

1.

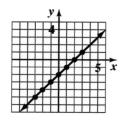

$y = 2x - 2$

$x = -3, y = -8$
$x = -2, y = -6$
$x = -1, y = -4$
$x = 0, y = -2$
$x = 1, y = 0$
$x = 2, y = 2$
$x = 3, y = 4$

2.

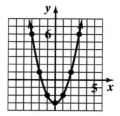

$y = x^2 - 3$

$x = -3, y = 6$
$x = -2, y = 1$
$x = -1, y = -2$
$x = 0, y = -3$
$x = 1, y = -2$
$x = 2, y = 1$
$x = 3, y = 6$

104

3.

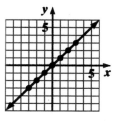

$y = x$

$x = -3, y = -3$
$x = -2, y = -2$
$x = -1, y = -1$
$x = 0, y = 0$
$x = 1, y = 1$
$x = 2, y = 2$
$x = 3, y = 3$

4.

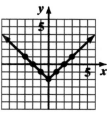

$y = |x| - 2$

$x = -3, y = 1$
$x = -2, y = 0$
$x = -1, y = -1$
$x = 0, y = -2$
$x = 1, y = -1$
$x = 2, y = 0$
$x = 3, y = 1$

5. A portion of Cartesian coordinate plane with minimum x-value equal to -20, maximum x-value equal to 40, x-scale equal to 10 and with minimum y-value equal to -5, maximum y-value equal to 5, and y-scale equal to 1.

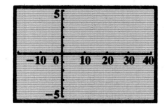

6. x-intercept: -2; The graph intersects the x-axis at $(-2, 0)$.
y-intercept: 2; The graph intersects the y-axis at $(0, 2)$.

7. x-intercepts: $2, -2$; The graph intersects the x-axis at $(-2, 0)$ and $(2, 0)$.
y-intercept: -4; The graph intercepts the y-axis at $(0, -4)$.

8. x-intercept: 5; The graph intersects the x-axis at $(5, 0)$.
y-intercept: None; The graph does not intersect the y-axis.

9. Point A is $(91, 125)$. This means that in 1991, 125,000 acres were used for cultivation

10. Opium cultivation was 150,000 acres in 1997.

11. Opium cultivation was at a minimum in 2001 when approximately 25,000 acres were used.

12. Opium cultivation was at a maximum in 2004 when approximately 300,000 acres were used.

13. Opium cultivation did not change between 1991 and 1992.

14. Opium cultivation increased at the greatest rate between 2001 and 2002. The increase in acres used for opium cultivation in this time period was approximately $180,000 - 25,000 = 155,000$ acres.

15. $2x - 5 = 7$
$\quad\quad 2x = 12$
$\quad\quad\; x = 6$
The solution set is $\{6\}$.
This is a conditional equation.

16. $5x + 20 = 3x$
$\quad\quad 2x = -20$
$\quad\quad\; x = -10$
The solution set is $\{-10\}$.
This is a conditional equation.

17. $7(x - 4) = x + 2$
$7x - 28 = x + 2$
$\quad\quad 6x = 30$
$\quad\quad\; x = 5$
The solution set is $\{5\}$.
This is a conditional equation.

18. $1 - 2(6 - x) = 3x + 2$

$\quad 1 - 12 + 2x = 3x + 2$

$\quad\quad -11 - x = 2$

$\quad\quad\quad -x = 13$

$\quad\quad\quad\quad x = -13$

The solution set is $\{-13\}$.

This is a conditional equation.

19. $2(x - 4) + 3(x + 5) = 2x - 2$

$\quad 2x - 8 + 3x + 15 = 2x - 2$

$\quad\quad\quad 5x + 7 = 2x - 2$

$\quad\quad\quad\quad\quad 3x = -9$

$\quad\quad\quad\quad\quad x = -3$

The solution set is $\{-3\}$.

This is a conditional equation.

20. $2x - 4(5x + 1) = 3x + 17$

$\quad 2x - 20x - 4 = 3x + 17$

$\quad\quad -18x - 4 = 3x + 17$

$\quad\quad\quad -21x = 21$

$\quad\quad\quad\quad x = -1$

The solution set is $\{-1\}$.

This is a conditional equation.

21. $7x + 5 = 5(x + 3) + 2x$

$\quad 7x + 5 = 5x + 15 + 2x$

$\quad 7x + 5 = 7x + 15$

$\quad\quad 5 = 15$

The solution set is $\varnothing$.

This is an inconsistent equation.

22. $7x + 13 = 2(2x - 5) + 3x + 23$

$\quad 7x + 13 = 2(2x - 5) + 3x + 23$

$\quad 7x + 13 = 4x - 10 + 3x + 23$

$\quad 7x + 13 = 7x + 13$

$\quad\quad 13 = 13$

The solution set is all real numbers.

This is an identity.

23. $\dfrac{2x}{3} = \dfrac{x}{6} + 1$

$\quad 2(2x) = x + 6$

$\quad\quad 4x = x + 6$

$\quad\quad 3x = 6$

$\quad\quad\quad x = 2$

The solution set is $\{2\}$.

This is a conditional equation.

24. $\dfrac{x}{2} - \dfrac{1}{10} = \dfrac{x}{5} + \dfrac{1}{2}$

$\quad 5x - 1 = 2x + 5$

$\quad\quad 3x = 6$

$\quad\quad\quad x = 2$

The solution set is $\{2\}$.

This is a conditional equation.

25. $\dfrac{2x}{3} = 6 - \dfrac{x}{4}$

$\quad 4(2x) = 12(6) - 3x$

$\quad\quad 8x = 72 - 3x$

$\quad\quad 11x = 72$

$\quad\quad\quad x = \dfrac{72}{11}$

The solution set is $\left\{\dfrac{72}{11}\right\}$.

This is a conditional equation.

26. $\dfrac{x}{4} = 2 - \dfrac{x - 3}{3}$

$\quad \dfrac{12 \cdot x}{4} = 12(2) - \dfrac{12(x - 3)}{3}$

$\quad\quad 3x = 24 - 4x + 12$

$\quad\quad 7x = 36$

$\quad\quad\quad x = \dfrac{36}{7}$

The solution set is $\left\{\dfrac{36}{7}\right\}$.

This is a conditional equation.

27. $\dfrac{3x + 1}{3} - \dfrac{13}{2} = \dfrac{1 - x}{4}$

$\quad 4(3x + 1) - 6(13) = 3(1 - x)$

$\quad\quad 12x + 4 - 78 = 3 - 3x$

$\quad\quad\quad 12x - 74 = 3 - 3x$

$\quad\quad\quad\quad 15x = 77$

$\quad\quad\quad\quad\quad x = \dfrac{77}{15}$

The solution set is $\left\{\dfrac{77}{15}\right\}$.

This is a conditional equation.

28. $\dfrac{9}{4} - \dfrac{1}{2x} = \dfrac{4}{x}$

$9x - 2 = 16$

$9x = 18$

$x = 2$

The solution set is $\{2\}$.
This is a conditional equation.

29. $\dfrac{7}{x-5} + 2 = \dfrac{x+2}{x-5}$

$7 + 2(x-5) = x + 2$

$7 + 2x - 10 = x + 2$

$2x - 3 = x + 2$

$x = 5$

5 does not check and must be rejected.
The solution set is the empty set, $\varnothing$.
This is an inconsistent equation.

30. $\dfrac{1}{x-1} - \dfrac{1}{x+1} = \dfrac{2}{x^2-1}$

$\dfrac{1}{x-1} - \dfrac{1}{x+1} = \dfrac{2}{(x+1)(x-1)}$

$x + 1 - (x-1) = 2$

$x + 1 - x + 1 = 2$

$2 = 2$

The solution set is all real numbers except -1 and 1. This is a conditional equation.

31. $\dfrac{5}{x+3} + \dfrac{1}{x-2} = \dfrac{8}{x^2+x-6}$

$\dfrac{5}{x+3} + \dfrac{1}{x-2} = \dfrac{8}{(x+3)(x-2)}$

$\dfrac{5(x+3)(x-2)}{x+3} + \dfrac{(x+3)(x-2)}{x-2} = \dfrac{8(x+3)(x-2)}{(x+3)(x-2)}$

$5(x-2) + 1(x+3) = 8$

$5x - 10 + x + 3 = 8$

$6x - 7 = 8$

$6x = 15$

$x = \dfrac{15}{6}$

$x = \dfrac{5}{2}$

The solution set is $\left\{\dfrac{5}{2}\right\}$.
This is a conditional equation.

32. $\dfrac{1}{x+5} = 0$

$(x+5)\dfrac{1}{x+5} = (x+5)(0)$

$1 = 0$

The solution set is the empty set, $\varnothing$.
This is an inconsistent equation.

33. $\dfrac{4}{x+2} + \dfrac{3}{x} = \dfrac{10}{x^2+2x}$

$\dfrac{4}{x+2} + \dfrac{3}{x} = \dfrac{10}{x(x+2)}$

$\dfrac{4 \cdot x(x+2)}{x+2} + \dfrac{3 \cdot x(x+2)}{x} = \dfrac{10 \cdot x(x+2)}{x(x+2)}$

$4x + 3(x+2) = 10$

$4x + 3x + 6 = 10$

$7x + 6 = 10$

$7x = 4$

$x = \dfrac{4}{7}$

The solution set is $\left\{\dfrac{4}{7}\right\}$.
This is a conditional equation.

34. $3 - 5(2x+1) - 2(x-4) = 0$

$3 - 5(2x+1) - 2(x-4) = 0$

$3 - 10x - 5 - 2x + 8 = 0$

$-12x + 6 = 0$

$-12x = -6$

$x = \dfrac{-6}{-12}$

$x = \dfrac{1}{2}$

The solution set is $\left\{\dfrac{1}{2}\right\}$.
This is a conditional equation.

35. $\dfrac{x+2}{x+3}+\dfrac{1}{x^2+2x-3}-1=0$

$\dfrac{x+2}{x+3}+\dfrac{1}{(x+3)(x-1)}-1=0$

$\dfrac{x+2}{x+3}+\dfrac{1}{(x+3)(x-1)}=1$

$\dfrac{(x+2)(x+3)(x-1)}{x+3}+1=(x+3)(x-1)$

$(x+2)(x-1)+1=(x+3)(x-1)$

$x^2+x-2+1=x^2+2x-3$

$x-1=2x-3$

$-x=-2$

$x=2$

The solution set is $\{2\}$.

This is a conditional equation.

36.   Let x = the number of calories in Burger King's Chicken Caesar.

$x+125$ = the number of calories in Taco Bell's Express Taco Salad.

$x+95$ = the number of calories in Wendy's Mandarin Chicken Salad.

$x+(x+125)+(x+95)=1705$

$3x+220=1705$

$3x=1485$

$x=495$

$x+125=495+125=620$

$x+95=495+95=590$

There are 495 calories in the Chicken Caesar, 620 calories in the Express Taco Salad, and 590 calories in the Mandarin Chicken Salad.

37.   Let x = the number of years after 1970.

$P=-0.5x+37.4$

$18.4=-0.5x+37.4$

$-19=-0.5x$

$\dfrac{-19}{-0.5}=\dfrac{-0.5x}{-0.5}$

$38=x$

If the trend continues only 18.4% of U.S. adults will smoke cigarettes 38 years after 1970, or 2008.

38. $15+.05x=5+.07x$

$10=.02x$

$500=x$

Both plans cost the same at 500 minutes.

39.   Let x = the original price of the phone

$48=x-0.20x$

$48=0.80x$

$60=x$

The original price is $60.

40.   Let x = the amount sold to earn $800 in one week

$800=300+0.05x$

$500=0.05x$

$10,000=x$

Sales must be $10,000 in one week to earn $800.

41.   Let x = the amount invested at 4%

Let y = the amount invested at 7%

$x+\quad y=9000$

$0.04x+0.07y=555$

Multiply the first equation by -0.04 and add.

$-0.04x-0.04y=-360$

$\underline{0.04x+0.07y=555}$

$0.03y=195$

$y=6500$

Back-substitute 6500 for y in one of the original equations to find x.

$x+y=9000$

$x+6500=9000$

$x=2500$

There was $2500 invested at 4% and $6500 invested at 7%.

42.   Let x = the amount invested at 2%

Let $8000-x$ = the amount invested at 5%.

$0.05(8000-x)=0.02x+85$

$400-0.05x=0.02x+85$

$-0.05x-0.02x=85-400$

$-0.07x=-315$

$\dfrac{-0.07x}{-0.07}=\dfrac{-315}{-0.07}$

$x=4500$

$8000-x=3500$

$4500 was invested at 2% and $3500 was invested at 5%.

43. Let w = the width of the playing field,
Let $3w - 6$ = the length of the playing field

$$P = 2(\text{length}) + 2(\text{width})$$

$$340 = 2(3w - 6) + 2w$$

$$340 = 6w - 12 + 2w$$

$$340 = 8w - 12$$

$$352 = 8w$$

$$44 = w$$

The dimensions are 44 yards by 126 yards.

44. a. Let x = the number of years (after 2007).
College A's enrollment: $14,100 + 1500x$
College B's enrollment: $41,700 - 800x$
$$14,100 + 1500x = 41,700 - 800x$$

b. Check some points to determine that
$y_1 = 14,100 + 1500x$ and
$y_2 = 41,700 - 800x$. Since
$y_1 = y_2 = 32,100$ when $x = 12$, the two
colleges will have the same enrollment in the
year $2007 + 12 = 2019$. That year the
enrollments will be 32,100 students.

45. $vt + gt^2 = s$

$$gt^2 = s - vt$$

$$\frac{gt^2}{t^2} = \frac{s - vt}{t^2}$$

$$g = \frac{s - vt}{t^2}$$

46. $T = gr + gvt$

$$T = g(r + vt)$$

$$\frac{T}{r + vt} = \frac{g(r + vt)}{r + vt}$$

$$\frac{T}{r + vt} = g$$

$$g = \frac{T}{r + vt}$$

47. $$T = \frac{A - P}{\text{Pr}}$$

$$\text{Pr}(T) = \text{Pr}\frac{A - P}{\text{Pr}}$$

$$\text{Pr}T = A - P$$

$$\text{Pr}T + P = A$$

$$P(rT + 1) = A$$

$$P = \frac{A}{1 + rT}$$

48. $(8 - 3i) - (17 - 7i) = 8 - 3i - 17 + 7i$
$$= -9 + 4i$$

49. $4i(3i - 2) = (4i)(3i) + (4i)(-2)$
$$= 12i^2 - 8i$$
$$= -12 - 8i$$

50. $(7 - i)(2 + 3i)$
$$= 7 \cdot 2 + 7(3i) + (-i)(2) + (-i)(3i)$$
$$= 14 + 21i - 2i + 3$$
$$= 17 + 19i$$

51. $(3 - 4i)^2 = 3^2 + 2 \cdot 3(-4i) + (-4i)^2$
$$= 9 - 24i - 16$$
$$= -7 - 24i$$

52. $(7 + 8i)(7 - 8i) = 7^2 + 8^2 = 49 + 64 = 113$

53. $\dfrac{6}{5 + i} = \dfrac{6}{5 + i} \cdot \dfrac{5 - i}{5 - i}$

$$= \frac{30 - 6i}{25 + 1}$$

$$= \frac{30 - 6i}{26}$$

$$= \frac{15 - 3i}{13}$$

$$= \frac{15}{13} - \frac{3}{13}i$$

54. $\dfrac{3 + 4i}{4 - 2i} = \dfrac{3 + 4i}{4 - 2i} \cdot \dfrac{4 + 2i}{4 + 2i}$

$$= \frac{12 + 6i + 16i + 8i^2}{16 - 4i^2}$$

$$= \frac{12 + 22i - 8}{16 + 4}$$

$$= \frac{4 + 22i}{20}$$

$$= \frac{1}{5} + \frac{11}{10}i$$

55. $\sqrt{-32} - \sqrt{-18} = i\sqrt{32} - i\sqrt{18}$
$$= i\sqrt{16 \cdot 2} - i\sqrt{9 \cdot 2}$$
$$= 4i\sqrt{2} - 3i\sqrt{2}$$
$$= (4i - 3i)\sqrt{2}$$
$$= i\sqrt{2}$$

56. $(-2+\sqrt{-100})^2 = (-2+i\sqrt{100})^2$

$\qquad\qquad = (-2+10i)^2$

$\qquad\qquad = 4-40i+(10i)^2$

$\qquad\qquad = 4-40i-100$

$\qquad\qquad = -96-40i$

57. $\dfrac{4+\sqrt{-8}}{2} = \dfrac{4+i\sqrt{8}}{2} = \dfrac{4+2i\sqrt{2}}{2} = 2+i\sqrt{2}$

58. $\qquad 2x^2+15x = 8$

$\qquad 2x^2+15x-8 = 0$

$\qquad (2x-1)(x+8) = 0$

$\qquad 2x-1 = 0 \quad x+8 = 0$

$\qquad x = \dfrac{1}{2} \text{ or } x = -8$

The solution set is $\left\{\dfrac{1}{2}, -8\right\}$.

59. $5x^2+20x = 0$

$\qquad 5x(x+4) = 0$

$\qquad 5x = 0 \quad x+4 = 0$

$\qquad x = 0 \text{ or } x = -4$

The solution set is $\{0, -4\}$.

60. $2x^2-3 = 125$

$\qquad 2x^2 = 128$

$\qquad x^2 = 64$

$\qquad x = \pm 8$

The solution set is $\{8, -8\}$.

61. $\dfrac{x^2}{2}+5 = -3$

$\qquad \dfrac{x^2}{2} = -8$

$\qquad x^2 = -16$

$\qquad \sqrt{x^2} = \pm\sqrt{-16}$

$\qquad x = \pm 4i$

62. $(x+3)^2 = -10$

$\qquad \sqrt{(x+3)^2} = \pm\sqrt{-10}$

$\qquad x+3 = \pm i\sqrt{10}$

$\qquad x = -3 \pm i\sqrt{10}$

63. $(3x-4)^2 = 18$

$\qquad \sqrt{(3x-4)^2} = \pm\sqrt{18}$

$\qquad 3x-4 = \pm 3\sqrt{2}$

$\qquad 3x = 4 \pm 3\sqrt{2}$

$\qquad \dfrac{3x}{3} = \dfrac{4 \pm 3\sqrt{2}}{3}$

$\qquad x = \dfrac{4 \pm 3\sqrt{2}}{3}$

64. x^2+20x

$\qquad \left(\dfrac{20}{2}\right)^2 = 10^2 = 100$

$\qquad x^2+20x+100 = (x+10)^2$

65. x^2-3x

$\qquad \left(\dfrac{3}{2}\right)^2 = \dfrac{9}{4}$

$\qquad x^2-3x+\dfrac{9}{4} = \left(x-\dfrac{3}{2}\right)^2$

66. $\qquad x^2-12x = -27$

$\qquad x^2-12x+36 = -27+36$

$\qquad (x-6)^2 = 9$

$\qquad x-6 = \pm 3$

$\qquad x = 6 \pm 3$

$\qquad x = 9, 3$

The solution set is $\{9, 3\}$.

67. $3x^2-12x+11 = 0$

$\qquad x^2-4x = -\dfrac{11}{3}$

$\qquad x^2-4x+4 = -\dfrac{11}{3}+4$

$\qquad (x-2)^2 = \dfrac{1}{3}$

$\qquad x-2 = \pm\sqrt{\dfrac{1}{3}}$

$\qquad x = 2 \pm \dfrac{\sqrt{3}}{3}$

The solution set is $\left\{2+\dfrac{\sqrt{3}}{3}, 2-\dfrac{\sqrt{3}}{3}\right\}$.

68.
$$x^2 = 2x + 4$$
$$x^2 - 2x - 4 = 0$$
$$x = \frac{2 \pm \sqrt{(-2)^2 - 4(1)(-4)}}{2(1)}$$
$$x = \frac{2 \pm \sqrt{4 + 16}}{2}$$
$$x = \frac{2 \pm \sqrt{20}}{2}$$
$$x = \frac{2 \pm 2\sqrt{5}}{2}$$
$$x = 1 \pm \sqrt{5}$$

The solution set is $\left\{1 + \sqrt{5}, 1 - \sqrt{5}\right\}$.

69. $x^2 - 2x + 19 = 0$
$$x = \frac{2 \pm \sqrt{(-2)^2 - 4(1)(19)}}{2(1)}$$
$$x = \frac{2 \pm \sqrt{4 - 76}}{2}$$
$$x = \frac{2 \pm \sqrt{-72}}{2}$$
$$x = \frac{2 \pm 6i\sqrt{2}}{2}$$
$$x = 1 \pm 3i\sqrt{2}$$

The solution set is $\left\{1 + 3i\sqrt{2}, 1 - 3i\sqrt{2}\right\}$.

70.
$$2x^2 = 3 - 4x$$
$$2x^2 + 4x - 3 = 0$$
$$x = \frac{-4 \pm \sqrt{4^2 - 4(2)(-3)}}{2(2)}$$
$$x = \frac{-4 \pm \sqrt{16 + 24}}{4}$$
$$x = \frac{-4 \pm \sqrt{40}}{4}$$
$$x = \frac{-4 \pm 2\sqrt{10}}{4}$$
$$x = \frac{-2 \pm \sqrt{10}}{2}$$

The solution set is $\left\{\frac{-2 + \sqrt{10}}{2}, \frac{-2 - \sqrt{10}}{2}\right\}$.

71. $x^2 - 4x + 13 = 0$
$$(-4)^2 - 4(1)(13)$$
$$= 16 - 52$$
$$= -36; \text{ 2 complex imaginary solutions}$$

72. $9x^2 = 2 - 3x$
$$9x^2 + 3x - 2 = 0$$
$$3^2 - 4(9)(-2)$$
$$= 9 + 72$$
$$= 81; \text{ 2 unequal real solutions}$$

73. $2x^2 - 11x + 5 = 0$
$$(2x - 1)(x - 5) = 0$$
$$2x - 1 = 0 \quad x - 5 = 0$$
$$x = \frac{1}{2} \text{ or } x = 5$$

The solution set is $\left\{5, \frac{1}{2}\right\}$.

74.
$$(3x + 5)(x - 3) = 5$$
$$3x^2 + 5x - 9x - 15 = 5$$
$$3x^2 - 4x - 20 = 0$$
$$x = \frac{4 \pm \sqrt{(-4)^2 - 4(3)(-20)}}{2(3)}$$
$$x = \frac{4 \pm \sqrt{16 + 240}}{6}$$
$$x = \frac{4 \pm \sqrt{256}}{6}$$
$$x = \frac{4 \pm 16}{6}$$
$$x = \frac{20}{6}, \frac{-12}{6}$$
$$x = \frac{10}{3}, -2$$

The solution set is $\left\{-2, \frac{10}{3}\right\}$.

75. $3x^2 - 7x + 1 = 0$
$$x = \frac{7 \pm \sqrt{(-7)^2 - 4(3)(1)}}{2(3)}$$
$$x = \frac{7 \pm \sqrt{49 - 12}}{6}$$
$$x = \frac{7 \pm \sqrt{37}}{6}$$

The solution set is $\left\{\frac{7 + \sqrt{37}}{6}, \frac{7 - \sqrt{37}}{6}\right\}$.

76. $x^2 - 9 = 0$

$x^2 = 9$

$x = \pm 3$

The solution set is $\{-3, 3\}$.

77. $(x-3)^2 - 25 = 0$

$(x-3)^2 = 25$

$x - 3 = \pm 5$

$x = 3 \pm 5$

$x = 8, -2$

The solution set is $\{8, -2\}$.

78. $3x^2 - x + 2 = 0$

$x = \dfrac{1 \pm \sqrt{(-1)^2 - 4(3)(2)}}{2(3)}$

$x = \dfrac{1 \pm \sqrt{1 - 24}}{6}$

$x = \dfrac{1 \pm \sqrt{-23}}{6}$

$x = \dfrac{1 \pm i\sqrt{23}}{6}$

The solution set is $\left\{ \dfrac{1 + i\sqrt{23}}{6}, \dfrac{1 - i\sqrt{23}}{6} \right\}$.

79. $3x^2 - 10x = 8$

$3x^2 - 10x - 8 = 0$

$(3x + 2)(x - 4) = 0$

$3x + 2 = 0 \quad$ or $\quad x - 4 = 0$

$3x = -2 \qquad\qquad x = 4$

$x = -\dfrac{2}{3}$

The solution set is $\left\{ -\dfrac{2}{3}, 4 \right\}$.

80. $(x+2)^2 + 4 = 0$

$(x+2)^2 = -4$

$\sqrt{(x+2)^2} = \pm\sqrt{-4}$

$x + 2 = \pm 2i$

$x = -2 \pm 2i$

The solution set is $\{-2 + 2i, -2 - 2i\}$.

81. $\dfrac{5}{x+1} + \dfrac{x-1}{4} = 2$

$\dfrac{5 \cdot 4(x+1)}{x+1} + \dfrac{(x-1) \cdot 4(x+1)}{4} = 2 \cdot 4(x+1)$

$20 + (x-1)(x+1) = 8(x+1)$

$20 + x^2 - 1 = 8x + 8$

$x^2 - 8x - 11 = 0$

$x = \dfrac{-b \pm \sqrt{b^2 - 4ac}}{2a}$

$x = \dfrac{-(-8) \pm \sqrt{(-8)^2 - 4(1)(11)}}{2(1)}$

$x = \dfrac{8 \pm \sqrt{20}}{2}$

$x = \dfrac{8 \pm 2\sqrt{5}}{2}$

$x = 4 \pm \sqrt{5}$

The solution set is $\left\{ 4 + \sqrt{5}, 4 - \sqrt{5} \right\}$.

82. $W(t) = 3t^2$

$588 = 3t^2$

$196 = t^2$

Apply the square root property.

$t^2 = 196$

$t = \pm\sqrt{196}$

$t = \pm 14$

The solutions are -14 and 14. We disregard -14, because we cannot have a negative time measurement. The fetus will weigh 588 grams after 14 weeks.

83. $P = -0.035x^2 + 0.65x + 7.6$

$0 = -0.035x^2 + 0.65x + 7.6$

$x = \dfrac{-b \pm \sqrt{b^2 - 4ac}}{2a}$

$x = \dfrac{-(0.65) \pm \sqrt{(0.65)^2 - 4(-0.035)(7.6)}}{2(-0.035)}$

$x \approx 27 \quad x \approx -8 \text{ (rejected)}$

If this trend continues, corporations will pay no taxes 27 years after 1985, or 2012.

84.
$$A = lw$$
$$15 = l(2l - 7)$$
$$15 = 2l^2 - 7l$$
$$0 = 2l^2 - 7l - 15$$
$$0 = (2l + 3)(l - 5)$$
$$l = 5$$
$$2l - 7 = 3$$
The length is 5 yards, the width is 3 yards.

85. Let x = height of building
$2x$ = shadow height
$$x^2 + (2x)^2 = 300^2$$
$$x^2 + 4x^2 = 90,000$$
$$5x^2 = 90,000$$
$$x^2 = 18,000$$
$$x \approx \pm 134.164$$
Discard negative height.
The building is approximately 134 meters high.

86.
$$2x^4 = 50x^2$$
$$2x^4 - 50x^2 = 0$$
$$2x^2(x^2 - 25) = 0$$
$$x = 0$$
$$x = \pm 5$$
The solution set is $\{-5, 0, 5\}$.

87.
$$2x^3 - x^2 - 18x + 9 = 0$$
$$x^2(2x - 1) - 9(2x - 1) = 0$$
$$(x^2 - 9)(2x - 1) = 0$$
$$x = \pm 3, \ x = \frac{1}{2}$$
The solution set is $\left\{-3, \frac{1}{2}, 3\right\}$.

88.
$$\sqrt{2x - 3} + x = 3$$
$$\sqrt{2x - 3} = 3 - x$$
$$2x - 3 = 9 - 6x + x^2$$
$$x^2 - 8x + 12 = 0$$
$$x^2 - 8x = -12$$
$$x^2 - 8x + 16 = -12 + 16$$
$$(x - 4)^2 = 4$$
$$x - 4 = \pm 2$$
$$x = 4 + 2$$
$$x = 6, 2$$
The solution set is $\{2\}$.

89.
$$\sqrt{x - 4} + \sqrt{x + 1} = 5$$
$$\sqrt{x - 4} = 5 - \sqrt{x + 1}$$
$$x - 4 = 25 - 10\sqrt{x + 1} + (x + 1)$$
$$x - 4 = 26 + x - 10\sqrt{x + 1}$$
$$-30 = -10\sqrt{x + 1}$$
$$3 = \sqrt{x + 1}$$
$$9 = x + 1$$
$$x = 8$$
The solution set is $\{8\}$.

90.
$$3x^{\frac{3}{4}} - 24 = 0$$
$$3x^{\frac{3}{4}} = 24$$
$$x^{\frac{3}{4}} = 8$$
$$\left(x^{\frac{3}{4}}\right)^{\frac{4}{3}} = (8)^{\frac{4}{3}}$$
$$x = 16$$
The solution set is $\{16\}$.

91.
$$(x - 7)^{\frac{2}{3}} = 25$$
$$\left[(x - 7)^{\frac{2}{3}}\right]^{\frac{3}{2}} = 25^{\frac{3}{2}}$$
$$x - 7 = \left(5^2\right)^{\frac{3}{2}}$$
$$x - 7 = 5^3$$
$$x - 7 = 125$$
$$x = 132$$
The solution set is $\{132\}$.

92. $x^4 - 5x^2 + 4 = 0$

Let $t = x^2$

$t^2 - 5t + 4 = 0$

$t = 4$ or $t = 1$

$x^2 = 4$ $x^2 = 1$

$x = \pm 2$ $x = \pm 1$

The solution set is $\{-2, -1, 1, 2\}$.

93. $x^{1/2} + 3x^{1/4} - 10 = 0$

Let $t = x^{1/4}$

$t^2 + 3t - 10 = 0$

$(t+5)(t-2) = 0$

$t = -5$ or $t = 2$

$x^{\frac{1}{4}} = -5$ $x^{\frac{1}{4}} = 2$

$\left(x^{\frac{1}{4}}\right)^4 = (-5)^4$ $\left(x^{\frac{1}{4}}\right)^4 = (2)^4$

$x = 625$ $x = 16$

625 does not check and must be rejected.
The solution set is $\{16\}$.

94. $|2x+1| = 7$

$2x + 1 = 7$ or $2x + 1 = -7$

$2x = 6$ $2x = -8$

$x = 3$ $x = -8$

The solution set is $\{-4, 3\}$.

95. $2|x-3| - 6 = 10$

$2|x-3| = 16$

$|x-3| = 8$

$x - 3 = 8$ or $x - 3 = -8$

$x = 11$ $x = -5$

The solution set is $\{-5, 11\}$.

96. $3x^{4/3} - 5x^{2/3} + 2 = 0$

Let $t = x^{\frac{2}{3}}$.

$3t^2 - 5t + 2 = 0$

$(3t-2)(t-1) = 0$

$3t - 2 = 0$ or $t - 1 = 0$

$3t = 2$ $t = 1$

$t = \frac{2}{3}$ $x^{\frac{2}{3}} = 1$

$x^{\frac{2}{3}} = \frac{2}{3}$ $\left(x^{\frac{2}{3}}\right)^{\frac{3}{2}} = \pm(1)^{\frac{3}{2}}$

$\left(x^{\frac{2}{3}}\right)^{\frac{3}{2}} = \pm\left(\frac{2}{3}\right)^{\frac{3}{2}}$ $x = \pm 1$

$x = \pm\sqrt[2]{\left(\frac{2}{3}\right)^3}$

$x = \pm\frac{2}{3}\sqrt{\frac{2}{3}}$

$x = \pm\frac{2}{3} \cdot \frac{\sqrt{2}}{\sqrt{3}} \cdot \frac{\sqrt{3}}{\sqrt{3}}$

$x = \pm\frac{2\sqrt{6}}{9}$

The solution set is $\left\{-\frac{2\sqrt{6}}{9}, \frac{2\sqrt{6}}{9}, -1, 1\right\}$.

97. $2\sqrt{x-1} = x$

$4(x-1) = x^2$

$4x - 4 = x^2$

$x^2 - 4x + 4 = 0$

$(x-2)^2 = 0$

$x = 2$

The solution set is $\{2\}$.

98. $|2x-5| - 3 = 0$

$2x - 5 = 3$ or $2x - 5 = -3$

$2x = 8$ $2x = 2$

$x = 4$ $x = 1$

The solution set is $\{4, 1\}$.

99. $x^3 + 2x^2 - 9x - 18 = 0$

$x^2(x+2) - 9(x+2) = 0$

$(x+2)(x^2 - 9) = 0$

$(x+2)(x+3)(x-3) = 0$

The solution set is $\{-3, -2, 3\}$.

100. $\sqrt{8-2x}-x=0$

$\sqrt{8-2x}=x$

$\left(\sqrt{8-2x}\right)^2=(x)^2$

$8-2x=x^2$

$0=x^2+2x-8$

$0=(x+4)(x-2)$

$x+4=0$ or $x-2=0$

$x=-4$ $\qquad$ $x=2$

-4 does not check.

The solution set is $\{2\}$.

101. $x^3+3x^2-2x-6=0$

$x^2(x+3)-2(x+3)=0$

$(x+3)(x^2-2)=0$

$x+3=0$ or $x^2-2=0$

$x=-3$ $\qquad$ $x^2=2$

$\qquad\qquad\qquad x=\pm\sqrt{2}$

The solution set is $\left\{-3,-\sqrt{2},\sqrt{2}\right\}$.

102. $-4|x+1|+12=0$

$-4|x+1|=-12$

$|x+1|=3$

$x+1=3$ or $x+1=-3$

$x=2$ $\qquad$ $x=-4$

The solution set is $\{-4,2\}$.

103. We need to solve $4.3=0.3\sqrt{x}+3.4$ for x.

$4.3=0.3\sqrt{x}+3.4$

$0.9=0.3\sqrt{x}$

$3=\sqrt{x}$

$3^2=\left(\sqrt{x}\right)^2$

$9=x$

The model indicates that the number of HIV infections in India will reach 4.3 million in 2007 ($x=9$ years after 1998).

104. $\{x|-3\le x<5\}$

105. $\{x|x>-2\}$

106. $\{x|x\le 0\}$

107. Graph $(-2,1]$:

Graph $[-1,3)$:

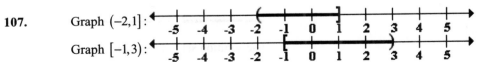

To find the intersection, take the portion of the number line that the two graphs have in common.

Numbers in both $(-2,1]$ and $[-1,3)$:

Thus, $(-2,1]\cap[-1,3)=[-1,1]$.

108. Graph $(-2,1]$:

Graph $[-1,3)$:

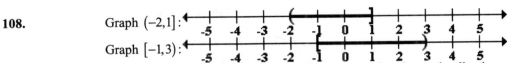

To find the union, take the portion of the number line representing the total collection of numbers in the two graphs.

Numbers in either $(-2,1]$ or $[-1,3)$ or both:

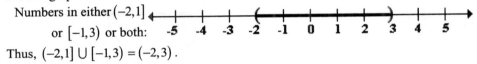

Thus, $(-2,1]\cup[-1,3)=(-2,3)$.

109. Graph $[1,3)$: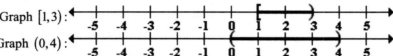

Graph $(0,4)$: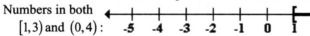

To find the intersection, take the portion of the number line that the two graphs have in common.

Numbers in both
$[1,3)$ and $(0,4)$: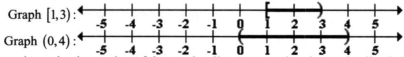

Thus, $[1,3) \cap (0,4) = [1,3)$.

110. Graph $[1,3)$: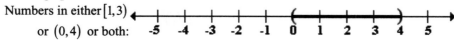

Graph $(0,4)$:

To find the union, take the portion of the number line representing the total collection of numbers in the two graphs.

Numbers in either $[1,3)$
or $(0,4)$ or both:

Thus, $[1,3) \cup (0,4) = (0,4)$.

111. $-6x + 3 \le 15$
$-6x \le 12$
$x \ge 2$

The solution set is $[-2, \infty)$.

112. $6x - 9 \ge -4x - 3$
$10x \ge 6$
$x \ge \dfrac{3}{5}$

The solution set is $\left[\dfrac{3}{5}, \infty\right)$.

113. $\dfrac{x}{3} - \dfrac{3}{4} - 1 > \dfrac{x}{2}$

$12\left(\dfrac{x}{3} - \dfrac{3}{4} - 1\right) > 12\left(\dfrac{x}{2}\right)$

$4x - 9 - 12 > 6x$
$-21 > 2x$
$-\dfrac{21}{2} > x$

The solution set is $\left(-\infty, -\dfrac{21}{2}\right)$.

114. $6x + 5 > -2(x - 3) - 25$
$6x + 5 > -2x + 6 - 25$
$8x + 5 > -19$
$8x > -24$
$x > -3$

The solution set is $(-3, \infty)$.

115. $3(2x - 1) - 2(x - 4) \ge 7 + 2(3 + 4x)$
$6x - 3 - 2x + 8 \ge 7 + 6 + 8x$
$4x + 5 \ge 8x + 13$
$-4x \ge 8$
$x \le -2$

The solution set is $[-\infty, -2)$.

116. $5(x - 2) - 3(x + 4) \ge 2x - 20$
$5x - 10 - 3x - 12 \ge 2x - 20$
$2x - 22 \ge 2x - 20$
$-22 \ge -20$

The solution set is $\varnothing$.

117. $7 < 2x + 3 \le 9$
$4 < 2x \le 6$
$2 < x \le 3$
$(2, 3]$

The solution set is $[2, 3)$.

116

118. $|2x+3| \le 15$

$-15 \le 2x+3 \le 15$

$-18 \le 2x \le 12$

$-9 \le x \le 6$

The solution set is $[-9,6]$.

119. $\left|\dfrac{2x+6}{3}\right| > 2$

$\dfrac{2x+6}{3} > 2 \qquad \dfrac{2x+6}{3} < -2$

$2x+6 > 6 \qquad 2x+6 < -6$

$2x > 0 \qquad\quad 2x < -12$

$x > 0 \qquad\qquad x < -6$

The solution set is $(-\infty,-6)$ or $(0,\infty)$.

120. $|2x+5| - 7 \ge -6$

$|2x+5| \ge 1$

$2x+5 \ge 1$ or $2x+5 \le -1$

$2x \ge -4 \qquad\quad 2x \le -6$

$x \ge -2 \quad$ or $\quad x \le -3$

The solution set is $(-\infty,-3]$ or $[-2,\infty)$.

121. $-4|x+2| + 5 \le -7$

$-4|x+2| \le -12$

$|x+2| \ge 3$

$\begin{array}{cc} x+2 \ge 3 & x+2 \le -3 \\ \text{or} & \\ x \ge 1 & x \le -5 \end{array}$

The solution set is $(-\infty,-5] \cup [1,\infty)$.

122.

$y_1 > y_2$

$-10 - 3(2x+1) > 8x+1$

$-10 - 6x - 3 > 8x+1$

$-6x - 13 > 8x+1$

$-14x > 14$

$\dfrac{-14x}{-14} < \dfrac{14}{-14}$

$x < -1$

The solution set is $(-\infty,-1)$.

123. $3 - |2x-5| \ge -6$

$-|2x-5| \ge -9$

$\dfrac{-|2x-5|}{-1} \le \dfrac{-9}{-1}$

$|2x-5| \le 9$

$-9 \le 2x-5 \le 9$

$-4 \le 2x \le 14$

$-2 \le x \le 7$

The solution set is $[-2,7]$.

124. $0.20x + 24 \le 40$

$0.20x \le 16$

$\dfrac{0.20x}{0.20} \le \dfrac{16}{0.20}$

$x \le 80$

A customer can drive no more than 80 miles.

125. $80 \le \dfrac{95+79+91+86+x}{5} < 90$

$400 \le 95+79+91+86+x < 450$

$400 \le 351+x < 450$

$49 \le x < 99$

A grade of at least 49% but less than 99% will result in a B.

126. $0.075x \ge 9000$

$\dfrac{0.075x}{0.075} \ge \dfrac{9000}{0.075}$

$x \ge 120,000$

The investment must be at least $120,000.

Chapter 1 Test

1. $7(x-2) = 4(x+1) - 21$

$7x - 14 = 4x + 4 - 21$

$7x - 14 = 4x - 17$

$3x = -3$

$x = -1$

The solution set is $\{-1\}$.

2. $-10 - 3(2x+1) - 8x - 1 = 0$

$-10 - 6x - 3 - 8x - 1 = 0$

$-14x - 14 = 0$

$-14x = 14$

$x = -1$

The solution set is $\{-1\}$.

117

3. $\dfrac{2x-3}{4} = \dfrac{x-4}{2} - \dfrac{x+1}{4}$

$2x - 3 = 2(x-4) - (x+1)$

$2x - 3 = 2x - 8 - x - 1$

$2x - 3 = x - 9$

$x = -6$

The solution set is $\{-6\}$.

4. $\dfrac{2}{x-3} - \dfrac{4}{x+3} = \dfrac{8}{(x-3)(x+3)}$

$2(x+3) - 4(x-3) = 8$

$2x + 6 - 4x + 12 = 8$

$-2x + 18 = 8$

$-2x = -10$

$x = 5$

The solution set is $\{5\}$.

5. $2x^2 - 3x - 2 = 0$

$(2x+1)(x-2) = 0$

$2x + 1 = 0 \quad \text{or} \quad x - 2 = 0$

$x = -\dfrac{1}{2} \quad \text{or} \quad x = 2$

The solution set is $\left\{-\dfrac{1}{2}, 2\right\}$.

6. $(3x-1)^2 = 75$

$3x - 1 = \pm\sqrt{75}$

$3x = 1 \pm 5\sqrt{3}$

$x = \dfrac{1 \pm 5\sqrt{3}}{3}$

The solution set is $\left\{\dfrac{1 - 5\sqrt{3}}{3}, \dfrac{1 + 5\sqrt{3}}{3}\right\}$.

7. $(x+3)^2 + 25 = 0$

$(x+3)^2 = -25$

$x + 3 = \pm\sqrt{-25}$

$x = -3 \pm 5i$

The solution set is $\{-3 + 5i, -3 - 5i\}$.

8. $x(x-2) = 4$

$x^2 - 2x - 4 = 0$

$x = \dfrac{-b \pm \sqrt{b^2 - 4ac}}{2a}$

$x = \dfrac{2 \pm \sqrt{(-2)^2 - 4(1)(-4)}}{2}$

$x = \dfrac{2 \pm 2\sqrt{5}}{2}$

$x = 1 \pm \sqrt{5}$

The solution set is $\left\{1 - \sqrt{5}, 1 + \sqrt{5}\right\}$.

9. $4x^2 = 8x - 5$

$4x^2 - 8x + 5 = 0$

$x = \dfrac{-b \pm \sqrt{b^2 - 4ac}}{2a}$

$x = \dfrac{8 \pm \sqrt{(-8)^2 - 4(4)(5)}}{2(4)}$

$x = \dfrac{8 \pm \sqrt{-16}}{8}$

$x = \dfrac{8 \pm 4i}{8}$

$x = 1 \pm \dfrac{1}{2}i$

The solution set is $\left\{1 + \dfrac{1}{2}i, 1 - \dfrac{1}{2}i\right\}$.

10. $x^3 - 4x^2 - x + 4 = 0$

$x^2(x-4) - 1(x-4) = 0$

$(x^2 - 1)(x-4) = 0$

$(x-1)(x+1)(x-4) = 0$

$x = 1 \text{ or } x = -1 \text{ or } x = 4$

The solution set is $\{-1, 1, 4\}$.

11.　$\sqrt{x-3}+5=x$

$$\sqrt{x-3}=x-5$$

$$x-3=x^2-10x+25$$

$$x^2-11x+28=0$$

$$x=\frac{11\pm\sqrt{11^2-4(1)(28)}}{2(1)}$$

$$x=\frac{11\pm\sqrt{121-112}}{2}$$

$$x=\frac{11\pm\sqrt{9}}{2}$$

$$x=\frac{11\pm3}{2}$$

$x=7$ or $x=4$

4 does not check and must be rejected.
The solution set is $\{7\}$.

12.　$\sqrt{8-2x}-x=0$

$$\sqrt{8-2x}=x$$

$$\left(\sqrt{8-2x}\right)^2=(x)^2$$

$$8-2x=x^2$$

$$0=x^2+2x-8$$

$$0=(x+4)(x-2)$$

$x+4=0$　　or　　$x-2=0$
　　$x=-4$　　　　　　$x=2$

−4 does not check and must be rejected.
The solution set is $\{2\}$.

13.　$\sqrt{x+4}+\sqrt{x-1}=5$

$$\sqrt{x+4}=5-\sqrt{x-1}$$

$$x+4=25-10\sqrt{x-1}+(x-1)$$

$$x+4=25-10\sqrt{x-1}+x-1$$

$$-20=-10\sqrt{x-1}$$

$$2=\sqrt{x-1}$$

$$4=x-1$$

$$x=5$$

The solution set is $\{5\}$.

14.　$5x^{3/2}-10=0$

$$5x^{3/2}=10$$

$$x^{3/2}=2$$

$$x=2^{2/3}$$

$$x=\sqrt[3]{4}$$

The solution set is $\left\{\sqrt[3]{4}\right\}$.

15.　$x^{2/3}-9x^{1/3}+8=0$ let $t=x^{1/3}$

$$t^2-9t+8=0$$

$$(t-1)(t-8)=0$$

$t=1$　　　$t=8$

$x^{1/3}=1$　$x^{1/3}=8$

　$x=1$　　　$x=512$

The solution set is $\{1,\,512\}$.

16.　$\left|\frac{2}{3}x-6\right|=2$

$\frac{2}{3}x-6=2$　　　$\frac{2}{3}x-6=-2$

　$\frac{2}{3}x=8$　　　　$\frac{2}{3}x=4$

　$x=12$　　　　$x=6$

The solution set is $\{6,\,12\}$.

17.　$-3|4x-7|+15=0$

$$-3|4x-7|=-15$$

$$|4x-7|=5$$

$4x-7=5$　　　　$4x-7=-5$
$4x=12$　　or　　$4x=2$
$x=3$　　　　　　$x=\frac{1}{2}$

The solution set is $\left\{\frac{1}{2},3\right\}$

18.　$\frac{1}{x^2}-\frac{4}{x}+1=0$

$$\frac{x^2}{x^2}-\frac{4x^2}{x}+x^2=0$$

$$1-4x+x^2=0$$

$$x^2-4x+1=0$$

$$x=\frac{-b\pm\sqrt{b^2-4ac}}{2a}$$

$$x=\frac{-(-4)\pm\sqrt{(-4)^2-4(1)(1)}}{2(1)}$$

$$x=\frac{4\pm\sqrt{12}}{2}$$

$$x=\frac{4\pm2\sqrt{3}}{2}$$

$$x=2\pm\sqrt{3}$$

The solution set is $\left\{2+\sqrt{3},2-\sqrt{3}\right\}$.

19. $\dfrac{2x}{x^2+6x+8}+\dfrac{2}{x+2}=\dfrac{x}{x+4}$

$$\dfrac{2x}{(x+4)(x+2)}+\dfrac{2}{x+2}=\dfrac{x}{x+4}$$

$$\dfrac{2x(x+4)(x+2)}{(x+4)(x+2)}+\dfrac{2(x+4)(x+2)}{x+2}=\dfrac{x(x+4)(x+2)}{x+4}$$

$$2x+2(x+4)=x(x+2)$$

$$2x+2x+8=x^2+2x$$

$$2x+8=x^2$$

$$0=x^2-2x-8$$

$$0=(x-4)(x+2)$$

$x-4=0$ or $x+2=0$

$x=4$ $\qquad\qquad$ $x=-2$ (rejected)

The solution set is $\{4\}$.

20. $3(x+4)\ge 5x-12$

$3x+12\ge 5x-12$

$-2x\ge -24$

$x\le 12$

The solution set is $(-\infty,12]$.

21. $\dfrac{x}{6}+\dfrac{1}{8}\le\dfrac{x}{2}-\dfrac{3}{4}$

$4x+3\le 12x-18$

$-8x\le -21$

$x\ge\dfrac{21}{8}$

The solution set is $\left[\dfrac{21}{8},\infty\right)$.

22. $-3\le\dfrac{2x+5}{3}<6$

$-9\le 2x+5<18$

$-14\le 2x<13$

$-7\le x<\dfrac{13}{2}$

The solution set is $\left[-7,\dfrac{13}{2}\right)$.

23. $|3x+2|\ge 3$

$3x+2\ge 3$ or $3x+2\le -3$

$3x\ge 1$ $\qquad\qquad$ $3x\le -5$

$x\ge\dfrac{1}{3}$ $\qquad\qquad$ $x\le -\dfrac{5}{3}$

The solution set is $\left(-\infty,-\dfrac{5}{3}\right]\cup\left[\dfrac{1}{3},\infty\right)$.

24. $-3\le y\le 7$

$-3\le 2x-5\le 7$

$2\le 2x\le 12$

$1\le x\le 6$

The solution set is $[1,6]$.

25. $\qquad\quad$ $y\ge 1$

$$\left|\dfrac{2-x}{4}\right|\ge 1$$

$\dfrac{2-x}{4}\ge 1$ or $\dfrac{2-x}{4}\le -1$

$2-x\ge 4$ $\qquad\qquad$ $2-x\le -4$

$-x\ge 2$ $\qquad\qquad$ $-x\le -6$

$x\le -2$ $\qquad\qquad$ $x\ge 6$

The solution set is $(-\infty,-2]\cup[6,\infty)$.

26.   Graph $[-1,2)$: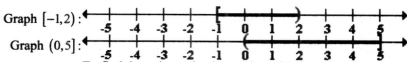

Graph $(0,5]$: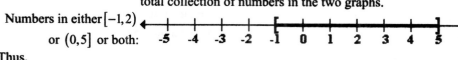

To find the union, take the portion of the number line representing the total collection of numbers in the two graphs.

Numbers in either $[-1,2)$ or $(0,5]$ or both: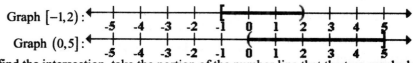

Thus,

$[-1,2) \cup (0,5] = [-1,5]$.

27.   Graph $[-1,2)$: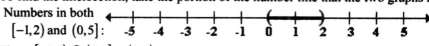

Graph $(0,5]$:

To find the intersection, take the portion of the number line that the two graphs have in common.

Numbers in both $[-1,2)$ and $(0,5]$:

Thus, $[-1,2) \cap (0,5] = (0,2)$.

28. $V = \dfrac{1}{3}lwh$

$3V = lwh$

$\dfrac{3V}{lw} = \dfrac{lwh}{lw}$

$\dfrac{3V}{lw} = h$

$h = \dfrac{3V}{lw}$

29. $y - y_1 = m(x - x_1)$

$y - y_1 = mx - mx_1$

$-mx = y_1 - mx_1 - y$

$\dfrac{-mx}{-m} = \dfrac{y_1 - mx_1 - y}{-m}$

$x = \dfrac{y - y_1}{m} + x_1$

30.

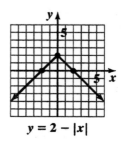

$y = 2 - |x|$

31.

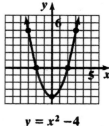

$y = x^2 - 4$

32. $(6 - 7i)(2 + 5i) = 12 + 30i - 14i - 35i^2$

$= 12 + 16i + 35$

$= 47 + 16i$

33. $\dfrac{5}{2-i} = \dfrac{5}{2-i} \cdot \dfrac{2+i}{2+i}$

$= \dfrac{5(2+i)}{4+1}$

$= \dfrac{5(2+i)}{5}$

$= 2 + i$

34. $2\sqrt{-49} + 3\sqrt{-64} = 2(7i) + 3(8i)$

$= 14i + 24i$

$= 38i$

35. $43x + 575 = 1177$

$43x = 602$

$x = 14$

The system's income will be $1177 billion 14 years after 2004, or 2018.

36.
$$B = 0.07x^2 + 47.4x + 500$$
$$1177 = 0.07x^2 + 47.4x + 500$$
$$0 = 0.07x^2 + 47.4x - 677$$
$$0 = 0.07x^2 + 47.4x - 677$$
$$x = \frac{-b \pm \sqrt{b^2 - 4ac}}{2a}$$
$$x = \frac{-(47.4) \pm \sqrt{(47.4)^2 - 4(0.07)(-677)}}{2(0.07)}$$
$$x \approx 14, \quad x \approx -691 \text{ (rejected)}$$
The system's income will be $1177 billion 14 years after 2004, or 2018.

37. The formulas model the data quite well.

38. Let x = the number of books in 2002.
Let $x + 62$ = the number of books in 2003.
Let $x + 190$ = the number of books in 2004.
$$(x) + (x + 62) + (x + 190) = 2598$$
$$x + x + 62 + x + 190 = 2598$$
$$3x + 252 = 2598$$
$$3x = 2346$$
$$x = 782$$
$$x + 62 = 844$$
$$x + 190 = 972$$
The number of books in 2002, 2003, and 2004 were 782, 844, and 972 respectively.

39.
$$29700 + 150x = 5000 + 1100x$$
$$24700 = 950x$$
$$26 = x$$
In 26 years, the cost will be $33,600.

40. Let x = amount invested at 8%
$10000 - x$ = amount invested at 10%
$$.08x + .1(10000 - x) = 940$$
$$.08x + 1000 - .1x = 940$$
$$-.02x = -60$$
$$x = 3000$$
$$10000 - x = 7000$$
$3000 at 8%, $7000 at 10%

41.
$$l = 2w + 4$$
$$A = lw$$
$$48 = (2w + 4)w$$
$$48 = 2w^2 + 4w$$
$$0 = 2w^2 + 4w - 48$$
$$0 = w^2 + 2w - 24$$
$$0 = (w + 6)(w - 4)$$

$$w + 6 = 0 \qquad w - 4 = 0$$
$$w = -6 \qquad w = 4$$
$$2w + 4 = 2(4) + 4 = 12$$
width is 4 feet, length is 12 feet

42.
$$24^2 + x^2 = 26^2$$
$$576 + x^2 = 676$$
$$x^2 = 100$$
$$x = \pm 10$$
The wire should be attached 10 feet up the pole.

43. Let x = the original selling price
$$20 = x - 0.60x$$
$$20 = 0.40x$$
$$50 = x$$
The original price is $50.

44. Let x = the number of local calls
The monthly cost using Plan A is $C_A = 25$.
The monthly cost using Plan B is $C_B = 13 + 0.06x$.
For Plan A to be better deal, it must cost less than Plan B.
$$C_A < C_B$$
$$25 < 13 + 0.06x$$
$$12 < 0.06x$$
$$200 < x$$
$$x > 200$$
Plan A is a better deal when more than 200 local calls are made per month.

Chapter 2

Section 2.1

Check Point Exercises

1. The domain is the set of all first components: $\{5, 10, 15, 20, 25\}$. The range is the set of all second components: $\{12.8, 16.2, 18.9, 20.7, 21.8\}$.

2. a. The relation is not a function since the two ordered pairs $(5, 6)$ and $(5, 8)$ have the same first component but different second components.

   b. The relation is a function since no two ordered pairs have the same first component and different second components.

3. a. $2x + y = 6$

      $$y = -2x + 6$$

      For each value of x, there is one and only one value for y, so the equation defines y as a function of x.

   b. $x^2 + y^2 = 1$

      $$y^2 = 1 - x^2$$

      $$y = \pm\sqrt{1 - x^2}$$

      Since there are values of x (all values between -1 and 1 exclusive) that give more than one value for y (for example, if $x = 0$, then $y = \pm\sqrt{1 - 0^2} = \pm 1$), the equation does not define y as a function of x.

4. a. $f(-5) = (-5)^2 - 2(-5) + 7$

      $$= 25 - (-10) + 7$$

      $$= 42$$

   b. $f(x + 4) = (x + 4)^2 - 2(x + 4) + 7$

      $$= x^2 + 8x + 16 - 2x - 8 + 7$$

      $$= x^2 + 6x + 15$$

   c. $f(-x) = (-x)^2 - 2(-x) + 7$

      $$= x^2 - (-2x) + 7$$

      $$= x^2 + 2x + 7$$

5.

x	$f(x) = 2x$	(x, y)
-2	−4	$(-2, -4)$
-1	−2	$(-1, -2)$
0	0	$(0, 0)$
1	2	$(1, 2)$
2	4	$(2, 4)$

x	$g(x) = 2x - 3$	(x, y)
-2	$g(-2) = 2(-2) - 3 = -7$	$(-2, -7)$
-1	$g(-1) = 2(-1) - 3 = -5$	$(-1, -5)$
0	$g(0) = 2(0) - 3 = -3$	$(0, -3)$
1	$g(1) = 2(1) - 3 = -1$	$(1, -1)$
2	$g(2) = 2(2) - 3 = 1$	$(2, 1)$

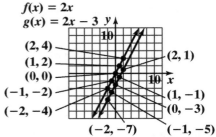

$f(x) = 2x$

$g(x) = 2x - 3$

The graph of g is the graph of f shifted down 3 units.

6. The graph (c) fails the vertical line test and is therefore not a function.
   y is a function of x for the graphs in (a) and (b).

7. **a.** $f(10) \approx 16$ **b.** $x \approx 8$

8. **a.** Domain $= \{x | -2 \le x \le 1\}$ or $[-2, 1]$.
   Range $= \{y | 0 \le y \le 3\}$ or $[0, 3]$.

   b. Domain $= \{x | -2 < x \le 1\}$ or $(-2, 1]$.
   Range $= \{y | -1 \le y < 2\}$ or $[-1, 2)$.

   c. Domain $= \{x | -3 \le x < 0\}$ or $[-3, 0)$.
   Range $= \{y | y = -3, -2, -1\}$.

Exercise Set 2.1

1. The relation is a function since no two ordered pairs have the same first component and different second components. The domain is {1, 3, 5} and the range is {2, 4, 5}.

3. The relation is not a function since the two ordered pairs (3, 4) and (3, 5) have the same first component but different second components (the same could be said for the ordered pairs (4, 4) and (4, 5)). The domain is {3, 4} and the range is {4, 5}.

5. The relation is a function because no two ordered pairs have the same first component and different second components The domain is
   {3, 4, 5, 7} and the range is {–2, 1, 9}.

7. The relation is a function since there are no same first components with different second components. The domain is {–3, –2, –1, 0} and the range is {–3, –2, –1, 0}.

9. The relation is not a function since there are ordered pairs with the same first component and different second components. The domain is $\{1\}$ and the range is $\{4, 5, 6\}$.

11. $x + y = 16$

    $y = 16 - x$

    Since only one value of y can be obtained for each value of x, y is a function of x.

13. $x^2 + y = 16$

    $y = 16 - x^2$

    Since only one value of y can be obtained for each value of x, y is a function of x.

15. $x^2 + y^2 = 16$

    $y^2 = 16 - x^2$

    $y = \pm\sqrt{16 - x^2}$

    If $x = 0$, $y = \pm 4$.

    Since two values, $y = 4$ and $y = -4$, can be obtained for one value of x, y is not a function of x.

17. $x = y^2$

    $y = \pm\sqrt{x}$

    If $x = 1$, $y = \pm 1$.

    Since two values, $y = 1$ and $y = -1$, can be obtained for $x = 1$, y is not a function of x.

19. $y = \sqrt{x + 4}$

    Since only one value of y can be obtained for each value of x, y is a function of x.

21. $x + y^3 = 8$

    $y^3 = 8 - x$

    $y = \sqrt[3]{8 - x}$

    Since only one value of y can be obtained for each value of x, y is a function of x.

23. $xy + 2y = 1$

    $y(x + 2) = 1$

    $y = \dfrac{1}{x + 2}$

    Since only one value of y can be obtained for each value of x, y is a function of x.

25. $|x| - y = 2$

    $-y = -|x| + 2$

    $y = |x| - 2$

    Since only one value of y can be obtained for each value of x, y is a function of x.

27. **a.** $f(6) = 4(6) + 5 = 29$

    b. $f(x + 1) = 4(x + 1) + 5 = 4x + 9$

    c. $f(-x) = 4(-x) + 5 = -4x + 5$

29. a. $g(-1) = (-1)^2 + 2(-1) + 3$
$= 1 - 2 + 3$
$= 2$

b. $g(x+5) = (x+5)^2 + 2(x+5) + 3$
$= x^2 + 10x + 25 + 2x + 10 + 3$
$= x^2 + 12x + 38$

c. $g(-x) = (-x)^2 + 2(-x) + 3$
$= x^2 - 2x + 3$

31. a. $h(2) = 2^4 - 2^2 + 1$
$= 16 - 4 + 1$
$= 13$

b. $h(-1) = (-1)^4 - (-1)^2 + 1$
$= 1 - 1 + 1$
$= 1$

c. $h(-x) = (-x)^4 - (-x)^2 + 1 = x^4 - x^2 + 1$

d. $h(3a) = (3a)^4 - (3a)^2 + 1$
$= 81a^4 - 9a^2 + 1$

33. a. $f(-6) = \sqrt{-6+6} + 3 = \sqrt{0} + 3 = 3$

b. $f(10) = \sqrt{10+6} + 3$
$= \sqrt{16} + 3$
$= 4 + 3$
$= 7$

c. $f(x-6) = \sqrt{x-6+6} + 3 = \sqrt{x} + 3$

35. a. $f(2) = \dfrac{4(2)^2 - 1}{2^2} = \dfrac{15}{4}$

b. $f(-2) = \dfrac{4(-2)^2 - 1}{(-2)^2} = \dfrac{15}{4}$

c. $f(-x) = \dfrac{4(-x)^2 - 1}{(-x)^2} = \dfrac{4x^2 - 1}{x^2}$

37. a. $f(6) = \dfrac{6}{|6|} = 1$

  b. $f(-6) = \dfrac{-6}{|-6|} = \dfrac{-6}{6} = -1$

  c. $f(r^2) = \dfrac{r^2}{|r^2|} = \dfrac{r^2}{r^2} = 1$

39.

x	$f(x) = x$	(x, y)
-2	$f(-2) = -2$	$(-2, -2)$
-1	$f(-1) = -1$	$(-1, -1)$
0	$f(0) = 0$	$(0, 0)$
1	$f(1) = 1$	$(1, 1)$
2	$f(2) = 2$	$(2, 2)$

x	$g(x) = x + 3$	(x, y)
-2	$g(-2) = -2 + 3 = 1$	$(-2, 1)$
-1	$g(-1) = -1 + 3 = 2$	$(-1, 2)$
0	$g(0) = 0 + 3 = 3$	$(0, 3)$
1	$g(1) = 1 + 3 = 4$	$(1, 4)$
2	$g(2) = 2 + 3 = 5$	$(2, 5)$

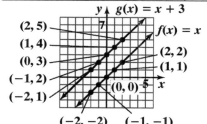

The graph of g is the graph of f shifted up 3 units.

41.

x	$f(x) = -2x$	(x, y)
-2	$f(-2) = -2(-2) = 4$	$(-2, 4)$
-1	$f(-1) = -2(-1) = 2$	$(-1, 2)$
0	$f(0) = -2(0) = 0$	$(0, 0)$
1	$f(1) = -2(1) = -2$	$(1, -2)$
2	$f(2) = -2(2) = -4$	$(2, -4)$

x	$g(x) = -2x - 1$	(x, y)
-2	$g(-2) = -2(-2) - 1 = 3$	$(-2, 3)$
-1	$g(-1) = -2(-1) - 1 = 1$	$(-1, 1)$
0	$g(0) = -2(0) - 1 = -1$	$(0, -1)$
1	$g(1) = -2(1) - 1 = -3$	$(1, -3)$
2	$g(2) = -2(2) - 1 = -5$	$(2, -5)$

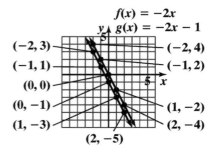

The graph of g is the graph of f shifted down 1 unit.

43.

x	$f(x) = x^2$	(x, y)
-2	$f(-2) = (-2)^2 = 4$	$(-2, 4)$
-1	$f(-1) = (-1)^2 = 1$	$(-1, 1)$
0	$f(0) = (0)^2 = 0$	$(0, 0)$
1	$f(1) = (1)^2 = 1$	$(1, 1)$
2	$f(2) = (2)^2 = 4$	$(2, 4)$

x	$g(x) = x^2 + 1$	(x, y)
-2	$g(-2) = (-2)^2 + 1 = 5$	$(-2, 5)$
-1	$g(-1) = (-1)^2 + 1 = 2$	$(-1, 2)$
0	$g(0) = (0)^2 + 1 = 1$	$(0, 1)$
1	$g(1) = (1)^2 + 1 = 2$	$(1, 2)$
2	$g(2) = (2)^2 + 1 = 5$	$(2, 5)$

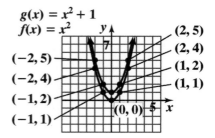

The graph of g is the graph of f shifted up 1 unit.

128

45.

x	$f(x) = \lvert x \rvert$	(x, y)
-2	$f(-2) = \lvert -2 \rvert = 2$	$(-2, 2)$
-1	$f(-1) = \lvert -1 \rvert = 1$	$(-1, 1)$
0	$f(0) = \lvert 0 \rvert = 0$	$(0, 0)$
1	$f(1) = \lvert 1 \rvert = 1$	$(1, 1)$
2	$f(2) = \lvert 2 \rvert = 2$	$(2, 2)$

x	$g(x) = \lvert x \rvert - 2$	(x, y)
-2	$g(-2) = \lvert -2 \rvert - 2 = 0$	$(-2, 0)$
-1	$g(-1) = \lvert -1 \rvert - 2 = -1$	$(-1, -1)$
0	$g(0) = \lvert 0 \rvert - 2 = -2$	$(0, -2)$
1	$g(1) = \lvert 1 \rvert - 2 = -1$	$(1, -1)$
2	$g(2) = \lvert 2 \rvert - 2 = 0$	$(2, 0)$

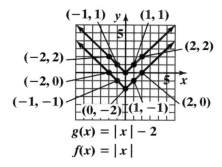

$$g(x) = \lvert x \rvert - 2$$
$$f(x) = \lvert x \rvert$$

The graph of g is the graph of f shifted down 2 units.

47.

x	$f(x) = x^3$	(x, y)
-2	$f(-2) = (-2)^3 = -8$	$(-2, -8)$
-1	$f(-1) = (-1)^3 = -1$	$(-1, -1)$
0	$f(0) = (0)^3 = 0$	$(0, 0)$
1	$f(1) = (1)^3 = 1$	$(1, 1)$
2	$f(2) = (2)^3 = 8$	$(2, 8)$

x	$g(x) = x^3 + 2$	(x, y)
-2	$g(-2) = (-2)^3 + 2 = -6$	$(-2, -6)$
-1	$g(-1) = (-1)^3 + 2 = 1$	$(-1, 1)$
0	$g(0) = (0)^3 + 2 = 2$	$(0, 2)$
1	$g(1) = (1)^3 + 2 = 3$	$(1, 3)$
2	$g(2) = (2)^3 + 2 = 10$	$(2, 10)$

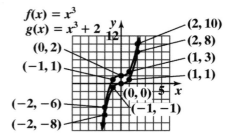

The graph of g is the graph of f shifted up 2 units.

49.

x	$f(x) = 3$	(x, y)
–2	$f(-2) = 3$	$(-2, 3)$
–1	$f(-1) = 3$	$(-1, 3)$
0	$f(0) = 3$	$(0, 3)$
1	$f(1) = 3$	$(1, 3)$
2	$f(2) = 3$	$(2, 3)$

x	$g(x) = 5$	(x, y)
–2	$g(-2) = 5$	$(-2, 5)$
–1	$g(-1) = 5$	$(-1, 5)$
0	$g(0) = 5$	$(0, 5)$
1	$g(1) = 5$	$(1, 5)$
2	$g(2) = 5$	$(2, 5)$

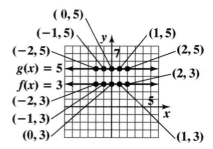

The graph of g is the graph of f shifted up 2 units.

51.

x	$f(x) = \sqrt{x}$	(x, y)
0	$f(0) = \sqrt{0} = 0$	$(0, 0)$
1	$f(1) = \sqrt{1} = 1$	$(1, 1)$
4	$f(4) = \sqrt{4} = 2$	$(4, 2)$
9	$f(9) = \sqrt{9} = 3$	$(9, 3)$

x	$g(x) = \sqrt{x} - 1$	(x, y)
0	$g(0) = \sqrt{0} - 1 = -1$	$(0, -1)$
1	$g(1) = \sqrt{1} - 1 = 0$	$(1, 0)$
4	$g(4) = \sqrt{4} - 1 = 1$	$(4, 1)$
9	$g(9) = \sqrt{9} - 1 = 2$	$(9, 2)$

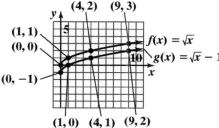

The graph of g is the graph of f shifted down 1 unit.

53.

x	$f(x) = \sqrt{x}$	(x, y)
0	$f(0) = \sqrt{0} = 0$	$(0, 0)$
1	$f(1) = \sqrt{1} = 1$	$(1, 1)$
4	$f(4) = \sqrt{4} = 2$	$(4, 2)$
9	$f(9) = \sqrt{9} = 3$	$(9, 3)$

x	$g(x) = \sqrt{x - 1}$	(x, y)
1	$g(1) = \sqrt{1 - 1} = 0$	$(1, 0)$
2	$g(2) = \sqrt{2 - 1} = 1$	$(2, 1)$
5	$g(5) = \sqrt{5 - 1} = 2$	$(5, 2)$
10	$g(10) = \sqrt{10 - 1} = 3$	$(10, 3)$

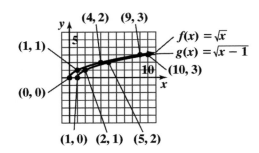

The graph of g is the graph of *f* shifted right 1 unit.

55. function

57. function

59. not a function

61. function

63. function

65. $f(-2) = -4$

67. $f(4) = 4$

69. $f(-3) = 0$

71. $g(-4) = 2$

73. $g(-10) = 2$

75. When $x = -2$, $g(x) = 1$.

77. a. domain: $(-\infty, \infty)$

    b. range: $[-4, \infty)$

    c. x-intercepts: -3 and 1

    d. y-intercept: -3

    e. $f(-2) = -3$ and $f(2) = 5$

79. a. domain: $(-\infty, \infty)$

    b. range: $[1, \infty)$

    c. x-intercept: none

    d. y-intercept: 1

    e. $f(-1) = 2$ and $f(3) = 4$

81. a. domain: $[0, 5)$

    b. range: $[-1, 5)$

    c. x-intercept: 2

    d. y-intercept: -1

    e. $f(3) = 1$

83. a. domain: $[0, \infty)$

    b. range: $[1, \infty)$

    c. x-intercept: none

    d. y-intercept: 1

    e. $f(4) = 3$

85. a. domain: $[-2, 6]$

    b. range: $[-2, 6]$

    c. x-intercept: 4

    d. y-intercept: 4

    e. $f(-1) = 5$

87. a. domain: $(-\infty, \infty)$

    b. range: $(-\infty, -2]$

    c. x-intercept: none

    d. y-intercept: -2

    e. $f(-4) = -5$ and $f(4) = -2$

89. a.   domain: $(-\infty, \infty)$

b.   range: $(0, \infty)$

c. x-intercept: none

d. y-intercept: 1.5

e. $f(4) = 6$

91. a.   domain: $\{-5, -2, 0, 1, 3\}$

b.   range: $\{2\}$

c. x-intercept: none

d. y-intercept: 2

e. $f(-5) + f(3) = 2 + 2 = 4$

93.
$$g(1) = 3(1) - 5 = 3 - 5 = -2$$
$$f(g(1)) = f(-2) = (-2)^2 - (-2) + 4$$
$$= 4 + 2 + 4 = 10$$

95.
$$\sqrt{3 - (-1)} - (-6)^2 + 6 \div (-6) \cdot 4$$
$$= \sqrt{3 + 1} - 36 + 6 \div (-6) \cdot 4$$
$$= \sqrt{4} - 36 + -1 \cdot 4$$
$$= 2 - 36 + -4$$
$$= -34 + -4$$
$$= -38$$

97. $f(-x) - f(x)$
$$= (-x)^3 + (-x) - 5 - (x^3 + x - 5)$$
$$= -x^3 - x - 5 - x^3 - x + 5 = -2x^3 - 2x$$

99. a. $\{(\text{U.S.}, 80\%), (\text{Japan}, 64\%),$
$(\text{France}, 64\%), (\text{Germany}, 61\%),$
$(\text{England}, 59\%), (\text{China}, 47\%)\}$

b.   Yes, the relation is a function. Each element in the domain corresponds to only one element in the range.

c. $\{(80\%, \text{U.S.}), (64\%, \text{Japan}),$
$(64\%, \text{France}), (61\%, \text{Germany}),$
$(59\%, \text{England}), (47\%, \text{China})\}$

d.   No, the relation is not a function. 64% in the domain corresponds to both Japan and France in the range.

101. $W(16) = 0.07(16) + 4.1$
$$= 1.12 + 4.1 = 5.22$$
In 2000 there were 5.22 million women enrolled in U.S. colleges.
(2000, 5.22)

103. $W(20) = 0.07(20) + 4.1$

$\qquad = 1.4 + 4.1 = 5.5$

$\quad M(20) = 0.01(20) + 3.9$

$\qquad = 0.2 + 3.9 = 4.1$

$\quad W(20) - M(20) = 5.5 - 4.1 = 1.4$

In 2004, there will be 1.4 million more women than men enrolled in U.S. colleges.

105. a.   According to the graph, women's earnings were about 73% of men's in 2000.

    b. $P(x) = 0.012x^2 - 0.16x + 60$

$\qquad P(40) = 0.012(40)^2 - 0.16(40) + 60 = 72.8$

According to the function, women's earnings were about 72.8% of men's in 2000.

    c. $\dfrac{27,355}{37,339} \approx 0.733 = 73.3\%$

The answers in parts (a) and (b) model the actual data quite well.

107. $C(x) = 100,000 + 100x$

$\quad C(90) = 100,000 + 100(90) = \$109,000$

It will cost \$109,000 to produce 90 bicycles.

109.
$$T(x) = \frac{40}{x} + \frac{40}{x+30}$$
$$T(30) = \frac{40}{30} + \frac{40}{30+30}$$
$$= \frac{80}{60} + \frac{40}{60}$$
$$= \frac{120}{60}$$
$$= 2$$

If you travel 30 mph going and 60 mph returning, your total trip will take 2 hours.

121. a.   false; the domain of f is $[-4, 4]$

    b.   false; the range of f is $[-2, 2)$

    c.   true; $f(-1) - f(4) = 1 - (-1) = 2$

    d.   false; $f(0) < 1$ x

(c) is true.

123. Answers may vary.
An example is $\{(1,1),(2,1)\}$

Section 2.2

Check Point Exercises

1. **a.** $f(x) = -2x^2 + x + 5$

$$f(x+h) = -2(x+h)^2 + (x+h) + 5$$
$$= -2(x^2 + 2xh + h^2) + x + h + 5$$
$$= -2x^2 - 4xh - 2h^2 + x + h + 5$$

b. $\dfrac{f(x+h) - f(x)}{h}$

$$= \frac{-2x^2 - 4xh - 2h^2 + x + h + 5 - \left(-2x^2 + x + 5\right)}{h}$$

$$= \frac{-2x^2 - 4xh - 2h^2 + x + h + 5 + 2x^2 - x - 5}{h}$$

$$= \frac{-4xh - 2h^2 + h}{h}$$

$$= \frac{h\left(-4x - 2h + 1\right)}{h}$$

$$= -4x - 2h + 1$$

2. $C(t) = \begin{cases} 20 & \text{if } 0 \le t \le 60 \\ 20 + 0.40(t - 60) & \text{if } t > 60 \end{cases}$

b.   Since $0 \le 40 \le 60$, $C(40) = 20$
With 40 calling minutes, the cost is \$20.
This is represented by $(40, 20)$.

c.   Since $80 > 60$, $C(80) = 20 + 0.40(80 - 60) = 28$
With 80 calling minutes, the cost is \$28.
This is represented by $(80, 28)$.

3. The function is increasing on the interval $(-\infty, -1)$, decreasing on the interval $(-1, 1)$, and increasing on the interval $(1, \infty)$.

4. **a.** $f(-x) = (-x)^2 + 6 = x^2 + 6 = f(x)$
The function is even.

b. $g(-x) = 7(-x)^3 - (-x) = -7x^3 + x = -f(x)$
The function is odd.

c. $h(-x) = (-x)^5 + 1 = -x^5 + 1$
The function is neither even nor odd.

Exercise Set 2.2

1.

$$\frac{f(x+h)-f(x)}{h}$$
$$=\frac{4(x+h)-4x}{h}$$
$$=\frac{4x+4h-4x}{h}$$
$$=\frac{4h}{h}$$
$$=4$$

3.

$$\frac{f(x+h)-f(x)}{h}$$
$$=\frac{3(x+h)+7-(3x+7)}{h}$$
$$=\frac{3x+3h+7-3x-7}{h}$$
$$=\frac{3h}{h}$$
$$=3$$

5.

$$\frac{f(x+h)-f(x)}{h}$$
$$=\frac{(x+h)^2-x^2}{h}$$
$$=\frac{x^2+2xh+h^2-x^2}{h}$$
$$=\frac{2xh+h^2}{h}$$
$$=\frac{h(2x+h)}{h}$$
$$=2x+h$$

7.

$$\frac{f(x+h)-f(x)}{h}$$
$$=\frac{(x+h)^2-4(x+h)+3-(x^2-4x+3)}{h}$$
$$=\frac{x^2+2xh+h^2-4x-4h+3-x^2+4x-3}{h}$$
$$=\frac{2xh+h^2-4h}{h}$$
$$=\frac{h(2x+h-4)}{h}$$
$$=2x+h-4$$

9.

$$\frac{f(x+h)-f(x)}{h}$$
$$=\frac{2(x+h)^2+(x+h)-1-(2x^2+x-1)}{h}$$
$$=\frac{2x^2+4xh+2h^2+x+h-1-2x^2-x+1}{h}$$
$$=\frac{4xh+2h^2+h}{h}$$
$$=\frac{h(4x+2h+1)}{h}$$
$$=4x+2h+1$$

11.

$$\frac{f(x+h)-f(x)}{h}$$
$$=\frac{-(x+h)^2+2(x+h)+4-(-x^2+2x+4)}{h}$$
$$=\frac{-x^2-2xh-h^2+2x+2h+4+x^2-2x-4}{h}$$
$$=\frac{-2xh-h^2+2h}{h}$$
$$=\frac{h(-2x-h+2)}{h}$$
$$=-2x-h+2$$

13.

$$\frac{f(x+h)-f(x)}{h}$$
$$=\frac{-2(x+h)^2+5(x+h)+7-(-2x^2+5x+7)}{h}$$
$$=\frac{-2x^2-4xh-2h^2+5x+5h+7+2x^2-5x-7}{h}$$
$$=\frac{-4xh-2h^2+5h}{h}$$
$$=\frac{h(-4x-2h+5)}{h}$$
$$=-4x-2h+5$$

15. $\dfrac{f(x+h)-f(x)}{h}$

$= \dfrac{-2(x+h)^2 - (x+h) + 3 - (-2x^2 - x + 3)}{h}$

$= \dfrac{-2x^2 - 4xh - 2h^2 - x - h + 3 + 2x^2 + x - 3}{h}$

$= \dfrac{-4xh - 2h^2 - h}{h}$

$= \dfrac{h(-4x - 2h - 1)}{h}$

$= -4x - 2h - 1$

17. $\dfrac{f(x+h)-f(x)}{h} = \dfrac{6-6}{h} = \dfrac{0}{h} = 0$

19. $\dfrac{f(x+h)-f(x)}{h}$

$= \dfrac{\dfrac{1}{x+h} - \dfrac{1}{x}}{h}$

$= \dfrac{\dfrac{x}{x(x+h)} + \dfrac{-(x+h)}{x(x+h)}}{h}$

$= \dfrac{\dfrac{x - x - h}{x(x+h)}}{h}$

$= \dfrac{\dfrac{-h}{x(x+h)}}{h}$

$= \dfrac{-h}{x(x+h)} \cdot \dfrac{1}{h}$

$= \dfrac{-1}{x(x+h)}$

21. $\dfrac{f(x+h)-f(x)}{h}$

$= \dfrac{\sqrt{x+h} - \sqrt{x}}{h}$

$= \dfrac{\sqrt{x+h} - \sqrt{x}}{h} \cdot \dfrac{\sqrt{x+h} + \sqrt{x}}{\sqrt{x+h} + \sqrt{x}}$

$= \dfrac{x + h - x}{h\left(\sqrt{x+h} + \sqrt{x}\right)}$

$= \dfrac{h}{h\left(\sqrt{x+h} + \sqrt{x}\right)}$

$= \dfrac{1}{\sqrt{x+h} + \sqrt{x}}$

23. **a.** $f(-2) = 3(-2) + 5 = -1$

 b. $f(0) = 4(0) + 7 = 7$

 c. $f(3) = 4(3) + 7 = 19$

25. **a.** $g(0) = 0 + 3 = 3$

 b. $g(-6) = -(-6 + 3) = -(-3) = 3$

 c. $g(-3) = -3 + 3 = 0$

27. **a.** $h(5) = \dfrac{5^2 - 9}{5 - 3} = \dfrac{25 - 9}{2} = \dfrac{16}{2} = 8$

 b. $h(0) = \dfrac{0^2 - 9}{0 - 3} = \dfrac{-9}{-3} = 3$

 c. $h(3) = 6$

29. **a.** increasing: $(-1, \infty)$

 b. decreasing: $(-\infty, -1)$

 c. constant: none

31. **a.** increasing: $(0, \infty)$

 b. decreasing: none

 c. constant: none

33. **a.** increasing: none

 b. decreasing: $(-2, 6)$

 c. constant: none

35. a.   increasing: $(-\infty, -1)$

    b.   decreasing: none

    c.   constant: $(-1, \infty)$

37. a.   increasing: $(-\infty, 0)$ or $(1.5, 3)$

    b.   decreasing: $(0, 1.5)$ or $(3, \infty)$

    c.   constant: none

39. a.   increasing: $(-2, 4)$

    b.   decreasing: none

    c.   constant: $(-\infty, -2)$ or $(4, \infty)$

41.   **a.** $x = 0$, relative maximum $= 4$

    b. $x = -3, 3$, relative minimum $= 0$

43.   **a.** $x = -2$, relative maximum $= 21$

    b. $x = 1$, relative minimum $= -6$

45. $f(x) = x^3 + x$
$f(-x) = (-x)^3 + (-x)$
$f(-x) = -x^3 - x = -(x^3 + x)$
$f(-x) = -f(x)$, odd function

47. $g(x) = x^2 + x$
$g(-x) = (-x)^2 + (-x)$
$g(-x) = x^2 - x$, neither

49. $h(x) = x^2 - x^4$
$h(-x) = (-x)^2 - (-x)^4$
$h(-x) = x^2 - x^4$
$h(-x) = h(x)$, even function

51. $f(x) = x^2 - x^4 + 1$
$f(-x) = (-x)^2 - (-x)^4 + 1$
$f(-x) = x^2 - x^4 + 1$
$f(-x) = f(x)$, even function

53. $f(x) = \dfrac{1}{5}x^6 - 3x^2$
$f(-x) = \dfrac{1}{5}(-x)^6 - 3(-x)^2$
$f(-x) = \dfrac{1}{5}x^6 - 3x^2$
$f(-x) = f(x)$, even function

55. $f(x) = x\sqrt{1 - x^2}$
$f(-x) = -x\sqrt{1 - (-x)^2}$
$f(-x) = -x\sqrt{1 - x^2}$
$\qquad = -\left(x\sqrt{1 - x^2}\right)$
$f(-x) = -f(x)$, odd function

57.   The graph is symmetric with respect to the y-axis. The function is even.

59.   The graph is symmetric with respect to the origin. The function is odd.

61. a.   Domain: $(-\infty, \infty)$

    b.   Range: $[-4, \infty)$

    c. x-intercepts: 1, 7

    d. y-intercept: 4

    e. $(4, \infty)$

    f. $(0, 4)$

    g. $(-\infty, 0)$

    h. $x = 4$

    i. $y = -4$

    j. $f(-3) = 4$

    k. $f(2) = -2$ and $f(6) = -2$

    l.   neither ; $f(-x) \neq x$, $f(-x) \neq -x$

63. **a.**   Domain: $(-\infty, 3]$

    b.   Range: $(-\infty, 4]$

    c. x-intercepts: $-3, 3$

    d. $f(0) = 3$

    e. $(-\infty, 1)$

    f. $(1, 3)$

    g. $(-\infty, -3]$

    h. $f(1) = 4$

    i. $x = 1$

    j.   positive; $f(-1) = +2$

65. $f(1.06) = 1$

67. $f\left(\dfrac{1}{3}\right) = 0$

69. $f(-2.3) = -3$

71. $\sqrt{f(-1.5) + f(-0.9)} - [f(\pi)]^2 + f(-3) \div f(1) \cdot f(-\pi)$

$= \sqrt{1 + 0} - [-4]^2 + 2 \div (-2) \cdot 3$

$= \sqrt{1} - 16 + (-1) \cdot 3$

$= 1 - 16 - 3$

$= -18$

73. $30 + 0.30(t - 120) = 30 + 0.3t - 36 = 0.3t - 6$

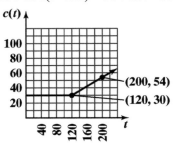

75. $C(t) = \begin{cases} 50 & \text{if } 0 \le t \le 400 \\ 50 + 0.30(t - 400) & \text{if } t > 400 \end{cases}$

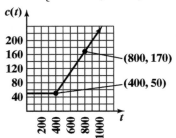

77. $f(60) \approx 3.1$

In 1960, about 3.1% of the population were Jewish-Americans.

79. $x \approx 19$ and $x \approx 64$

In 1919 and 1964, about 3% of the population were Jewish-Americans.

81. In 1940, the maximum of 3.7% of the population were Jewish-American.

83. Each year corresponds to only 1 percentage.

85. Increasing: (45, 74)
Decreasing: (16, 45)
The number of accidents occurring per 50 million miles driven increases with age starting at age 45, while it decreases with age starting at age 16.

87. Answers may vary. An example is 16 and 74 year olds will have 526.4 accidents per 50 million miles.

89. $f(30) = 61.9(30) + 132 = 1989$ cigarettes per adult
This describes the actual data quite well.

91. The maximum occurred in 1960. Graph estimates will vary near 4100.
$f(50) = -2.2(50)^2 + 256(50) - 3503 = 3797$ cigarettes per adult
The function does not describe the actual data reasonably well.

93.

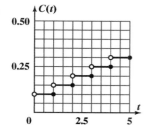

103.

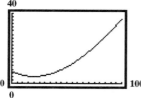

The number of doctor visits decreases during childhood and then increases as you get older. The minimum is (20.29, 3.99), which means that the minimum number of doctor visits, about 4, occurs at around age 20.

105.

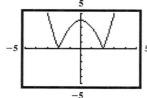

Increasing: $(-2, 0)$ or $(2, \infty)$
Decreasing: $(-\infty, -2)$ or $(0, 2)$

107.

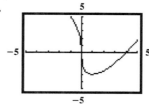

Increasing: $(1, \infty)$
Decreasing: $(-\infty, 1)$

109.

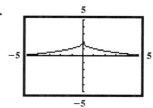

Increasing: $(-\infty, 0)$
Decreasing: $(0, \infty)$

113. a. h is even if both f and g are even or if both f and g are odd.
  f and g are both even:

$$h(-x) = \frac{f(-x)}{g(-x)} = \frac{f(x)}{g(x)} = h(x)$$

  f and g are both odd:

$$h(-x) = \frac{f(-x)}{g(-x)} = \frac{-f(x)}{-g(x)} = \frac{f(x)}{g(x)} = h(x)$$

b. h is odd if f is odd and g is even or if f is even and g is odd.
  f is odd and g is even:

$$h(-x) = \frac{f(-x)}{g(-x)} = \frac{-f(x)}{g(x)} = -\frac{f(x)}{g(x)} = -h(x)$$

  f is even and g is odd:

$$h(-x) = \frac{f(-x)}{g(-x)} = \frac{f(x)}{-g(x)} = -\frac{f(x)}{g(x)} = -h(x)$$

Section 2.3

Check Point Exercises

1. a. $m = \dfrac{-2-4}{-4-(-3)} = \dfrac{-6}{-1} = 6$

b. $m = \dfrac{5-(-2)}{-1-4} = \dfrac{7}{-5} = -\dfrac{7}{5}$

2. $y - y_1 = m(x - x_1)$
$y - (-5) = 6(x - 2)$
$y + 5 = 6x - 12$
$y = 6x - 17$

3. $m = \dfrac{-6 - (-1)}{-1 - (-2)} = \dfrac{-5}{1} = -5$,

so the slope is –5. Using the point $(-2, -1)$, we get the point slope equation:
$y - y_1 = m(x - x_1)$
$y - (-1) = -5[x - (-2)]$
$y + 1 = -5(x + 2).$ Solve the equation for y:
$y + 1 = -5x - 10$
$y = -5x - 11$.

4.   The slope m is $\frac{3}{5}$ and the y-intercept is 1, so one point on the line is $(1, 0)$. We can find a second point on the line by using the slope $m = \frac{3}{5} = \frac{\text{Rise}}{\text{Run}}$: starting at the point $(0, 1)$, move 3 units up and 5 units to the right, to obtain the point $(5, 4)$.

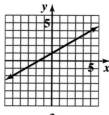

$f(x) = \dfrac{3}{5}x + 1$

5.   All ordered pairs that are solutions of $x = -3$ have a value of x that is always –3. Any value can be used for y.

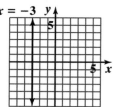

6. $3x + 6y - 12 = 0$

$$6y = -3x + 12$$
$$y = \frac{-3}{6}x + \frac{12}{6}$$
$$y = -\frac{1}{2}x + 2$$

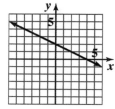

3x + 6y − 12 = 0

The slope is $-\dfrac{1}{2}$ and the y-intercept is 2.

7. Find the x-intercept:

$$3x - 2y - 6 = 0$$
$$3x - 2(0) - 6 = 0$$
$$3x - 6 = 0$$
$$3x = 6$$
$$x = 2$$

Find the y-intercept:

$$3x - 2y - 6 = 0$$
$$3(0) - 2y - 6 = 0$$
$$-2y - 6 = 0$$
$$-2y = 6$$
$$y = -3$$

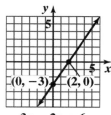

3x − 2y = 6

8. $m = \dfrac{\text{Change in } y}{\text{Change in } x} = \dfrac{32.8 - 30.0}{20 - 10} = \dfrac{2.8}{10} = 0.28$

$$y - y_1 = m(x - x_1)$$
$$y - 30.0 = 0.28(x - 10)$$
$$y - 30.0 = 0.28x - 2.8$$
$$y = 0.28x + 27.2$$

2020 is 50 years after 1970.

$$y = 0.28x + 27.2$$
$$y = 0.28(50) + 27.2$$
$$y = 41.2$$

In 2020 the median age is expected to be 41.2.

Exercise Set 2.3

1. $m = \dfrac{10 - 7}{8 - 4} = \dfrac{3}{4}$; rises

3. $m = \dfrac{2 - 1}{2 - (-2)} = \dfrac{1}{4}$; rises

5. $m = \dfrac{2 - (-2)}{3 - 4} = \dfrac{0}{-1} = 0$; horizontal

7. $m = \dfrac{-1 - 4}{-1 - (-2)} = \dfrac{-5}{1} = -5$; falls

9. $m = \dfrac{-2 - 3}{5 - 5} = \dfrac{-5}{0}$ undefined; vertical

11. $m = 2,\ x_1 = 3,\ y_1 = 5;$
point-slope form: $y - 5 = 2(x - 3);$
slope-intercept form: $y - 5 = 2x - 6$
$$y = 2x - 1$$

13. $m = 6,\ x_1 = -2,\ y_1 = 5;$
point-slope form: $y - 5 = 6(x + 2);$
slope-intercept form: $y - 5 = 6x + 12$
$$y = 6x + 17$$

15. $m = -3,\ x_1 = -2,\ y_1 = -3;$
point-slope form: $y + 3 = -3(x + 2);$
slope-intercept form: $y + 3 = -3x - 6$
$$y = -3x - 9$$

17. $m = -4,\ x_1 = -4,\ y_1 = 0;$
point-slope form: $y - 0 = -4(x + 4);$
slope-intercept form: $y = -4(x + 4)$
$$y = -4x - 16$$

19. $m = -1,\ x_1 = \dfrac{-1}{2},\ y_1 = -2;$

point-slope form: $y + 2 = -1\left(x + \dfrac{1}{2}\right);$

slope-intercept form: $y + 2 = -x - \dfrac{1}{2}$

$$y = -x - \dfrac{5}{2}$$

21. $m = \dfrac{1}{2}$, $x_1 = 0$, $y_1 = 0$;

    point-slope form: $y - 0 = \dfrac{1}{2}(x - 0)$;

    slope-intercept form: $y = \dfrac{1}{2}x$

23. $m = -\dfrac{2}{3}$, $x_1 = 6$, $y_1 = -2$;

    point-slope form: $y + 2 = -\dfrac{2}{3}(x - 6)$;

    slope-intercept form: $y + 2 = -\dfrac{2}{3}x + 4$

$$y = -\dfrac{2}{3}x + 2$$

25. $m = \dfrac{10 - 2}{5 - 1} = \dfrac{8}{4} = 2$;

    point-slope form: $y - 2 = 2(x - 1)$ using $(x_1, y_1) = (1, 2)$, or $y - 10 = 2(x - 5)$ using $(x_1, y_1) = (5, 10)$;

    slope-intercept form: $y - 2 = 2x - 2$ or

$$y - 10 = 2x - 10,$$
$$y = 2x$$

27. $m = \dfrac{3 - 0}{0 - (-3)} = \dfrac{3}{3} = 1$;

    point-slope form: $y - 0 = 1(x + 3)$ using $(x_1, y_1) = (-3, 0)$, or $y - 3 = 1(x - 0)$ using $(x_1, y_1) = (0, 3)$; slope-intercept form: $y = x + 3$

29. $m = \dfrac{4 - (-1)}{2 - (-3)} = \dfrac{5}{5} = 1$;

    point-slope form: $y + 1 = 1(x + 3)$ using $(x_1, y_1) = (-3, -1)$, or $y - 4 = 1(x - 2)$ using $(x_1, y_1) = (2, 4)$; slope-intercept form: $y + 1 = x + 3$ or

$$y - 4 = x - 2$$
$$y = x + 2$$

31. $m = \dfrac{6 - (-2)}{3 - (-3)} = \dfrac{8}{6} = \dfrac{4}{3}$;

    point-slope form: $y + 2 = \dfrac{4}{3}(x + 3)$ using $(x_1, y_1) = (-3, -2)$, or $y - 6 = \dfrac{4}{3}(x - 3)$ using $(x_1, y_1) = (3, 6)$;

    slope-intercept form: $y + 2 = \dfrac{4}{3x} + 4$ or

$$y - 6 = \dfrac{4}{3}x - 4,$$
$$y = \dfrac{4}{3}x + 2$$

33. $m = \dfrac{-1 - (-1)}{4 - (-3)} = \dfrac{0}{7} = 0$;

    point-slope form: $y + 1 = 0(x + 3)$ using $(x_1, y_1) = (-3, -1)$, or $y + 1 = 0(x - 4)$ using $(x_1, y_1) = (4, -1)$;

    slope-intercept form: $y + 1 = 0$, so

$$y = -1$$

35. $m = \dfrac{0-4}{-2-2} = \dfrac{-4}{-4} = 1$;

point-slope form: $y - 4 = 1(x - 2)$ using $(x_1, y_1) = (2, 4)$, or $y - 0 = 1(x + 2)$ using $(x_1, y_1) = (-2, 0)$;

slope-intercept form: $y - 9 = x - 2$, or

$$y = x + 2$$

37. $m = \dfrac{4-0}{0-\left(-\frac{1}{2}\right)} = \dfrac{4}{\frac{1}{2}} = 8$;

point-slope form: $y - 4 = 8(x - 0)$ using $(x_1, y_1) = (0, 4)$, or $y - 0 = 8\left(x + \frac{1}{2}\right)$ using $(x_1, y_1) = \left(-\frac{1}{2}, 0\right)$; or

$y - 0 = 8\left(x + \frac{1}{2}\right)$

slope-intercept form: $y = 8x + 4$

39. $m = 2;\ b = 1$

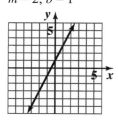

$y = 2x + 1$

41. $m = -2;\ b = 1$

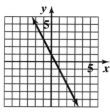

$f(x) = -2x + 1$

43. $m = \dfrac{3}{4};\ b = -2$

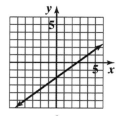

$f(x) = \dfrac{3}{4}x - 2$

45. $m = -\dfrac{3}{5};\ b = 7$

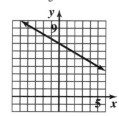

$y = -\dfrac{3}{5}x + 7$

47. $m = -\dfrac{1}{2};\ b = 0$

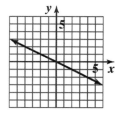

$g(x) = -\dfrac{1}{2}x$

49. $y = -2$

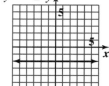

51. $y = -3$

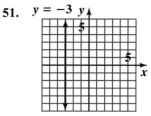

53. $y = 0$

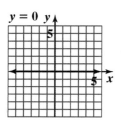

55. $f(x) = 1$

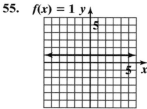

57. $3x - 18 = 0$
$3x = 18$
$x = 6$

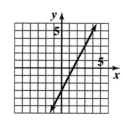

59. a. $3x + y - 5 = 0$
$y - 5 = -3x$
$y = -3x + 5$

b. $m = -3; b = 5$

c.

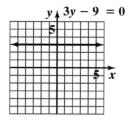

$3x + y - 5 = 0$

61. a. $2x + 3y - 18 = 0$
$2x - 18 = -3y$
$-3y = 2x - 18$
$y = \dfrac{2}{-3}x - \dfrac{18}{-3}$
$y = -\dfrac{2}{3}x + 6$

b. $m = -\dfrac{2}{3}; b = 6$

c.

$2x + 3y - 18 = 0$

63. a. $8x - 4y - 12 = 0$
$8x - 12 = 4y$
$4y = 8x - 12$
$y = \dfrac{8}{4}x - \dfrac{12}{4}$
$y = 2x - 3$

b. $m = 2; b = -3$

c.

$8x - 4y - 12 = 0$

65. a. $3y - 9 = 0$
$3y = 9$
$y = 3$

b. $m = 0; b = 3$

c.

$3y - 9 = 0$

146

67. Find the *x*-intercept:
$$6x - 2y - 12 = 0$$
$$6x - 2(0) - 12 = 0$$
$$6x - 12 = 0$$
$$6x = 12$$
$$x = 2$$
Find the *y*-intercept:
$$6x - 2y - 12 = 0$$
$$6(0) - 2y - 12 = 0$$
$$-2y - 12 = 0$$
$$-2y = 12$$
$$y = -6$$

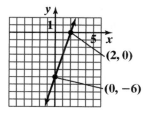

$$6x - 2y - 12 = 0$$

69. Find the *x*-intercept:
$$2x + 3y + 6 = 0$$
$$2x + 3(0) + 6 = 0$$
$$2x + 6 = 0$$
$$2x = -6$$
$$x = -3$$
Find the *y*-intercept:
$$2x + 3y + 6 = 0$$
$$2(0) + 3y + 6 = 0$$
$$3y + 6 = 0$$
$$3y = -6$$
$$y = -2$$

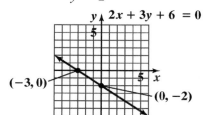

71. Find the *x*-intercept:
$$8x - 2y + 12 = 0$$
$$8x - 2(0) + 12 = 0$$
$$8x + 12 = 0$$
$$8x = -12$$
$$\frac{8x}{8} = \frac{-12}{8}$$
$$x = \frac{-3}{2}$$
Find the *y*-intercept:
$$8x - 2y + 12 = 0$$
$$8(0) - 2y + 12 = 0$$
$$-2y + 12 = 0$$
$$-2y = -12$$
$$y = -6$$

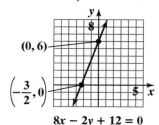

$$8x - 2y + 12 = 0$$

73. $m = \dfrac{0-a}{b-0} = \dfrac{-a}{b} = -\dfrac{a}{b}$

Since *a* and *b* are both positive, $-\dfrac{a}{b}$ is negative. Therefore, the line falls.

75. $m = \dfrac{(b+c)-b}{a-a} = \dfrac{c}{0}$
The slope is undefined.
The line is vertical.

77. $Ax + By = C$
$$By = -Ax + C$$
$$y = -\frac{A}{B}x + \frac{C}{B}$$

The slope is $-\dfrac{A}{B}$ and the *y* – intercept is $\dfrac{C}{B}$.

79.
$$-3 = \frac{4-y}{1-3}$$
$$-3 = \frac{4-y}{-2}$$
$$6 = 4-y$$
$$2 = -y$$
$$-2 = y$$

81.
$$3x - 4f(x) = 6$$
$$-4f(x) = -3x + 6$$
$$f(x) = \frac{3}{4}x - \frac{3}{2}$$

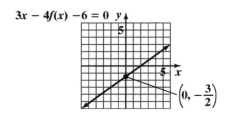

$3x - 4f(x) - 6 = 0$

$\left(0, -\frac{3}{2}\right)$

83. Using the slope-intercept form for the equation of a line:
$$-1 = -2(3) + b$$
$$-1 = -6 + b$$
$$5 = b$$

85. m_1, m_3, m_2, m_4

87. a. First we must find the slope using
$(10,16)$ and $(16,12.7)$.
$$m = \frac{12.7 - 16}{16 - 10} = \frac{3.3}{6} = -0.55$$
Then use the slope and one of the points to write the equation in point-slope form.
$$y - y_1 = m(x - x_1)$$
$$y - 16 = -0.55(x - 10)$$
or
$$y - 12.7 = -0.55(x - 16)$$

b.
$$y - 16 = -0.55(x - 10)$$
$$y - 16 = -0.55x + 5.5$$
$$y = -0.55x + 21.5$$
$$f(x) = -0.55x + 21.5$$

c. $f(20) = -0.55(20) + 21.5 = 10.5$
The linear function predicts 10.5% of adult women will be on weight-loss diets in 2007.

89. a. points: $(0, 73.7), (5, 74.7), (10, 75.4)$
$(15, 75.8), (19, 76.7), (20, 77.0), (21, 77.2)$

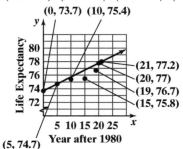

$(0, 73.7)$ $(10, 75.4)$

$(21, 77.2)$
$(20, 77)$
$(19, 76.7)$
$(15, 75.8)$

$(5, 74.7)$ Year after 1980

b. $m = \frac{\text{Change in } y}{\text{Change in } x} = \frac{77.0 - 74.7}{20 - 5} \approx 0.15$
$$y - y_1 = m(x - x_1)$$
$$y - 74.7 = 0.15(x - 5) \quad \text{[point-slope]}$$
$$y - 74.7 = 0.15x - 0.75$$
$$y = 0.15x + 73.95 \quad \text{[slope-intercept]}$$

c. $E(x) = 0.15x + 73.95$
$$E(40) = 0.15(40) + 73.95$$
$$= 79.95$$
In 2020 the life expectancy is expected to be 79.95.

91. $(10, 230)$ $(60, 110)$ Points may vary.
$$m = \frac{110 - 230}{60 - 10} = \frac{120}{50} = -2.4$$
$$y - 230 = -2.4(x - 10)$$
$$y - 230 = -2.4x + 24$$
$$y = -2.4x + 254$$
Answers may vary for predictions.

101. Two points are $(0, 6)$ and $(10, -24)$.
$$m = \frac{-24 - 6}{10 - 0} = \frac{-30}{10} = -3.$$
Check: $y = mx + b : y = -3x + 6$.

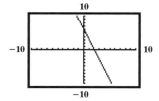

148

103. Two points are $(0, -2)$ and $(10, 5.5)$.

$$m = \frac{5.5 - (-2)}{10 - 0} = \frac{7.5}{10} = 0.75 \text{ or } \frac{3}{4}.$$

Check: $y = mx + b$: $y = \frac{3}{4}x - 2$.

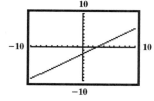

105. Statement **c.** is true.

Statement **a.** is false. One nonnegative slope is 0. A line with slope equal to zero does not rise from left to right.

Statement **b.** is false. Slope-intercept form is $y = mx + b$. Vertical lines have equations of the form $x = a$. Equations of this form have undefined slope and cannot be written in slope-intercept form.

Statement **d.** is false. The graph of $x = 7$ is a vertical line through the point $(7, 0)$.

107. We are given that the y-intercept is -6 and the slope is $\frac{1}{2}$.

So the equation of the line is $y = \frac{1}{2}x - 6$.

We can put this equation in the form $ax + by = c$ to find the missing coefficients.

$$y = \frac{1}{2}x - 6$$

$$y - \frac{1}{2}x = -6$$

$$2\left(y - \frac{1}{2}x\right) = 2(-6)$$

$$2y - x = -12$$

$$x - 2y = 12$$

Therefore, the coefficient of x is 1 and the coefficient of y is -2.

109. Let $(25, 40)$ and $(125, 280)$ be ordered pairs (M, E) where M is degrees Madonna and E is degrees Elvis. Then

$$m = \frac{280 - 40}{125 - 25} = \frac{240}{100} = 2.4. \text{ Using } (x_1, y_1) = (25, 40),$$

point-slope form tells us that
$E - 40 = 2.4\,(M - 25)$ or
$E = 2.4\,M - 20.$

Section 2.4

Check Point Exercises

1. The slope of the line $y = 3x + 1$ is 3.

   $y - y_1 = m(x - x_1)$
   $y - 5 = 3(x - (-2))$
   $y - 5 = 3(x + 2)$ point-slope
   $y - 5 = 3x + 6$
   $\quad y = 3x + 11$ slope-intercept

2. **a.** Write the equation in slope-intercept form:

   $x + 3y - 12 = 0$
   $3y = -x + 12$
   $y = -\dfrac{1}{3}x + 4$

   The slope of this line is $-\dfrac{1}{3}$ thus the slope of any line perpendicular to this line is 3.

   b. Use $m = 3$ and the point $(-2, -6)$ to write the equation.

   $y - y_1 = m(x - x_1)$
   $y - (-6) = 3(x - (-2))$
   $y + 6 = 3(x + 2)$
   $y + 6 = 3x + 6$
   $-3x + y = 0$
   $3x - y = 0$ general form

3. $m = \dfrac{\text{Change in } y}{\text{Change in } x} = \dfrac{12 - 10}{2010 - 1995} = \dfrac{2}{15} \approx 0.13$

   The slope indicates that the number of U.S. men living alone is projected to increase by 0.13 million each year.

4. **a.** $\dfrac{f(x_2) - f(x_1)}{x_2 - x_1} = \dfrac{1^3 - 0^3}{1 - 0} = 1$

   b. $\dfrac{f(x_2) - f(x_1)}{x_2 - x_1} = \dfrac{2^3 - 1^3}{2 - 1} = \dfrac{8 - 1}{1} = 7$

   c. $\dfrac{f(x_2) - f(x_1)}{x_2 - x_1} = \dfrac{0^3 - (-2)^3}{0 - (-2)} = \dfrac{8}{2} = 4$

5. $\dfrac{f(x_2) - f(x_1)}{x_2 - x_1} = \dfrac{f(3) - f(1)}{3 - 1} = \dfrac{0.05 - 0.03}{3 - 1} = 0.01$

Exercise Set 2.4

1. Since L is parallel to $y = 2x$, we know it will have slope $m = 2$. We are given that it passes through $(4, 2)$. We use the slope and point to write the equation in point-slope form.
    $$y - y_1 = m(x - x_1)$$
    $$y - 2 = 2(x - 4)$$
    Solve for y to obtain slope-intercept form.
    $$y - 2 = 2(x - 4)$$
    $$y - 2 = 2x - 8$$
    $$y = 2x - 6$$
    In function notation, the equation of the line is $f(x) = 2x - 6$.

3. Since L is perpendicular to $y = 2x$, we know it will have slope $m = -\dfrac{1}{2}$. We are given that it

    passes through
    $(2, 4)$. We use the slope and point to write the equation in point-slope form.
    $$y - y_1 = m(x - x_1)$$
    $$y - 4 = -\frac{1}{2}(x - 2)$$
    Solve for y to obtain slope-intercept form.
    $$y - 4 = -\frac{1}{2}(x - 2)$$
    $$y - 4 = -\frac{1}{2}x + 1$$
    $$y = -\frac{1}{2}x + 5$$

    In function notation, the equation of the line is $f(x) = -\dfrac{1}{2}x + 5$.

5. $m = -4$ since the line is parallel to $y = -4x + 3$; $x_1 = -8$, $y_1 = -10$;
    point-slope form: $y + 10 = -4(x + 8)$
    slope-intercept form: $y + 10 = -4x - 32$
    $ y = -4x - 42$

7. $m = -5$ since the line is perpendicular to $y = \dfrac{1}{5}x + 6$; $x_1 = 2$, $y_1 = -3$;

    point-slope form: $y + 3 = -5(x - 2)$
    slope-intercept form: $y + 3 = -5x + 10$
    $ y = -5x + 7$

9. $2x - 3y - 7 = 0$
    $$-3y = -2x + 7$$
    $$y = \frac{2}{3}x - \frac{7}{3}$$

    The slope of the given line is $\dfrac{2}{3}$, so $m = \dfrac{2}{3}$ since the lines are parallel.

    point-slope form: $y - 2 = \dfrac{2}{3}(x + 2)$
    general form: $2x - 3y + 10 = 0$

11. $x - 2y - 3 = 0$

$$-2y = -x + 3$$

$$y = \frac{1}{2}x - \frac{3}{2}$$

The slope of the given line is $\frac{1}{2}$, so $m = -2$ since the lines are perpendicular.

point-slope form: $y + 7 = -2(x - 4)$

general form: $2x + y - 1 = 0$

13. $\dfrac{15 - 0}{5 - 0} = \dfrac{15}{5} = 3$

15. $\dfrac{5^2 + 2 \cdot 5 - (3^2 + 2 \cdot 3)}{5 - 3}$

$$= \frac{25 + 10 - (9 + 6)}{2}$$

$$= \frac{20}{2}$$

$$= 10$$

17. $\dfrac{\sqrt{9} - \sqrt{4}}{9 - 4} = \dfrac{3 - 2}{5} = \dfrac{1}{5}$

19.   Since the line is perpendicular to $x = 6$ which is a vertical line, we know the graph of f is a horizontal line with 0 slope. The graph of f passes through $(-1, 5)$, so the equation of f is $f(x) = 5$.

21.   First we need to find the equation of the line with $x-$intercept of 2 and $y-$intercept of -4. This line will pass through $(2, 0)$ and $(0, -4)$. We use these points to find the slope.

$$m = \frac{-4 - 0}{0 - 2} = \frac{-4}{-2} = 2$$

Since the graph of f is perpendicular to this line, it will have slope $m = -\dfrac{1}{2}$.

Use the point $(-6, 4)$ and the slope $-\dfrac{1}{2}$ to find the equation of the line.

$$y - y_1 = m(x - x_1)$$

$$y - 4 = -\frac{1}{2}\left(x - (-6)\right)$$

$$y - 4 = -\frac{1}{2}(x + 6)$$

$$y - 4 = -\frac{1}{2}x - 3$$

$$y = -\frac{1}{2}x + 1$$

$$f(x) = -\frac{1}{2}x + 1$$

23. First put the equation $3x - 2y - 4 = 0$ in slope-intercept form.

$$3x - 2y - 4 = 0$$
$$-2y = -3x + 4$$
$$y = \frac{3}{2}x - 2$$

The equation of f will have slope $-\frac{2}{3}$ since it is perpendicular to the line above and the same $y-$ intercept -2.

So the equation of f is $f(x) = -\frac{2}{3}x - 2$.

25. The slope indicates that the global average temperature is projected to increase by 0.01 degrees Fahrenheit each year.

27. The slope indicates that the percentage of U.S. adults who smoked cigarettes decreased by 0.52% each year.

29. $f(x) = 13x + 222$

31. $f(x) = -2.40x + 52.40$

33. $\dfrac{f(x_2) - f(x_1)}{x_2 - x_1} = \dfrac{f(2003) - f(1997)}{2003 - 1997} = \dfrac{25.2 - 32.5}{2003 - 1997} \approx -1.22$

41. $y = \frac{1}{3}x + 1$
$y = -3x - 2$

    a. The lines are perpendicular because their slopes are negative reciprocals of each other. This is verified because product of their slopes is -1.

    b.
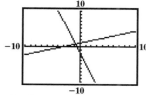

The lines do not appear to be perpendicular.

    c.
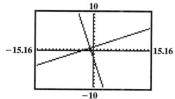

The lines appear to be perpendicular. The calculator screen is rectangular and does not have the same width and height. This causes the scale of the x–axis to differ from the scale on the y–axis despite using the same scale in the window settings. In part (b), this causes the lines not to appear perpendicular when indeed they are. The zoom square feature compensates for this and in part (c), the lines appear to be perpendicular.

43.

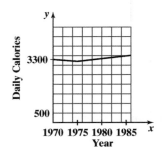

45.   The slope of the line containing $(1,-3)$ and $(-2,4)$ has slope
$$m = \frac{4-(-3)}{-2-1} = \frac{4+3}{-3} = \frac{7}{-3} = -\frac{7}{3}.$$
Solve $Ax + y - 2 = 0$ for y to obtain slope-intercept form.
$$Ax + y - 2 = 0$$
$$y = -Ax + 2$$
So the slope of this line is $-A$.

This line is perpendicular to the line above so its slope is $\frac{3}{7}$. Therefore, $-A = \frac{3}{7}$ so $A = -\frac{3}{7}$.

Mid-Chapter 2 Check Point

1.   The relation is not a function.
The domain is $\{1,2\}$.
The range is $\{-6,4,6\}$.

2.   The relation is a function.
The domain is $\{0,2,3\}$.
The range is $\{1,4\}$.

3.   The relation is a function.
The domain is $\{x \mid -2 \le x < 2\}$.
The range is $\{y \mid 0 \le y \le 3\}$.

4.   The relation is not a function.
The domain is $\{x \mid -3 < x \le 4\}$.
The range is $\{y \mid -1 \le y \le 2\}$.

5.   The relation is not a function.
The domain is $\{-2,-1,0,1,2\}$.
The range is $\{-2,-1,1,3\}$.

6.   The relation is a function.
The domain is $\{x \mid x \le 1\}$.
The range is $\{y \mid y \ge -1\}$.

7. $x^2 + y = 5$
$$y = -x^2 + 5$$
For each value of x, there is one and only one value for y, so the equation defines y as a function of x.

8. $x + y^2 = 5$
$$y^2 = 5 - x$$
$$y = \pm\sqrt{5-x}$$
Since there are values of x that give more than one value for y (for example, if $x = 4$, then $y = \pm\sqrt{5-4} = \pm 1$), the equation does not define y as a function of x.

9.   Each value of x corresponds to exactly one value of y.

10.   Domain: $(-\infty,\infty)$

11.   Range: $(-\infty,4]$

12. x-intercepts: -6 and 2

13. y-intercept: 3

14.   increasing: $(-\infty, -2)$

15.   decreasing: $(-2, \infty)$

154

16. $x = -2$

17. $f(-2) = 4$

18. $f(-4) = 3$

19. $f(-7) = -2$ and $f(3) = -2$

20. $f(-6) = 0$ and $f(2) = 0$

21. $(-6, 2)$

22. $f(100)$ is negative.

23. neither; $f(-x) \neq x$ and $f(-x) \neq -x$

24. $\dfrac{f(x_2) - f(x_1)}{x_2 - x_1} = \dfrac{f(4) - f(-4)}{4 - (-4)} = \dfrac{-5 - 3}{4 + 4} = -1$

25. $y = -2x$
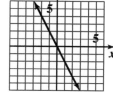

26. $y = -2$
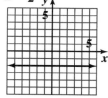

27. $x + y = -2$
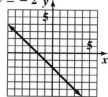

28. $y = \dfrac{1}{3}x - 2$
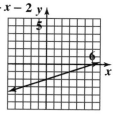

29. $x = 3.5$
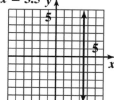

30.
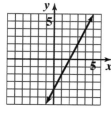
$$4x - 2y = 8$$

31.
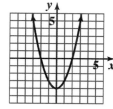
$$f(x) = x^2 - 4$$

32.
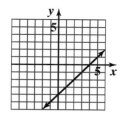
$$f(x) = x - 4$$

33.
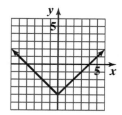
$$f(x) = |x| - 4$$

155

34. $5y = -3x$

$$y = -\frac{3}{5}x$$

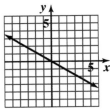

$5y = -3x$

35. $5y = 20$

$$y = 4$$

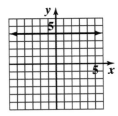

$5y = 20$

36.

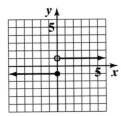

$$f(x) = \begin{cases} -1 \text{ if } x \le 0 \\ 1 \text{ if } x > 0 \end{cases}$$

37. a. $f(-x) = -2(-x)^2 - x - 5 = -2x^2 - x - 5$

neither; $f(-x) \ne x$ and $f(-x) \ne -x$

b. $\dfrac{f(x+h) - f(x)}{h}$

$$= \frac{-2(x+h)^2 + (x+h) - 5 - (-2x^2 + x - 5)}{h}$$

$$= \frac{-2x^2 - 4xh - 2h^2 + x + h - 5 + 2x^2 - x + 5}{h}$$

$$= \frac{-4xh - 2h^2 + h}{h}$$

$$= \frac{h(-4x - 2h + 1)}{h}$$

$$= -4x - 2h + 1$$

38. $C(x) = \begin{cases} 30 & \text{if} \quad 0 \le t \le 200 \\ 30 + 0.40(t - 200) & \text{if} \quad t > 200 \end{cases}$

a. $C(150) = 30$

b. $C(250) = 30 + 0.40(250 - 200) = 50$

39. $y - y_1 = m(x - x_1)$

$$y - 3 = -2(x - (-4))$$

$$y - 3 = -2(x + 4)$$

$$y - 3 = -2x - 8$$

$$y = -2x - 5$$

$$f(x) = -2x - 5$$

40. $m = \dfrac{\text{Change in } y}{\text{Change in } x} = \dfrac{1 - (-5)}{2 - (-1)} = \dfrac{6}{3} = 2$

$$y - y_1 = m(x - x_1)$$

$$y - 1 = 2(x - 2)$$

$$y - 1 = 2x - 4$$

$$y = 2x - 3$$

$$f(x) = 2x - 3$$

41. $3x - y - 5 = 0$

$$-y = -3x + 5$$

$$y = 3x - 5$$

The slope of the given line is 3, and the lines are parallel, so $m = 3$.

$$y - y_1 = m(x - x_1)$$

$$y - (-4) = 3(x - 3)$$

$$y + 4 = 3x - 9$$

$$y = 3x - 13$$

$$f(x) = 3x - 13$$

42.
$$2x - 5y - 10 = 0$$
$$-5y = -2x + 10$$
$$\frac{-5y}{-5} = \frac{-2x}{-5} + \frac{10}{-5}$$
$$y = \frac{2}{5}x - 2$$

The slope of the given line is $\frac{2}{5}$, and the lines

are perpendicular, so $m = -\frac{5}{2}$.

$$y - y_1 = m(x - x_1)$$
$$y - (-3) = -\frac{5}{2}(x - (-4))$$
$$y + 3 = -\frac{5}{2}x - 10$$
$$y = -\frac{5}{2}x - 13$$
$$f(x) = -\frac{5}{2}x - 13$$

43. $m_1 = \dfrac{\text{Change in } y}{\text{Change in } x} = \dfrac{0 - (-4)}{7 - 2} = \dfrac{4}{5}$

$m_2 = \dfrac{\text{Change in } y}{\text{Change in } x} = \dfrac{6 - 2}{1 - (-4)} = \dfrac{4}{5}$

The slope of the lines are equal thus the lines are parallel.

44. The slope indicates that the percentage of U.S. colleges offering distance learning is increasing by 7.8% each year.

45. $\dfrac{f(x_2) - f(x_1)}{x_2 - x_1} = \dfrac{f(2) - f(-1)}{2 - (-1)}$

$$= \frac{\left(3(2)^2 - 2\right) - \left(3(-1)^2 - (-1)\right)}{2 + 1}$$
$$= 2$$

Section 2.5

Check Point Exercises

1. Shift up vertically 3 units.

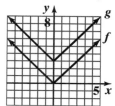

2. Shift to the right 4 units.

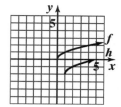

3. Shift to the right 1 unit and down 2 units.

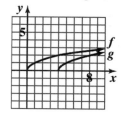

4. Reflect about the *x*-axis.

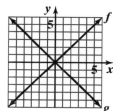

5. Reflect about the *y*-axis.

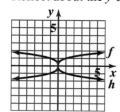

6. Vertically stretch the graph of $f(x) = |x|$.

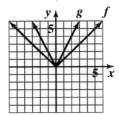

7. **a.** Horizontally shrink the graph of $y = f(x)$.

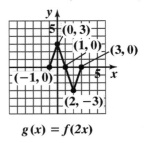

$$g(x) = f(2x)$$

b. Horizontally stretch the graph of $y = f(x)$.

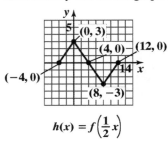

$$h(x) = f\left(\frac{1}{2}x\right)$$

8. The graph of $y = f(x)$ is shifted 1 unit left, shrunk by a factor of $\frac{1}{3}$, reflected about the x-axis, then shifted down 2 units.

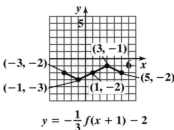

$$y = -\frac{1}{3}f(x + 1) - 2$$

9. The graph of $f(x) = x^2$ is shifted 1 unit right, stretched by a factor of 2, then shifted up 3 units.

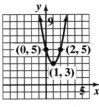

$$g(x) = 2(x - 1)^2 + 3$$

Exercise Set 2.5

1.

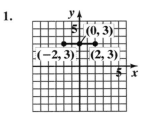

$$g(x) = f(x) + 1$$

3.

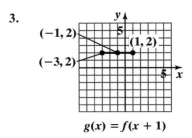

$$g(x) = f(x + 1)$$

5.

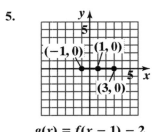

$$g(x) = f(x - 1) - 2$$

7.

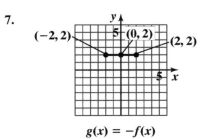

$$g(x) = -f(x)$$

9.

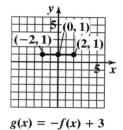

$$g(x) = -f(x) + 3$$

11.

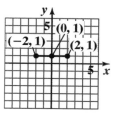

$$g(x) = \frac{1}{2}f(x)$$

13. $g(x) = f\left(\frac{1}{2}x\right)$

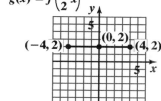

15.

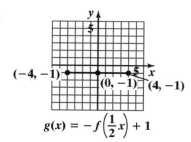

$$g(x) = -f\left(\frac{1}{2}x\right) + 1$$

17.

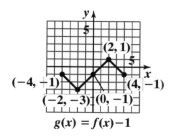

$$g(x) = f(x) - 1$$

19.

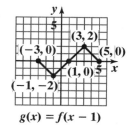

$$g(x) = f(x - 1)$$

21.

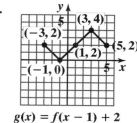

$$g(x) = f(x - 1) + 2$$

23.

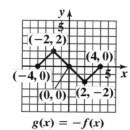

$$g(x) = -f(x)$$

25.

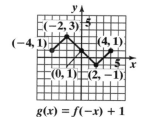

$$g(x) = f(-x) + 1$$

27.

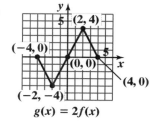

$$g(x) = 2f(x)$$

29.

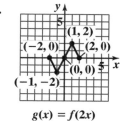

$$g(x) = f(2x)$$

31.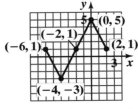

$g(x) = 2f(x + 2) + 1$

33.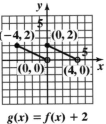

$g(x) = f(x) + 2$

35.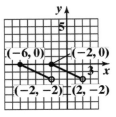

$g(x) = f(x + 2)$

37.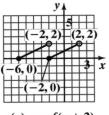

$g(x) = -f(x + 2)$

39.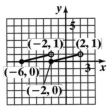

$g(x) = -\frac{1}{2}f(x + 2)$

41.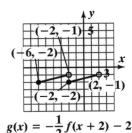

$g(x) = -\frac{1}{2}f(x + 2) - 2$

43.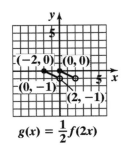

$g(x) = \frac{1}{2}f(2x)$

45.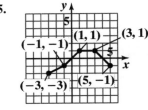

$g(x) = f(x - 1) - 1$

47.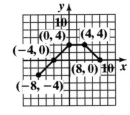

$g(x) = -f(x - 1) + 1$

49.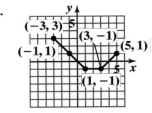

$g(x) = 2f\left(\frac{1}{2}x\right)$

51.

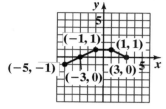

$$g(x) = \frac{1}{2}f(x + 1)$$

53.

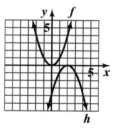

55.

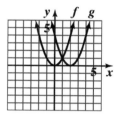

57.

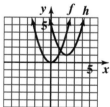

59.

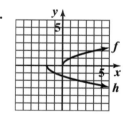

61.

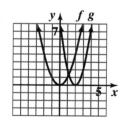

63.

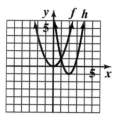

65.

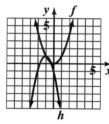

67.

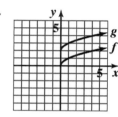

69.

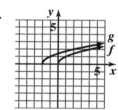

71.

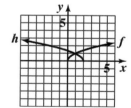

73.

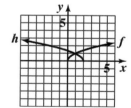

161

75.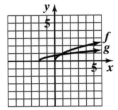

77.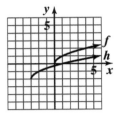

79.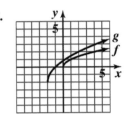

81.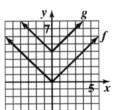

83.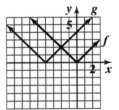

85.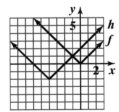

87.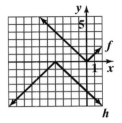

89.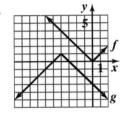

91.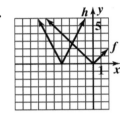

93.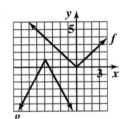

95.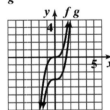

97.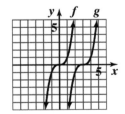

162

99.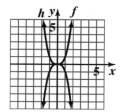

101.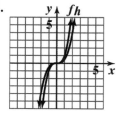

103.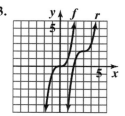

105.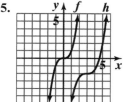

107.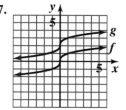

109.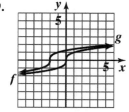

111.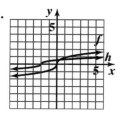

113.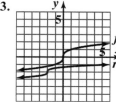

115.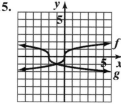

117.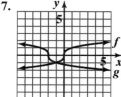

119.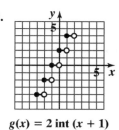

$g(x) = 2 \text{ int } (x + 1)$

121.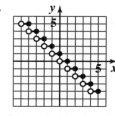

$h(x) = \text{int } (-x) + 1$

123. $y = \sqrt{x-2}$

125. $y = (x+1)^2 - 4$

163

127. a.   First, vertically stretch the graph of $f(x) = \sqrt{x}$ by the factor 2.9; then shift the result up 20.1 units.

b. $f(x) = 2.9\sqrt{x} + 20.1$

$f(48) = 2.9\sqrt{48} + 20.1 \approx 40.2$

The model describes the actual data very well.

c. $\dfrac{f(x_2) - f(x_1)}{x_2 - x_1}$

$= \dfrac{f(10) - f(0)}{10 - 0}$

$= \dfrac{\left(2.9\sqrt{10} + 20.1\right) - \left(2.9\sqrt{0} + 20.1\right)}{10 - 0}$

$= \dfrac{29.27 - 20.1}{10}$

≈ 0.9

0.9 inches per month

d. $\dfrac{f(x_2) - f(x_1)}{x_2 - x_1}$

$= \dfrac{f(60) - f(50)}{60 - 50}$

$= \dfrac{\left(2.9\sqrt{60} + 20.1\right) - \left(2.9\sqrt{50} + 20.1\right)}{60 - 50}$

$= \dfrac{42.5633 - 40.6061}{10}$

≈ 0.2

This rate of change is lower than the rate of change in part (c). The relative leveling off of the curve shows this difference.

135. a.
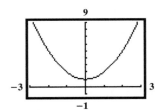

136. a.
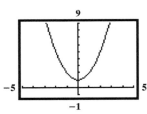

b.
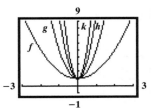

b.
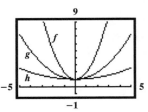

137. a.   False; the graph of g is a translation of three units upward and three units to the left of the graph of f.

b.   False; the graph of f is a reflection of the graph of $y = \sqrt{x}$ in the x-axis, while the graph of g is a reflection of the graph of $y = \sqrt{x}$ in the y-axis.

  c. False; $g(x) = 5x^2 - 10$, so the graph of g can be obtained by stretching f five units followed by a downward shift of ten units.

  d. True

  (d) is true.

139. $g(x) = -|x - 5| + 1$ **143.** $(a,\ 2b)$

                   145. $(a,\ b - 3)$

141. $g(x) = -\dfrac{1}{4}\sqrt{16 - x^2} - 1$

Section 2.6

Check Point Exercises

1. **a.** The function $f(x) = x^2 + 3x - 17$ contains neither division nor an even root. The domain of f is the set of all real numbers or $(-\infty, \infty)$.

  b. The denominator equals zero when $x = 7$ or $x = -7$. These values must be excluded from the domain. Domain of $g = (-\infty, -7) \cup (-7, 7) \cup (7, \infty)$.

  c. Since $h(x) = \sqrt{9x - 27}$ contains an even root; the quantity under the radical must be greater than or equal to 0.
$$9x - 27 \geq 0$$
$$9x \geq 27$$
$$x \geq 3$$
Thus, the domain of h is $\{x \mid x \geq 3\}$, or the interval $[3, \infty)$.

2. **a.** $(f + g)(x) = f(x) + g(x)$
$$= x - 5 + (x^2 - 1)$$
$$= x - 5 + x^2 - 1$$
$$= -x^2 + x - 6$$

  b. $(f - g)(x) = f(x) - g(x)$
$$= x - 5 - (x^2 - 1)$$
$$= x - 5 - x^2 + 1$$
$$= -x^2 + x - 4$$

  c. $(fg)(x) = (x - 5)(x^2 - 1)$
$$= x(x^2 - 1) - 5(x^2 - 1)$$
$$= x^3 - x - 5x^2 + 5$$
$$= x^3 - 5x^2 - x + 5$$

  d. $\left(\dfrac{f}{g}\right)(x) = \dfrac{f(x)}{g(x)}$
$$= \dfrac{x - 5}{x^2 - 1},\ x \neq \pm 1$$

3. a. $(f+g)(x) = f(x)+g(x)$

$$= \sqrt{x-3}+\sqrt{x+1}$$

   b. Domain of f: $x-3 \geq 0$

$$x \geq 3$$

$$[3, \infty)$$

   Domain of g: $x+1 \geq 0$

$$x \geq -1$$

$$[-1, \infty)$$

   The domain of $f+g$ is the set of all real numbers that are common to the domain of f and the domain of g.
   Thus, the domain of $f+g$ is $[3, \infty)$.

4. a. $(f \circ g)(x) = f(g(x))$

$$= 5(2x^2 - x - 1)+6$$

$$= 10x^2 - 5x - 5 + 6$$

$$= 10x^2 - 5x + 1$$

   b. $(g \circ f)(x) = g(f(x))$

$$= 2(5x+6)^2 - (5x+6) - 1$$

$$= 2(25x^2 + 60x + 36) - 5x - 6 - 1$$

$$= 50x^2 + 120x + 72 - 5x - 6 - 1$$

$$= 50x^2 + 115x + 65$$

5. a. $f \circ g(x) = \dfrac{4}{\dfrac{1}{x}+2} = \dfrac{4x}{1+2x}$

   b. $\left\{ x \mid x \neq 0, x \neq -\dfrac{1}{2} \right\}$

6. $h(x) = f \circ g$ where $f(x) = \sqrt{x}$; $g(x) = x^2 + 5$

Exercise Set 2.6

1. The function contains neither division nor an even root. The domain $= (-\infty, \infty)$

3. The denominator equals zero when $x = 4$. This value must be excluded from the domain.
    Domain: $(-\infty, 4) \cup (4, \infty)$.

5. The function contains neither division nor an even root. The domain $= (-\infty, \infty)$

7. The values that make the denominator equal zero must be excluded from the domain.
    Domain: $(-\infty, -3) \cup (-3, 5) \cup (5, \infty)$

9. The values that make the denominators equal zero must be excluded from the domain.
    Domain: $(-\infty, -7) \cup (-7, 9) \cup (9, \infty)$

11. The first denominator cannot equal zero. The values that make the second denominator equal zero must be excluded from the domain.
Domain: $(-\infty,-1)\cup(-1,1)\cup(1,\infty)$

13. Exclude x for $x=0$.

Exclude x for $\dfrac{3}{x}-1=0$.

$$\dfrac{3}{x}-1=0$$

$$x\left(\dfrac{3}{x}-1\right)=x(0)$$

$$3-x=0$$

$$-x=-3$$

$$x=3$$

Domain: $(-\infty,0)\cup(0,3)\cup(3,\infty)$

15. Exclude x for $x-1=0$.

$$x-1=0$$

$$x=1$$

Exclude x for $\dfrac{4}{x-1}-2=0$.

$$\dfrac{4}{x-1}-2=0$$

$$(x-1)\left(\dfrac{4}{x-1}-2\right)=(x-1)(0)$$

$$4-2(x-1)=0$$

$$4-2x+2=0$$

$$-2x+6=0$$

$$-2x=-6$$

$$x=3$$

Domain: $(-\infty,1)\cup(1,3)\cup(3,\infty)$

17. The expression under the radical must not be negative.
$$x-3\geq0$$

$$x\geq3$$

Domain: $[3,\infty)$

19. The expression under the radical must be positive.
$$x-3>0$$

$$x>3$$

Domain: $(3,\infty)$

21. The expression under the radical must not be negative.
$$5x+35\geq0$$

$$5x\geq-35$$

$$x\geq-7$$

Domain: $[-7,\infty)$

23. The expression under the radical must not be negative.
$$24 - 2x \geq 0$$
$$-2x \geq -24$$
$$\frac{-2x}{-2} \leq \frac{-24}{-2}$$
$$x \leq 12$$
Domain: $(-\infty, 12]$

25. The expressions under the radicals must not be negative.
$$x - 2 \geq 0 \quad \text{and} \quad x + 3 \geq 0$$
$$x \geq 2 \qquad\qquad x \geq -3$$
To make both inequalities true, $x \geq 2$.
Domain: $[2, \infty)$

27. The expression under the radical must not be negative.
$$x - 2 \geq 0$$
$$x \geq 2$$
The denominator equals zero when $x = 5$.
Domain: $[2, 5) \cup (5, \infty)$.

29. Find the values that make the denominator equal zero and must be excluded from the domain.
$$x^3 - 5x^2 - 4x + 20$$
$$= x^2(x - 5) - 4(x - 5)$$
$$= (x - 5)(x^2 - 4)$$
$$= (x - 5)(x + 2)(x - 2)$$
-2, 2, and 5 must be excluded.
Domain: $(-\infty, -2) \cup (-2, 2) \cup (2, 5) \cup (5, \infty)$

31. $(f + g)(x) = 3x + 2$
Domain: $(-\infty, \infty)$
$(f - g)(x) = f(x) - g(x)$
$\qquad = (2x + 3) - (x - 1)$
$\qquad = x + 4$
Domain: $(-\infty, \infty)$
$(fg)(x) = f(x) \cdot g(x)$
$\qquad = (2x + 3) \cdot (x - 1)$
$\qquad = 2x^2 + x - 3$
Domain: $(-\infty, \infty)$
$\left(\dfrac{f}{g}\right)(x) = \dfrac{f(x)}{g(x)} = \dfrac{2x + 3}{x - 1}$
Domain: $(-\infty, 1) \cup (1, \infty)$

33. $(f + g)(x) = 3x^2 + x - 5$
Domain: $(-\infty, \infty)$
$(f - g)(x) = -3x^2 + x - 5$
Domain: $(-\infty, \infty)$
$(fg)(x) = (x - 5)(3x^2) = 3x^3 - 15x^2$
Domain: $(-\infty, \infty)$
$\left(\dfrac{f}{g}\right)(x) = \dfrac{x - 5}{3x^2}$
Domain: $(-\infty, 0) \cup (0, \infty)$

35. $(f+g)(x) = 2x^2 - 2$

Domain: $(-\infty, \infty)$

$(f-g)(x) = 2x^2 - 2x - 4$

Domain: $(-\infty, \infty)$

$(fg)(x) = (2x^2 - x - 3)(x+1)$

$\qquad = 2x^3 + x^2 - 4x - 3$

Domain: $(-\infty, \infty)$

$\left(\dfrac{f}{g}\right)(x) = \dfrac{2x^2 - x - 3}{x+1}$

$\qquad = \dfrac{(2x-3)(x+1)}{(x+1)} = 2x - 3$

Domain: $(-\infty, -1) \cup (-1, \infty)$

37. $(f+g)(x) = (3 - x^2) + (x^2 + 2x - 15)$

$\qquad = 2x - 12$

Domain: $(-\infty, \infty)$

$(f-g)(x) = (3 - x^2) - (x^2 + 2x - 15)$

$\qquad = -2x^2 - 2x + 18$

Domain: $(-\infty, \infty)$

$(fg)(x) = (3 - x^2)(x^2 + 2x - 15)$

$\qquad = -x^4 - 2x^3 + 18x^2 + 6x - 45$

Domain: $(-\infty, \infty)$

$\left(\dfrac{f}{g}\right)(x) = \dfrac{3 - x^2}{x^2 + 2x - 15}$

Domain: $(-\infty, -5) \cup (-5, 3) \cup (3, \infty)$

39. $(f+g)(x) = \sqrt{x} + x - 4$

Domain: $[0, \infty)$

$(f-g)(x) = \sqrt{x} - x + 4$

Domain: $[0, \infty)$

$(fg)(x) = \sqrt{x}(x-4)$

Domain: $[0, \infty)$

$\left(\dfrac{f}{g}\right)(x) = \dfrac{\sqrt{x}}{x-4}$

Domain: $[0, 4) \cup (4, \infty)$

41. $(f+g)(x) = 2 + \dfrac{1}{x} + \dfrac{1}{x} = 2 + \dfrac{2}{x} = \dfrac{2x+2}{x}$

Domain: $(-\infty, 0) \cup (0, \infty)$

$(f-g)(x) = 2 + \dfrac{1}{x} - \dfrac{1}{x} = 2$

Domain: $(-\infty, 0) \cup (0, \infty)$

$(fg)(x) = \left(2 + \dfrac{1}{x}\right) \cdot \dfrac{1}{x} = \dfrac{2}{x} + \dfrac{1}{x^2} = \dfrac{2x+1}{x^2}$

Domain: $(-\infty, 0) \cup (0, \infty)$

$\left(\dfrac{f}{g}\right)(x) = \dfrac{2 + \frac{1}{x}}{\frac{1}{x}} = \left(2 + \dfrac{1}{x}\right) \cdot x = 2x + 1$

Domain: $(-\infty, 0) \cup (0, \infty)$

43. $(f+g)(x) = f(x) + g(x)$

$\qquad = \dfrac{5x+1}{x^2-9} + \dfrac{4x-2}{x^2-9}$

$\qquad = \dfrac{9x-1}{x^2-9}$

Domain: $(-\infty, -3) \cup (-3, 3) \cup (3, \infty)$

$(f-g)(x) = f(x) - g(x)$

$\qquad = \dfrac{5x+1}{x^2-9} - \dfrac{4x-2}{x^2-9}$

$\qquad = \dfrac{x+3}{x^2-9}$

$\qquad = \dfrac{1}{x-3}$

Domain: $(-\infty, -3) \cup (-3, 3) \cup (3, \infty)$

$(fg)(x) = f(x) \cdot g(x)$

$\qquad = \dfrac{5x+1}{x^2-9} \cdot \dfrac{4x-2}{x^2-9}$

$\qquad = \dfrac{(5x+1)(4x-2)}{\left(x^2-9\right)^2}$

Domain: $(-\infty, -3) \cup (-3, 3) \cup (3, \infty)$

$\left(\dfrac{f}{g}\right)(x) = \dfrac{\frac{5x+1}{x^2-9}}{\frac{4x-2}{x^2-9}}$

$\qquad = \dfrac{5x+1}{x^2-9} \cdot \dfrac{x^2-9}{4x-2}$

$\qquad = \dfrac{5x+1}{4x-2}$

The domain must exclude -3, 3, and any values that make $4x - 2 = 0$.

$4x - 2 = 0$

$\quad 4x = 2$

$\qquad x = \dfrac{1}{2}$

Domain: $(-\infty, -3) \cup \left(-3, \tfrac{1}{2}\right) \cup \left(\tfrac{1}{2}, 3\right) \cup (3, \infty)$

45. $(f+g)(x) = \sqrt{x+4} + \sqrt{x-1}$
Domain: $[1, \infty)$
$(f-g)(x) = \sqrt{x+4} - \sqrt{x-1}$
Domain: $[1, \infty)$
$(fg)(x) = \sqrt{x+4} \cdot \sqrt{x-1} = \sqrt{x^2+3x-4}$
Domain: $[1, \infty)$
$\left(\dfrac{f}{g}\right)(x) = \dfrac{\sqrt{x+4}}{\sqrt{x-1}}$
Domain: $(1, \infty)$

47. $(f+g)(x) = \sqrt{x-2} + \sqrt{2-x}$
Domain: $\{2\}$
$(f-g)(x) = \sqrt{x-2} - \sqrt{2-x}$
Domain: $\{2\}$
$(fg)(x) = \sqrt{x-2} \cdot \sqrt{2-x} = \sqrt{-x^2+4x-4}$
Domain: $\{2\}$
$\left(\dfrac{f}{g}\right)(x) = \dfrac{\sqrt{x-2}}{\sqrt{2-x}}$
Domain: $\varnothing$

49. $f(x) = 2x;\ g(x) = x+7$

   a. $(f \circ g)(x) = 2(x+7) = 2x+14$

   b. $(g \circ f)(x) = 2x+7$

   c. $(f \circ g)(2) = 2(2)+14 = 18$

51. $f(x) = x+4;\ g(x) = 2x+1$

   a. $(f \circ g)(x) = (2x+1)+4 = 2x+5$

   b. $(g \circ f)(x) = 2(x+4)+1 = 2x+9$

   c. $(f \circ g)(2) = 2(2)+5 = 9$

53. $f(x) = 4x-3;\ g(x) = 5x^2-2$

   a. $(f \circ g)(x) = 4(5x^2-2)-3$
            $= 20x^2-11$

   b. $(g \circ f)(x) = 5(4x-3)^2-2$
            $= 5(16x^2-24x+9)-2$
            $= 80x^2-120x+43$

   c. $(f \circ g)(2) = 20(2)^2-11 = 69$

55. $f(x) = x^2+2;\ g(x) = x^2-2$

   a. $(f \circ g)(x) = (x^2-2)^2+2$
            $= x^4-4x^2+4+2$
            $= x^4-4x^2+6$

   b. $(g \circ f)(x) = (x^2+2)^2-2$
            $= x^4+4x^2+4-2$
            $= x^4+4x^2+2$

   c. $(f \circ g)(2) = 2^4-4(2)^2+6 = 6$

57. $f(x) = 4-x;\ g(x) = 2x^2+x+5$

   a. $(f \circ g)(x) = 4-\left(2x^2+x+5\right)$
            $= 4-2x^2-x-5$
            $= -2x^2-x-1$

   b. $(g \circ f)(x) = 2(4-x)^2+(4-x)+5$
            $= 2(16-8x+x^2)+4-x+5$
            $= 32-16x+2x^2+4-x+5$
            $= 2x^2-17x+41$

   c. $(f \circ g)(2) = -2(2)^2-2-1 = -11$

59. $f(x) = \sqrt{x};\ g(x) = x-1$

   a. $(f \circ g)(x) = \sqrt{x-1}$

   b. $(g \circ f)(x) = \sqrt{x}-1$

   c. $(f \circ g)(2) = \sqrt{2-1} = \sqrt{1} = 1$

61. $f(x) = 2x-3;\ g(x) = \dfrac{x+3}{2}$

   a. $(f \circ g)(x) = 2\left(\dfrac{x+3}{2}\right)-3$
            $= x+3-3$
            $= x$

   b. $(g \circ f)(x) = \dfrac{(2x-3)+3}{2} = \dfrac{2x}{2} = x$

   c. $(f \circ g)(2) = 2$

170

63. $f(x) = \dfrac{1}{x}; \quad g(x) = \dfrac{1}{x}$

     a. $(f \circ g)(x) = \dfrac{1}{\frac{1}{x}} = x$

     b. $(g \circ f)(x) = \dfrac{1}{\frac{1}{x}} = x$

     c. $(f \circ g)(2) = 2$

65.   **a.** $(f \circ g)(x) = f\left(\dfrac{1}{x}\right) = \dfrac{2}{\frac{1}{x} + 3}, x \neq 0$

            $= \dfrac{2(x)}{\left(\frac{1}{x} + 3\right)(x)}$

            $= \dfrac{2x}{1 + 3x}$

     b. We must exclude 0 because it is excluded from *g*.

        We must exclude $-\dfrac{1}{3}$ because it causes the denominator of $f \circ g$ to be 0.

        Domain: $\left(-\infty, -\dfrac{1}{3}\right) \cup \left(-\dfrac{1}{3}, 0\right) \cup (0, \infty)$.

67.   **a.** $(f \circ g)(x) = f\left(\dfrac{4}{x}\right) = \dfrac{\frac{4}{x}}{\frac{4}{x} + 1}$

            $= \dfrac{\left(\frac{4}{x}\right)(x)}{\left(\frac{4}{x} + 1\right)(x)}$

            $= \dfrac{4}{4 + x}, x \neq -4$

     b. We must exclude 0 because it is excluded from *g*.
        We must exclude -4 because it causes the denominator of $f \circ g$ to be 0.
        Domain: $(-\infty, -4) \cup (-4, 0) \cup (0, \infty)$.

69.   **a.** $f \circ g(x) = f(x - 2) = \sqrt{x - 2}$

     b. The expression under the radical in $f \circ g$ must not be negative.
        $x - 2 \geq 0$
          $x \geq 2$
        Domain: $[2, \infty)$.

71. a.
$$(f \circ g)(x) = f(\sqrt{1-x})$$
$$= \left(\sqrt{1-x}\right)^2 + 4$$
$$= 1 - x + 4$$
$$= 5 - x$$

b. The domain of $f \circ g$ must exclude any values that are excluded from g.
$$1 - x \geq 0$$
$$-x \geq -1$$
$$x \leq 1$$
Domain: $(-\infty, 1]$.

73. $f(x) = x^4 \quad g(x) = 3x - 1$

75. $f(x) = \sqrt[3]{x} \quad g(x) = x^2 - 9$

77. $f(x) = |x| \quad g(x) = 2x - 5$

79. $f(x) = \dfrac{1}{x} \quad g(x) = 2x - 3$

81. $(f + g)(-3) = f(-3) + g(-3) = 4 + 1 = 5$

83. $(fg)(2) = f(2)g(2) = (-1)(1) = -1$

85. The domain of $f + g$ is $[-4, 3]$.

87. The graph of $f + g$

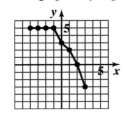

89. $(f \circ g)(-1) = f(g(-1)) = f(-3) = 1$

91. $(g \circ f)(0) = g(f(0)) = g(2) = -6$

93.
$$(f \circ g)(x) = 7$$
$$2(x^2 - 3x + 8) - 5 = 7$$
$$2x^2 - 6x + 16 - 5 = 7$$
$$2x^2 - 6x + 11 = 7$$
$$2x^2 - 6x + 4 = 0$$
$$x^2 - 3x + 2 = 0$$
$$(x - 1)(x - 2) = 0$$
$$x - 1 = 0 \quad \text{or} \quad x - 2 = 0$$
$$x = 1 \qquad\qquad x = 2$$

95. Domain: $\{0, 1, 2, 3, 4, 5, 6, 7, 8\}$

97. a. $(B - D)(x) = (26,208x + 3,869,910) - (17,964x + 2,300,198)$
$$= 26,208x + 3,869,910 - 17,964x - 2,300,198$$
$$= 8244x + 1,569,712$$
This function represents the net change in population from births and deaths.

b. $(B - D)(x) = 8244x + 1,569,712$
$(B - D)(8) = 8244(8) + 1,569,712 = 1,635,664$
The U.S. population increased by 1,635,664 in 2003.

c. $4,093,000 - 2,423,000 = 1,670,000$
The difference of the functions modeled this value reasonably well.

99. $f + g$ represents the total world population in year x.

101. $(f + g)(2000) \approx 6$ billion people.

103. $(R-C)(20,000)$

$= 65(20,000) - (600,000 + 45(20,000))$

$= -200,000$

The company lost $200,000 since costs exceeded revenues.

$(R - C)(30,000)$

$= 65(30,000) - (600,000 + 45(30,000))$

$= 0$

The company broke even.

105. a. f gives the price of the computer after a $400 discount. g gives the price of the computer after a 25% discount.

    b. $(f \circ g)(x) = 0.75x - 400$

This models the price of a computer after first a 25% discount and then a $400 discount.

    c. $(g \circ f)(x) = 0.75(x - 400)$

This models the price of a computer after first a $400 discount and then a 25% discount.

    d.   The function $f \circ g$ models the greater discount, since the 25% discount is taken on the regular price first.

117. $(f \circ g)(x) = (f \circ g)(-x)$

$f(g(x)) = f(g(-x))$ since g is even

$f(g(x)) = f(g(x))$ so $f \circ g$ is even

119.

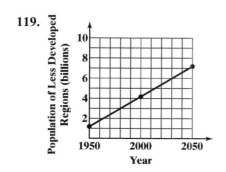

113.

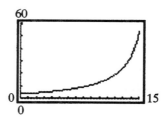

The per capita cost of Medicare is rising.

115.

$(f \circ g)(x) = \sqrt{2 - \sqrt{x}}$

The domain of g is $[0, \infty)$.

The expression under the radical in $f \circ g$ must not be negative.

$2 - \sqrt{x} \geq 0$

$-\sqrt{x} \geq -2$

$\sqrt{x} \leq 2$

$x \leq 4$

Domain: $[0, 4]$

Section 2.7

Check Point Exercises

1. $d = \sqrt{(x_2 - x_1)^2 + (y_2 - y_1)^2}$

    $d = \sqrt{(1-(-4))^2 + (-3-9)^2}$

    $= \sqrt{(5)^2 + (-12)^2}$

    $= \sqrt{25 + 144}$

    $= \sqrt{169}$

    $= 13$

2. $\left(\dfrac{1+7}{2}, \dfrac{2+(-3)}{2}\right) = \left(\dfrac{8}{2}, \dfrac{-1}{2}\right) = \left(4, -\dfrac{1}{2}\right)$

3. $h = 0,\ k = 0,\ r = 4;$

    $(x-0)^2 + (y-0)^2 = 4^2$

    $x^2 + y^2 = 16$

4. $h = 5,\ k = -6,\ r = 10;$

    $(x-5)^2 + [y-(-6)]^2 = 10^2$

    $(x-5)^2 + (y+6)^2 = 100$

5. a. $(x+3)^2 + (y-1)^2 = 4$

    $[x-(-3)]^2 + (y-1)^2 = 2^2$

    So in the standard form of the circle's
    equation $(x-h)^2 + (y-k)^2 = r^2$,
    we have $h = -3,\ k = 1,\ r = 2$.
    center: $(h, k) = (-3, 1)$
    radius: $r = 2$

    b.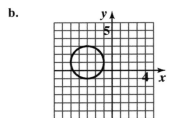

    $(x + 3)^2 + (y - 1)^2 = 4$

    c. Domain: $[-5, -1]$
        Range: $[-1, 3]$

6. $x^2 + y^2 + 4x - 4y - 1 = 0$

    $x^2 + y^2 + 4x - 4y - 1 = 0$

    $(x^2 + 4x\quad) + (y^2 - 4y\quad) = 0$

    $(x^2 + 4x + 4) + (y^2 + 4y + 4) = 1 + 4 + 4$

    $(x+2)^2 + (y-2)^2 = 9$

    $[x-(-x)]^2 + (y-2)^2 = 3^2$

    So in the standard form of the circle's equation
    $(x-h)^2 + (y-k)^2 = r^2$, we have
    $h = -2,\ k = 2,\ r = 3$.

    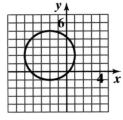

    $x^2 + y^2 + 4x - 4y - 1 = 0$

Exercise Set 2.7

1. $d = \sqrt{(14-2)^2 + (8-3)^2}$

    $= \sqrt{12^2 + 5^2}$

    $= \sqrt{144 + 25}$

    $= \sqrt{169}$

    $= 13$

3. $d = \sqrt{(-6-4)^2 + (3-(-1))^2}$

    $= \sqrt{(-10)^2 + (4)^2}$

    $= \sqrt{100 + 16}$

    $= \sqrt{116}$

    $= 2\sqrt{29}$

    ≈ 10.77

5. $d = \sqrt{(-3-0)^2 + (4-0)^2}$

    $= \sqrt{3^2 + 4^2}$

    $= \sqrt{9 + 16}$

    $= \sqrt{25}$

    $= 5$

7. $d = \sqrt{[3-(-2)]^2 + [-4-(-6)]^2}$
$= \sqrt{5^2 + 2^2}$
$= \sqrt{25 + 4}$
$= \sqrt{29}$
≈ 5.39

9. $d = \sqrt{(4-0)^2 + [1-(-3)]^2}$
$= \sqrt{4^2 + 4^2}$
$= \sqrt{16 + 16}$
$= \sqrt{32}$
$= 4\sqrt{2}$
≈ 5.66

11. $d = \sqrt{(-.5-3.5)^2 + (6.2-8.2)^2}$
$= \sqrt{(-4)^2 + (-2)^2}$
$= \sqrt{16 + 4}$
$= \sqrt{20}$
$= 2\sqrt{5}$
≈ 4.47

13. $d = \sqrt{(\sqrt{5}-0)^2 + [0-(-\sqrt{3})]^2}$
$= \sqrt{(\sqrt{5})^2 + (\sqrt{3})^2}$
$= \sqrt{5 + 3}$
$= \sqrt{8}$
$= 2\sqrt{2}$
≈ 2.83

15. $d = \sqrt{(-\sqrt{3}-3\sqrt{3})^2 + (4\sqrt{5}-\sqrt{5})^2}$
$= \sqrt{(-4\sqrt{3})^2 + (3\sqrt{5})^2}$
$= \sqrt{16(3) + 9(5)}$
$= \sqrt{48 + 45}$
$= \sqrt{93}$
≈ 9.64

17. $d = \sqrt{\left(\frac{1}{3}-\frac{7}{3}\right)^2 + \left(\frac{6}{5}-\frac{1}{5}\right)^2}$
$= \sqrt{(-2)^2 + 1^2}$
$= \sqrt{4 + 1}$
$= \sqrt{5}$
≈ 2.24

19. $\left(\frac{6+2}{2}, \frac{8+4}{2}\right) = \left(\frac{8}{2}, \frac{12}{2}\right) = (4, 6)$

21. $\left(\frac{-2+(-6)}{2}, \frac{-8+(-2)}{2}\right)$
$= \left(\frac{-8}{2}, \frac{-10}{2}\right) = (-4, -5)$

23. $\left(\frac{-3+6}{2}, \frac{-4+(-8)}{2}\right)$
$= \left(\frac{3}{2}, \frac{-12}{2}\right) = \left(\frac{3}{2}, -6\right)$

25. $\left(\frac{\frac{-7}{2}+\left(-\frac{5}{2}\right)}{2}, \frac{\frac{3}{2}+\left(-\frac{11}{2}\right)}{2}\right)$
$= \left(\frac{\frac{-12}{2}}{2}, \frac{\frac{-8}{2}}{2}\right) = \left(\frac{-6}{2}, \frac{-4}{2}\right) = (-3, -2)$

27. $\left(\frac{8+(-6)}{2}, \frac{3\sqrt{5}+7\sqrt{5}}{2}\right)$
$= \left(\frac{2}{2}, \frac{10\sqrt{5}}{2}\right) = \left(1, 5\sqrt{5}\right)$

29. $\left(\frac{\sqrt{18}+\sqrt{2}}{2}, \frac{-4+4}{2}\right)$
$= \left(\frac{3\sqrt{2}+\sqrt{2}}{2}, \frac{0}{2}\right) = \left(\frac{4\sqrt{2}}{2}, 0\right) = (2\sqrt{2}, 0)$

31. $(x-0)^2 + (y-0)^2 = 7^2$
$x^2 + y^2 = 49$

33. $(x-3)^2 + (y-2)^2 = 5^2$

$(x-3)^2 + (y-2)^2 = 25$

35. $[x-(-1)]^2 + (y-4)^2 = 2^2$

$(x+1)^2 + (y-4)^2 = 4$

37. $[x-(-3)]^2 + [y-(-1)]^2 = \left(\sqrt{3}\right)^2$

$(x+3)^2 + (y+1)^2 = 3$

39. $[x-(-4)]^2 + (y-0)^2 = 10^2$

$(x+4)^2 + (y-0)^2 = 100$

41. $x^2 + y^2 = 16$

$(x-0)^2 + (y-0)^2 = y^2$

$h=0,\ k=0,\ r=4;$

center $= (0, 0);$ radius $= 4$

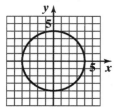

$x^2 + y^2 = 16$

Domain: $[-4, 4]$

Range: $[-4, 4]$

43. $(x-3)^2 + (y-1)^2 = 36$

$(x-3)^2 + (y-1)^2 = 6^2$

$h=3,\ k=1,\ r=6;$

center $= (3, 1);$ radius $= 6$

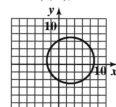

$(x-3)^2 + (y-1)^2 = 36$

Domain: $[-3, 9]$

Range: $[-5, 7]$

45. $(x+3)^2 + (y-2)^2 = 4$

$[x-(-3)]^2 + (y-2)^2 = 2^2$

$h=-3,\ k=2,\ r=2$

center $= (-3, 2);$ radius $= 2$

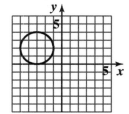

$(x+3)^2 + (y-2)^2 = 4$

Domain: $[-5, -1]$

Range: $[0, 4]$

47. $(x+2)^2 + (y+2)^2 = 4$

$[x-(-2)]^2 + [y-(-2)]^2 = 2^2$

$h=-2,\ k=-2,\ r=2$

center $= (-2, -2);$ radius $= 2$

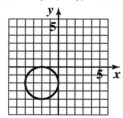

$(x+2)^2 + (y+2)^2 = 4$

Domain: $[-4, 0]$

Range: $[-4, 0]$

49. $x^2 + y^2 + 6x + 2y + 6 = 0$

$\left(x^2 + 6x\right) + \left(y^2 + 2y\right) = -6$

$\left(x^2 + 6x + 9\right) + \left(y^2 + 2y + 1\right) = 9 + 1 - 6$

$(x+3)^2 + (y+1)^2 = 4$

$[x-(-3)]^2 + [9-(-1)]^2 = 2^2$

center $= (-3, -1);$ radius $= 2$

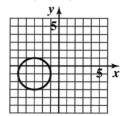

$x^2 + y^2 + 6x + 2y + 6 = 0$

51.
$$x^2 + y^2 - 10x - 6y - 30 = 0$$
$$\left(x^2 - 10x\right) + \left(y^2 - 6y\right) = 30$$
$$\left(x^2 - 10x + 25\right) + \left(y^2 - 6y + 9\right) = 25 + 9 + 30$$
$$(x - 5)^2 + (y - 3)^2 = 64$$
$$(x - 5)^2 + (y - 3)^2 = 8^2$$
center = (5, 3); radius = 8

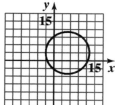

$$x^2 + y^2 - 10x - 6y - 30 = 0$$

53.
$$x^2 + y^2 + 8x - 2y - 8 = 0$$
$$\left(x^2 + 8x\right) + \left(y^2 - 2y\right) = 8$$
$$\left(x^2 + 8x + 16\right) + \left(y^2 - 2y + 1\right) = 16 + 1 + 8$$
$$(x + 4)^2 + (y - 1)^2 = 25$$
$$[x - (-4)]^2 + (y - 1)^2 = 5^2$$
center = (−4, 1); radius = 5

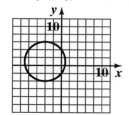

$$x^2 + y^2 + 8x - 2y - 8 = 0$$

55.
$$x^2 - 2x + y^2 - 15 = 0$$
$$\left(x^2 - 2x\right) + y^2 = 15$$
$$\left(x^2 - 2x + 1\right) + (y - 0)^2 = 1 + 0 + 15$$
$$(x - 1)^2 + (y - 0)^2 = 16$$
$$(x - 1)^2 + (y - 0)^2 = 4^2$$
center = (1, 0); radius = 4

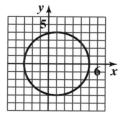

$$x^2 - 2x + y^2 - 15 = 0$$

57.
$$x^2 + y^2 - x + 2y + 1 = 0$$
$$x^2 - x \quad + y^2 + 2y \quad = -1$$
$$x^2 - x + \frac{1}{4} + y^2 + 2y + 1 = -1 + \frac{1}{4} + 1$$
$$\left(x - \frac{1}{2}\right)^2 + (y + 1)^2 = \frac{1}{4}$$

center = $\left(\dfrac{1}{2}, -1\right)$; radius = $\dfrac{1}{2}$

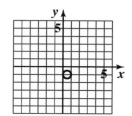

$$x^2 + y^2 - x + 2y + 1 = 0$$

59.
$$x^2 + y^2 + 3x - 2y - 1 = 0$$
$$x^2 + 3x \quad + y^2 - 2y \quad = 1$$
$$x^2 + 3x + \frac{9}{4} + y^2 - 2y + 1 = 1 + \frac{9}{4} + 1$$
$$\left(x + \frac{3}{2}\right)^2 + (y - 1)^2 = \frac{17}{4}$$
center = $\left(-\dfrac{3}{2}, 1\right)$; radius = $\dfrac{\sqrt{17}}{2}$

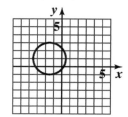

$$x^2 + y^2 + 3x - 2y - 1 = 0$$

61. a. Since the line segment passes through the center, the center is the midpoint of the segment.

$$M = \left(\frac{x_1 + x_2}{2}, \frac{y_1 + y_2}{2}\right)$$
$$= \left(\frac{3+7}{2}, \frac{9+11}{2}\right) = \left(\frac{10}{2}, \frac{20}{2}\right)$$
$$= (5, 10)$$

The center is $(5, 10)$.

b. The radius is the distance from the center to one of the points on the circle. Using the point $(3, 9)$, we get:

$$d = \sqrt{(5-3)^2 + (10-9)^2}$$
$$= \sqrt{2^2 + 1^2} = \sqrt{4+1}$$
$$= \sqrt{5}$$

The radius is $\sqrt{5}$ units.

c.
$$(x-5)^2 + (y-10)^2 = \left(\sqrt{5}\right)^2$$
$$(x-5)^2 + (y-10)^2 = 5$$

63. $x^2 + y^2 = 16$
$x - y = 4$

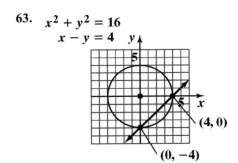

Intersection points: $(0, -4)$ and $(4, 0)$

Check $(0, -4)$:

$0^2 + (-4)^2 = 16$ $0 - (-4) = 4$
     $16 = 16$ true $4 = 4$ true

Check $(4, 0)$:

$4^2 + 0^2 = 16$ $4 - 0 = 4$
     $16 = 16$ true $4 = 4$ true

The solution set is $\{(0, -4), (4, 0)\}$.

65. $(x-2)^2 + (y+3)^2 = 4$
$y = x - 3$

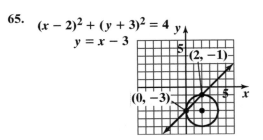

Intersection points: $(0, -3)$ and $(2, -1)$

Check $(0, -3)$:

$(0-2)^2 + (-3+3)^2 = 9$ $-3 = 0 - 3$
     $(-2)^2 + 0^2 = 4$ $-3 = -3$ true
         $4 = 4$
           true

Check $(2, -1)$:

$(2-2)^2 + (-1+3)^2 = 4$ $-1 = 2 - 3$
         $0^2 + 2^2 = 4$ $-1 = -1$ true
         $4 = 4$
           true

The solution set is $\{(0, -3), (2, -1)\}$.

67.
$$d = \sqrt{[65 - (-115)]^2 + (70 - 170)^2}$$
$$d = \sqrt{(65 + 115)^2 + (-100)^2}$$
$$d = \sqrt{180^2 + 10000}$$
$$d = \sqrt{32400 + 10000}$$
$$d = \sqrt{42400}$$
$$d = 205.9 \text{ miles}$$
$$\frac{205.9 \text{ miles}}{400} = 0.5 \text{ hours or 30 minutes}$$

69. If we place L.A. at the origin, then we want the equation of a circle with center at $(-2.4, -2.7)$ and radius 30.

$$\left(x - (-2.4)\right)^2 + \left(y - (-2.7)\right)^2 = 30^2$$
$$(x + 2.4)^2 + (y + 2.7)^2 = 900$$

77.

79.

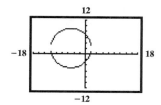

81. The distance for A to B:

$$\overline{AB} = \sqrt{(3-1)^2 + [3+d-(1+d)]^2}$$
$$= \sqrt{2^2 + 2^2}$$
$$= \sqrt{4+4}$$
$$= \sqrt{8}$$
$$= 2\sqrt{2}$$

The distance from B to C:

$$\overline{BC} = \sqrt{(6-3)^2 + [3+d-(6+d)]^2}$$
$$= \sqrt{3^2 + (-3)^2}$$
$$= \sqrt{9+9}$$
$$= \sqrt{18}$$
$$= 3\sqrt{2}$$

The distance for A to C:

$$\overline{AC} = \sqrt{(6-1)^2 + [6+d-(1+d)]^2}$$
$$= \sqrt{5^2 + 5^2}$$
$$= \sqrt{25+25}$$
$$= \sqrt{50}$$
$$= 5\sqrt{2}$$
$$\overline{AB} + \overline{BC} = \overline{AC}$$
$$2\sqrt{2} + 3\sqrt{2} = 5\sqrt{2}$$
$$5\sqrt{2} = 5\sqrt{2}$$

83. Both circles have center (2, –3). The smaller circle has radius 5 and the larger circle has radius 6. The smaller circle is inside of the larger circle. The area between them is given by

$$\pi(6)^2 - \pi(5)^2 = 36\pi - 25\pi$$
$$= 11\pi$$
$$\approx 34.56 \text{ square units.}$$

Chapter 2 Review Exercises

1. function
domain: {2, 3, 5}
range: {7}

2. function
domain: {1, 2, 13}
range: {10, 500, π}

3. not a function
domain: {12, 14}
range: {13, 15, 19}

179

4. $2x + y = 8$

   $y = -2x + 8$

Since only one value of y can be obtained for each value of x, y is a function of x.

5. $3x^2 + y = 14$

   $y = -3x^2 + 14$

Since only one value of y can be obtained for each value of x, y is a function of x.

6. $2x + y^2 = 6$

   $y^2 = -2x + 6$

   $y = \pm\sqrt{-2x + 6}$

Since more than one value of y can be obtained from some values of x, y is not a function of x.

7. $f(x) = 5 - 7x$

   a. $f(4) = 5 - 7(4) = -23$

   b. $f(x + 3) = 5 - 7(x + 3)$

   $= 5 - 7x - 21$

   $= -7x - 16$

   c. $f(-x) = 5 - 7(-x) = 5 + 7x$

8. $g(x) = 3x^2 - 5x + 2$

   a. $g(0) = 3(0)^2 - 5(0) + 2 = 2$

   b. $g(-2) = 3(-2)^2 - 5(-2) + 2$

   $= 12 + 10 + 2$

   $= 24$

   c. $g(x - 1) = 3(x - 1)^2 - 5(x - 1) + 2$

   $= 3(x^2 - 2x + 1) - 5x + 5 + 2$

   $= 3x^2 - 11x + 10$

   d. $g(-x) = 3(-x)^2 - 5(-x) + 2$

   $= 3x^2 + 5x + 2$

9.   **a.** $g(13) = \sqrt{13 - 4} = \sqrt{9} = 3$

   b. $g(0) = 4 - 0 = 4$

   c. $g(-3) = 4 - (-3) = 7$

10.   **a.** $f(-2) = \dfrac{(-2)^2 - 1}{-2 - 1} = \dfrac{3}{-3} = -1$

   b. $f(1) = 12$

   c. $f(2) = \dfrac{2^2 - 1}{2 - 1} = \dfrac{3}{1} = 3$

11.   The vertical line test shows that this is not the graph of a function.

12.   The vertical line test shows that this is the graph of a function.

13.   The vertical line test shows that this is the graph of a function.

14.   The vertical line test shows that this is not the graph of a function.

15.   The vertical line test shows that this is not the graph of a function.

16.   The vertical line test shows that this is the graph of a function.

17. $\dfrac{8(x + h) - 11 - (8x - 11)}{h}$

   $= \dfrac{8x + 8h - 11 - 8x + 11}{h}$

   $= \dfrac{8h}{8}$

   $= 8$

18. $\dfrac{-2(x + h)^2 + (x + h) + 10 - \left(-2x^2 + x + 10\right)}{h}$

   $= \dfrac{-2\left(x^2 + 2xh + h^2\right) + x + h + 10 + 2x^2 - x - 10}{h}$

   $= \dfrac{-2x^2 - 4xh - 2h^2 + x + h + 10 + 2x^2 - x - 10}{h}$

   $= \dfrac{-4xh - 2h^2 + h}{h}$

   $= \dfrac{h\left(-4x - 2h + 1\right)}{h}$

   $-4x - 2h + 1$

19. a. domain: $[-3, 5)$

 b. range: $[-5, 0]$

 c. x-intercept: -3

 d. y-intercept: -2

 e. increasing: $(-2, 0)$ or $(3, 5)$
   decreasing: $(-3, -2)$ or $(0, 3)$

 f. $f(-2) = -3$ and $f(3) = -5$

20. a. domain: $(-\infty, \infty)$

 b. range: $(-\infty, \infty)$

 c. x-intercepts: -2 and 3

 d. y-intercept: 3

 e. increasing: $(-5, 0)$
   decreasing: $(-\infty, -5)$ or $(0, \infty)$

 f. $f(-2) = 0$ and $f(6) = -3$

21. a. domain: $(-\infty, \infty)$

 b. range: $[-2, 2]$

 c. x-intercept: 0

 d. y-intercept: 0

 e. increasing: $(-2, 2)$
   constant: $(-\infty, -2)$ or $(2, \infty)$

 f. $f(-9) = -2$ and $f(14) = 2$

22. a. 0, relative maximum -2

 b. $-2, 3$, relative minimum $-3, -5$

23. a. 0, relative maximum 3

 b. -5, relative minimum -6

24. $f(x) = x^3 - 5x$
$f(-x) = (-x)^3 - 5(-x)$
$\quad = -x^3 + 5x$
$\quad = -f(x)$
The function is odd. The function is symmetric with respect to the origin.

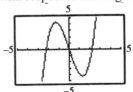

25. $f(x) = x^4 - 2x^2 + 1$
$f(-x) = (-x)^4 - 2(-x)^2 + 1$
$\quad = x^4 - 2x^2 + 1$
$\quad = f(x)$
The function is even. The function is symmetric with respect to the y-axis.

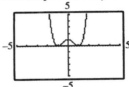

26. $f(x) = 2x\sqrt{1 - x^2}$
$f(-x) = 2(-x)\sqrt{1 - (-x)^2}$
$\quad = -2x\sqrt{1 - x^2}$
$\quad = -f(x)$
The function is odd. The function is symmetric with respect to the origin.

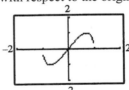

27. a. Yes, the eagle's height is a function of time since the graph passes the vertical line test.

 b. Decreasing: $(3, 12)$
   The eagle descended.

 c. Constant: $(0, 3)$ or $(12, 17)$
   The eagle's height held steady during the first 3 seconds and the eagle was on the ground for 5 seconds.

 d. Increasing: $(17, 30)$
   The eagle was ascending.

28.

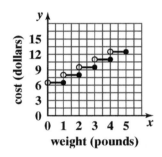

cost (dollars) / weight (pounds)

29. $m = \dfrac{1-2}{5-3} = \dfrac{-1}{2} = -\dfrac{1}{2}$; falls

30. $m = \dfrac{-4-(-2)}{-3-(-1)} = \dfrac{-2}{-2} = 1$; rises

31. $m = \dfrac{\frac{1}{4}-\frac{1}{4}}{6-(-3)} = \dfrac{0}{9} = 0$; horizontal

32. $m = \dfrac{10-5}{-2-(-2)} = \dfrac{5}{0}$ undefined; vertical

33. point-slope form: $y - 2 = -6(x + 3)$
slope-intercept form: $y = -6x - 16$

34. $m = \dfrac{2-6}{-1-1} = \dfrac{-4}{-2} = 2$
point-slope form: $y - 6 = 2(x - 1)$
or $y - 2 = 2(x + 1)$
slope-intercept form: $y = 2x + 4$

35. $3x + y - 9 = 0$
$y = -3x + 9$
$m = -3$
point-slope form:
$y + 7 = -3(x - 4)$
slope-intercept form:
$y = -3x + 12 - 7$
$y = -3x + 5$

36. perpendicular to $y = \dfrac{1}{3}x + 4$

$m = -3$
point-slope form:
$y - 6 = -3(x + 3)$
slope-intercept form:
$y = -3x - 9 + 6$
$y = -3x - 3$

37. Write $6x - y - 4 = 0$ in slope intercept form.
$6x - y - 4 = 0$
$-y = -6x + 4$
$y = 6x - 4$
The slope of the perpendicular line is 6, thus the

slope of the desired line is $m = -\dfrac{1}{6}$.

$$y - y_1 = m(x - x_1)$$
$$y - (-1) = -\tfrac{1}{6}(x - (-12))$$
$$y + 1 = -\tfrac{1}{6}(x + 12)$$
$$y + 1 = -\tfrac{1}{6}x - 2$$
$$6y + 6 = -x - 12$$
$$x + 6y + 18 = 0$$

38. slope: $\dfrac{2}{5}$; y-intercept: -1

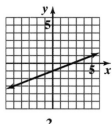

$$y = \dfrac{2}{5}x - 1$$

39. slope: -4; y-intercept: 5

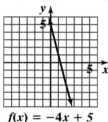

$$f(x) = -4x + 5$$

40. $2x + 3y + 6 = 0$

$$3y = -2x - 6$$

$$y = -\frac{2}{3}x - 2$$

slope: $-\frac{2}{3}$; y-intercept: -2

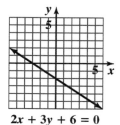

2x + 3y + 6 = 0

41. $2y - 8 = 0$

$$2y = 8$$

$$y = 4$$

slope: 0; y-intercept: 4

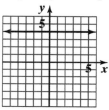

2y − 8 = 0

42. $2x - 5y - 10 = 0$

Find x-intercept:

$$2x - 5(0) - 10 = 0$$

$$2x - 10 = 0$$

$$2x = 10$$

$$x = 5$$

Find y-intercept:

$$2(0) - 5y - 10 = 0$$

$$-5y - 10 = 0$$

$$-5y = 10$$

$$y = -2$$

2x − 5y − 10 = 0

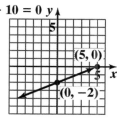

43. $2x - 10 = 0$

$$2x = 10$$

$$x = 5$$

2x − 10 = 0

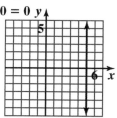

44.   **a.**   First, find the slope. $(1, 1.5)$ and $(3, 3.4)$.

$$m = \frac{3.4 - 1.5}{3 - 1} = \frac{1.9}{2} = 0.95$$

Next, use the slope and one of the points to write the point-slope equation of the line.

$$y - 1.5 = 0.95(x - 1) \text{ or } y - 3.4 = 0.95(x - 3)$$

     b. $y - 1.5 = 0.95(x - 1)$

$$y - 1.5 = 0.95x - 0.95$$

$$y = 0.95x - 0.55$$

     c.   Since 2009 is 2009-1999 = 10, let $x = 10$.

$$y = 0.95(10) + 0.55$$

$$= 9.5 + 0.55 = 10.05$$

$10.05 billion in revenue was earned from online gambling in 2009.

45.   **a.** $(1999, 41315)$ and $(2001, 41227)$

$$m = \frac{41227 - 41315}{2001 - 1999} = \frac{-88}{2} = -44$$

The number of new AIDS diagnoses decreased at a rate of 44 each year from 1999 to 2001.

     b. $(2001, 41227)$ and $(2003, 43045)$

$$m = \frac{43045 - 41227}{2003 - 2001} = \frac{1818}{2} = 909$$

The number of new AIDS diagnoses increased at a rate of 909 each year from 2001 to 2003.

     c. $(1999, 41315)$ and $(2003, 43045)$

$$m = \frac{43045 - 41315}{2003 - 1999} = \frac{1730}{4} = 432.5$$

$$\frac{-44 + 909}{2} = \frac{865}{2} = 432.5$$

Yes, the slope equals the average of the two values.

46. $\dfrac{9^2 - 4(9) - [4^2 - 4 \cdot 5]}{9 - 5} = \dfrac{40}{4} = 10$

47. $y = g(x)$
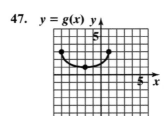

48. $y = g(x)$
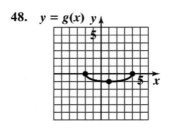

49.
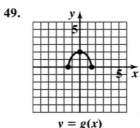
$y = g(x)$

50.
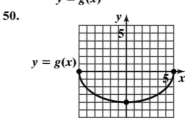
$y = g(x)$

51.
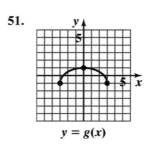
$y = g(x)$

52.
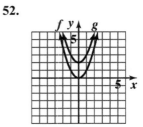

53.
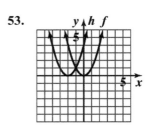

54.
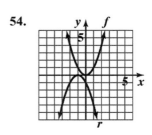

55.
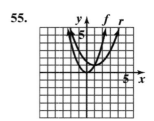

56.
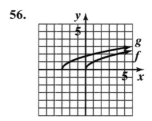

57.
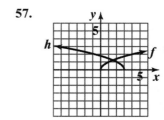

184

58.

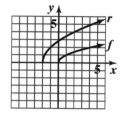

59.

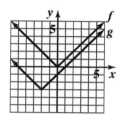

60.

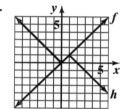

61.

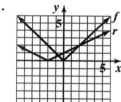

62.

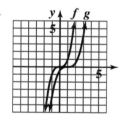

63.

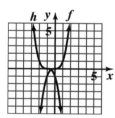

64.

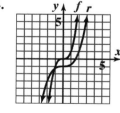

65.

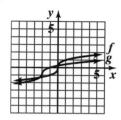

66.

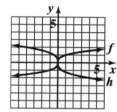

67.

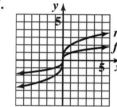

68. domain: $(-\infty, \infty)$

69. The denominator is zero when $x = 7$. The domain is $(-\infty, 7) \cup (7, \infty)$.

70. The expressions under each radical must not be negative.
$8 - 2x \geq 0$
$-2x \geq -8$
$x \leq 4$
Domain: $(-\infty, 4]$.

71. The denominator is zero when $x = -7$ or $x = 3$.
Domain: $(-\infty, -7) \cup (-7, 3) \cup (3, \infty)$

72. The expressions under each radical must not be negative. The denominator is zero when $x = 5$.
$x - 2 \geq 0$
$x \geq 2$
Domain: $[2, 5) \cup (5, \infty)$

73. The expressions under each radical must not be negative.
$x - 1 \geq 0$ and $x + 5 \geq 0$
$x \geq 1$ $x \geq -5$
Domain: $[1, \infty)$

185

74. $f(x) = 3x - 1; g(x) = x - 5$
$(f+g)(x) = 4x - 6$
Domain: $(-\infty, \infty)$
$(f-g)(x) = (3x-1) - (x-5) = 2x + 4$
Domain: $(-\infty, \infty)$
$(fg)(x) = (3x-1)(x-5) = 3x^2 - 16x + 5$
Domain: $(-\infty, \infty)$
$\left(\dfrac{f}{g}\right)(x) = \dfrac{3x-1}{x-5}$
Domain: $(-\infty, 5) \cup (5, \infty)$

75. $f(x) = x^2 + x + 1; g(x) = x^2 - 1$
$(f+g)(x) = 2x^2 + x$
Domain: $(-\infty, \infty)$
$(f-g)(x) = (x^2 + x + 1) - (x^2 - 1) = x + 2$
Domain: $(-\infty, \infty)$
$(fg)(x) = (x^2 + x + 1)(x^2 - 1)$
$= x^4 + x^3 - x - 1$
$\left(\dfrac{f}{g}\right)(x) = \dfrac{x^2 + x + 1}{x^2 - 1}$
Domain: $(-\infty, -1) \cup (-1, 1) \cup (1, \infty)$

76. $f(x) = \sqrt{x+7}; g(x) = \sqrt{x-2}$
$(f+g)(x) = \sqrt{x+7} + \sqrt{x-2}$
Domain: $[2, \infty)$
$(f-g)(x) = \sqrt{x+7} - \sqrt{x-2}$
Domain: $[2, \infty)$
$(fg)(x) = \sqrt{x+7} \cdot \sqrt{x-2}$
$= \sqrt{x^2 + 5x - 14}$
Domain: $[2, \infty)$
$\left(\dfrac{f}{g}\right)(x) = \dfrac{\sqrt{x+7}}{\sqrt{x-2}}$
Domain: $(2, \infty)$

77. $f(x) = x^2 + 3; g(x) = 4x - 1$

a. $(f \circ g)(x) = (4x-1)^2 + 3$
$= 16x^2 - 8x + 4$

b. $(g \circ f)(x) = 4(x^2 + 3) - 1$
$= 4x^2 + 11$

c. $(f \circ g)(3) = 16(3)^2 - 8(3) + 4 = 124$

78. $f(x) = \sqrt{x}; \ g(x) = x + 1$

a. $(f \circ g)(x) = \sqrt{x+1}$

b. $(g \circ f)(x) = \sqrt{x} + 1$

c. $(f \circ g)(3) = \sqrt{3+1} = \sqrt{4} = 2$

79. a. $(f \circ g)(x) = f\left(\dfrac{1}{x}\right)$

$= \dfrac{\dfrac{1}{x} + 1}{\dfrac{1}{x} - 2} = \dfrac{\left(\dfrac{1}{x} + 1\right)x}{\left(\dfrac{1}{x} - 2\right)x} = \dfrac{1+x}{1-2x}$

b. $x \neq 0$ $1 - 2x \neq 0$
$x \neq \dfrac{1}{2}$
$(-\infty, 0) \cup \left(0, \dfrac{1}{2}\right) \cup \left(\dfrac{1}{2}, \infty\right)$

80. a. $(f \circ g)(x) = f(x+3) = \sqrt{x+3-1} = \sqrt{x+2}$

b. $x + 2 \geq 0$
$x \geq -2$ $[-2, \infty)$

81. $f(x) = x^4$ $g(x) = x^2 + 2x - 1$

82. $f(x) = \sqrt[3]{x}$ $g(x) = 7x + 4$

83. $d = \sqrt{[3-(-2)]^2 + [9-(-3)]^2}$
$= \sqrt{5^2 + 12^2}$
$= \sqrt{25 + 144}$
$= \sqrt{169}$
$= 13$

84. $d = \sqrt{[-2-(-4)]^2 + (5-3)^2}$
$= \sqrt{2^2 + 2^2}$
$= \sqrt{4+4}$
$= \sqrt{8}$
$= 2\sqrt{2}$
≈ 2.83

85. $\left(\dfrac{2+(-12)}{2}, \dfrac{6+4}{2}\right) = \left(\dfrac{-10}{2}, \dfrac{10}{2}\right) = (-5, 5)$

86. $\left(\dfrac{4+(-15)}{2}, \dfrac{-6+2}{2}\right) = \left(\dfrac{-11}{2}, \dfrac{-4}{2}\right) = \left(\dfrac{-11}{2}, -2\right)$

87. $x^2 + y^2 = 3^2$
$x^2 + y^2 = 9$

88. $(x-(-2))^2 + (y-4)^2 = 6^2$
$(x+2)^2 + (y-4)^2 = 36$

89. center: (0, 0); radius: 1

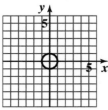

$x^2 + y^2 = 1$
Domain: $[-1,1]$
Range: $[-1,1]$

90. center: (–2, 3); radius: 3

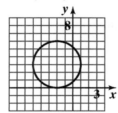

$(x + 2)^2 + (y - 3)^2 = 9$
Domain: $[-5,1]$
Range: $[0,6]$

91. $x^2 + y^2 - 4x + 2y - 4 = 0$
$x^2 - 4x \;\;\; + y^2 + 2y \;\; = 4$
$x^2 - 4x + 4 + y^2 + 2y + 1 = 4 + 4 + 1$
$(x-2)^2 + (y+1)^2 = 9$
center: (2, –1); radius: 3

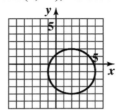

$x^2 + y^2 - 4x + 2y - 4 = 0$
Domain: $[-1,5]$
Range: $[-4,2]$

187

Chapter 2 Test

1.   (b), (c), and (d) are not functions.

2.   **a.** $f(4) - f(-3) = 3 - (-2) = 5$

     b.   domain: $(-5, 6]$

     c.   range: $[-4, 5]$

     d.   increasing: $(-1, 2)$

     e.   decreasing: $(-5, -1)$ or $(2, 6)$

     f. $2, f(2) = 5$

     g. $(-1, -4)$

     h. x-intercepts: $-4, 1$, and 5.

     i. y-intercept: -3

3.   **a.** $-2, 2$

     b. $-1, 1$

     c. 0

     d.   even; $f(-x) = f(x)$

     e. $f(0)$ is a relative minimum.

     f.

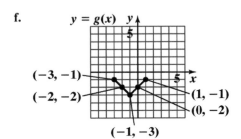

     g.

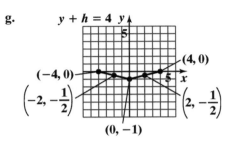

h.

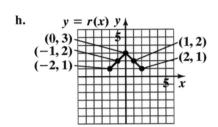

i. $\dfrac{f(x_2) - f(x_1)}{x_2 - x_1} = \dfrac{-1 - 0}{1 - (-2)} = -\dfrac{1}{3}$

4.

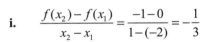

    Domain: $(-\infty, \infty)$

    Range: $(-\infty, \infty)$

5.

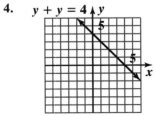

    Domain: $[-2, 2]$

    Range: $[-2, 2]$

6.

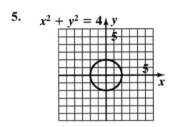

    Domain: $(-\infty, \infty)$

    Range: $\{4\}$

7.

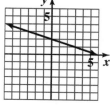

$$f(x) = -\frac{1}{3}x + 2$$

Domain: $(-\infty, \infty)$

Range: $(-\infty, \infty)$

8.

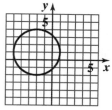

$$(x + 2)^2 + (y - 1)^2 = 9$$

Domain: $[-5, 1]$

Range: $[-2, 4]$

9.

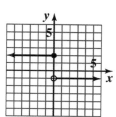

$$f(x) = \begin{cases} 2 \text{ if } x \le 0 \\ -1 \text{ if } x > 0 \end{cases}$$

Domain: $(-\infty, \infty)$

Range: $\{-1, 2\}$

10.

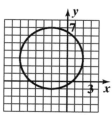

$$x^2 + y^2 + 4x + 6y - 3 = 0$$

Domain: $[-6, 2]$

Range: $[-1, 7]$

11.

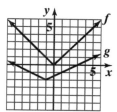

Domain of f: $(-\infty, \infty)$

Range of f: $[0, \infty)$

Domain of g: $(-\infty, \infty)$

Range of g: $[-2, \infty)$

12.

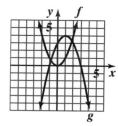

Domain of f: $(-\infty, \infty)$

Range of f: $[0, \infty)$

Domain of g: $(-\infty, \infty)$

Range of g: $(-\infty, 4]$

13. $f(x) = x^2 - x - 4$

$$\begin{aligned} f(x - 1) &= (x - 1)^2 - (x - 1) - 4 \\ &= x^2 - 2x + 1 - x + 1 - 4 \\ &= x^2 - 3x - 2 \end{aligned}$$

14. $\dfrac{f(x + h) - f(x)}{h}$

$$= \frac{(x + h)^2 - (x + h) - 4 - \left(x^2 - x - 4\right)}{h}$$

$$= \frac{x^2 + 2xh + h^2 - x - h - 4 - x^2 + x + 4}{h}$$

$$= \frac{2xh + h^2 - h}{h}$$

$$= \frac{h(2x + h - 1)}{h}$$

$$= 2x + h - 1$$

15. $\begin{aligned}(g - f)(x) &= 2x - 6 - \left(x^2 - x - 4\right) \\ &= 2x - 6 - x^2 + x + 4 \\ &= -x^2 + 3x - 2\end{aligned}$

16. $\left(\dfrac{f}{g}\right)(x) = \dfrac{x^2 - x - 4}{2x - 6}$

Domain: $(-\infty, 3) \cup (3, \infty)$

17. $(f \circ g)(x) = f(g(x))$

$\qquad = (2x - 6)^2 - (2x - 6) - 4$

$\qquad = 4x^2 - 24x + 36 - 2x + 6 - 4$

$\qquad = 4x^2 - 26x + 38$

18. $(g \circ f)(x) = g(f(x))$

$\qquad = 2(x^2 - x - 4) - 6$

$\qquad = 2x^2 - 2x - 8 - 6$

$\qquad = 2x^2 - 2x - 14$

19. $g(f(-1)) = 2((-1)^2 - (-1) - 4) - 6$

$\qquad = 2(1 + 1 - 4) - 6$

$\qquad = 2(-2) - 6$

$\qquad = -4 - 6$

$\qquad = -10$

20. $f(x) = x^2 - x - 4$

$\qquad f(-x) = (-x)^2 - (-x) - 4$

$\qquad\qquad = x^2 + x - 4$

f is neither even nor odd.

21. $m = \dfrac{-8 - 1}{-1 - 2} = \dfrac{-9}{-3} = 3$

point-slope form: $y - 1 = 3(x - 2)$
or $y + 8 = 3(x + 1)$
slope-intercept form: $y = 3x - 5$

22. $y = -\dfrac{1}{4}x + 5$ so $m = 4$

point-slope form: $y - 6 = 4(x + 4)$
slope-intercept form: $y = 4x + 22$

23. Write $4x + 2y - 5 = 0$ in slope intercept form.

$4x + 2y - 5 = 0$

$\qquad 2y = -4x + 5$

$\qquad y = -2x + \dfrac{5}{2}$

The slope of the parallel line is -2, thus the slope of the desired line is $m = -2$.

$\qquad y - y_1 = m(x - x_1)$

$\qquad y - (-10) = -2(x - (-7))$

$\qquad y + 10 = -2(x + 7)$

$\qquad y + 10 = -2x - 14$

$2x + y + 24 = 0$

24. **a.** $(2, 4.85)$ and $(5, 4.49)$

First, find the slope using the points $(2, 4.85)$ and $(5, 4.49)$

$m = \dfrac{4.49 - 4.85}{5 - 2} = \dfrac{-0.36}{3} = -0.12$

Then use the slope and one of the points to write the equation in point-slope form.

$y - y_1 = m(x - x_1)$

$y - 4.85 = -0.12(x - 2)$

or

$y - 4.49 = -0.12(x - 5)$

b. Solve for y to obtain slope-intercept form.

$y - 4.85 = -0.12(x - 2)$

$y - 4.85 = -0.12x + 0.24$

$\qquad y = -0.12x + 5.09$

$\qquad f(x) = -0.12x + 5.09$

c. To predict the minimum hourly inflation-adjusted wages in 2007, let $x = 2007 - 1997 = 10$.

$f(10) = -0.12(10) + 5.09 = 3.89$

The linear function predicts the minimum hourly inflation-adjusted wage in 2007 to $3.89.

25. $\dfrac{3(10)^2 - 5 - [3(6)^2 - 5]}{10 - 6}$

$= \dfrac{205 - 103}{4}$

$= \dfrac{192}{4}$

$= 48$

26. $g(-1) = 3 - (-1) = 4$

$g(7) = \sqrt{7-3} = \sqrt{4} = 2$

27. The denominator is zero when $x = 1$ or $x = -5$.

Domain: $(-\infty, -5) \cup (-5, 1) \cup (1, \infty)$

28. The expressions under each radical must not be negative.

$x + 5 \geq 0$ and $x - 1 \geq 0$

$x \geq -5$ $\qquad x \geq 1$

Domain: $[1, \infty)$

29. $(f \circ g)(x) = \dfrac{7}{\dfrac{2}{x} - 4} = \dfrac{7x}{2 - 4x}$

$x \neq 0, \quad 2 - 4x \neq 0$

$x \neq \dfrac{1}{2}$

Domain: $(-\infty, 0) \cup \left(0, \dfrac{1}{2}\right) \cup \left(\dfrac{1}{2}, \infty\right)$

30. $f(x) = x^7 \qquad g(x) = 2x + 3$

31. $d = \sqrt{(x_2 - x_1)^2 + (y_2 - y_1)^2}$

$d = \sqrt{(x_2 - x_1)^2 + (y_2 - y_1)^2}$

$= \sqrt{(5-2)^2 + (2-(-2))^2}$

$= \sqrt{3^2 + 4^2}$

$= \sqrt{9 + 16}$

$= \sqrt{25}$

$= 5$

$\left(\dfrac{x_1 + x_2}{2}, \dfrac{y_1 + y_2}{2}\right) = \left(\dfrac{2+5}{2}, \dfrac{-2+2}{2}\right)$

$= \left(\dfrac{7}{2}, 0\right)$

The length is 5 and the midpoint is $\left(\dfrac{7}{2}, 0\right)$.

Cumulative Review Exercises (Chapters 1–2)

1. Domain: $[0, 2)$

Range: $[0, 2]$

2. $f(x) = 1$ at $\dfrac{1}{2}$ and $\dfrac{3}{2}$.

3. relative maximum: 2

4.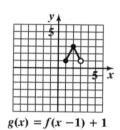

$g(x) = f(x - 1) + 1$

5.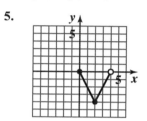

6. $(x + 3)(x - 4) = 8$

$x^2 - x - 12 = 8$

$x^2 - x - 20 = 0$

$(x + 4)(x - 5) = 0$

$x + 4 = 0$ or $x - 5 = 0$

$x = -4$ or $\qquad x = 5$

7. $3(4x - 1) = 4 - 6(x - 3)$

$12x - 3 = 4 - 6x + 18$

$18x = 25$

$x = \dfrac{25}{18}$

8. $\sqrt{x} + 2 = x$

$\sqrt{x} = x - 2$

$(\sqrt{x})^2 = (x - 2)^2$

$x = x^2 - 4x + 4$

$0 = x^2 - 5x + 4$

$0 = (x - 1)(x - 4)$

$x - 1 = 0$ or $x - 4 = 0$

$x = 1$ or $\qquad x = 4$

A check of the solutions shows that $x = 1$ is an extraneous solution. The only solution is $x = 4$.

191

9. $x^{2/3} - x^{1/3} - 6 = 0$

Let $u = x^{1/3}$. Then $u^2 = x^{2/3}$.

$u^2 - u - 6 = 0$

$(u+2)(u-3) = 0$

$u = -2$ or $u = 3$

$x^{1/3} = -2$ or $x^{1/3} = 3$

$x = (-2)^3$ or $x = 3^3$

$x = -8$ or $x = 27$

10. $\dfrac{x}{2} - 3 \le \dfrac{x}{4} + 2$

$4\left(\dfrac{x}{2} - 3\right) \le 4\left(\dfrac{x}{4} + 2\right)$

$2x - 12 \le x + 8$

$x \le 20$

The solution set is $(-\infty, 20]$.

11.

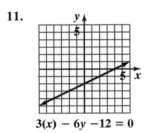

$3(x) - 6y - 12 = 0$

Domain: $(-\infty, \infty)$

Range: $(-\infty, \infty)$

12.

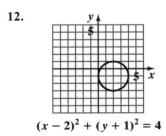

$(x-2)^2 + (y+1)^2 = 4$

Domain: $[0, 4]$

Range: $[-3, 1]$

13.

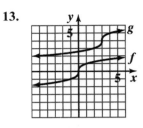

Domain of f: $(-\infty, \infty)$

Range of f: $(-\infty, \infty)$

Domain of g: $(-\infty, \infty)$

Range of g: $(-\infty, \infty)$

14. $\dfrac{f(x+h) - f(x)}{h}$

$= \dfrac{\left(4 - (x+h)^2\right) - \left(4 - x^2\right)}{h}$

$= \dfrac{4 - (x^2 + 2xh + h^2) - \left(4 - x^2\right)}{h}$

$= \dfrac{4 - x^2 - 2xh - h^2 - 4 + x^2}{h}$

$= \dfrac{-2xh - h^2}{h}$

$= \dfrac{h(-2x - h)}{h}$

$= -2x - h$

15. $(f \circ g)(x) = f\big(g(x)\big)$

$(f \circ g)(x) = f(x+5)$

$0 = 4 - (x+5)^2$

$0 = 4 - (x^2 + 10x + 25)$

$0 = 4 - x^2 - 10x - 25$

$0 = -x^2 - 10x - 21$

$0 = x^2 + 10x + 21$

$0 = (x+7)(x+3)$

The value of $(f \circ g)(x)$ will be 0 when $x = -3$ or $x = -7$.

16. $y = -\dfrac{1}{4}x + \dfrac{1}{3}$, so $m = 4$.

point-slope form: $y - 5 = 4(x + 2)$
slope-intercept form: $y = 4x + 13$
general form: $4x - y + 13 = 0$

17. $0.07x + 0.09(6000 - x) = 510$
$$0.07x + 540 - 0.09x = 510$$
$$-0.02x = -30$$
$$x = 1500$$
$$6000 - x = 4500$$

$1500 was invested at 7% and $4500 was invested at 9%.

18. $200 + 0.05x = .15x$
$$200 = 0.10x$$
$$2000 = x$$

For $2000 in sales, the earnings will be the same.

19. width $= w$
length $= 2w + 2$
$2(2w + 2) + 2w = 22$
$4w + 4 + 2w = 22$
$6w = 18$
$w = 3$
$2w + 2 = 8$
The garden is 3 feet by 8 feet.

Chapter 3

Section 3.1

Check Point Exercises

1.　a.　$2x = 3y = -4$

$2(1) - 3(2) = -4$

$2 - 6 = -4$

$-4 = -4$ true

$2x + y = 4$

$2(1) + 2 = 4$

$2 + 2 = 4$

$4 = 4$ true

$(1, 2)$ is a solution of the system.

　b.　$2x = 3y = -4$

$2(7) - 3(6) = -4$

$14 - 18 = -4$

$-4 = -4$ true

$2x + y = 4$

$2(7) + 6 = 4$

$14 + 6 = 4$

$20 = 4$ false

$(7, 6)$ is not a solution of the system.

2.　$3x + 2y = 4$

$2x + y = 1$

Solve $2x + y = 1$ for y.

$2x + y = 1$

$y = 1 - 2x$

Substitute $1 - 2x$ for y in the other equation and solve.

$$3x + 2\overbrace{\left(1 - 2x\right)}^{y} = 4$$

$3x + 2 - 4x = 4$

$-x = 2$

$x = -2$

Back-substitute the obtained value:

$3x + 2y = 4$

$3(-2) + 2y = 4$

$-6 + 2y = 4$

$2y = 10$

$y = 5$

Checking these values in both equations shows that $(-2, 5)$ is the solution of the system.

3.　Rewrite one or both equations:

$4x + 5y = 3 \xrightarrow{\text{No change}} 4x + 5y = 3$

$2x - 3y = 7 \xrightarrow{\text{Mult. by } -2} -4x + 6y = -14$

$\overline{11y = -11}$

$y = -1$

Back-substitute into either equation:

$4x + 5y = 3$

$4x + 5(-1) = 3$

$4x - 5 = 3$

$4x = 8$

$x = 2$

Checking confirms the solution set is $\{(2, -1)\}$.

4.　Rewrite both equations in the form $Ax + By = C$:

$2x = 9 + 3y \rightarrow 2x - 3y = 9$

$4y = 8 - 3x \rightarrow 3x + 4y = 8$

Rewrite with opposite coefficients, then add and solve:

$2x - 3y = 9 \xrightarrow{\text{Mult. by } 4} 8x - 12y = 36$

$3x + 4y = 8 \xrightarrow{\text{Mult. by } 3} 9x + 12y = 24$

$\overline{17x = 60}$

$$x = \frac{60}{17}$$

Back-substitute into either equation:

$4y = 8 - 3x$

$$4y = 8 - 3\left(\frac{60}{17}\right)$$

$$4y = -\frac{44}{17}$$

$$y = -\frac{11}{17}$$

Checking confirms the solution is $\left(\dfrac{60}{17}, -\dfrac{11}{17}\right)$.

5. Rewrite with a pair of opposite coefficients, then add:

$$5x - 2y = 4 \xrightarrow{\text{Mult. by 2}} 10x - 4y = 8$$
$$-10x + 4y = 7 \xrightarrow{\text{No change}} \underline{-10x + 4y = 7}$$
$$0 = 15$$

The statement $0 = 15$ is false which indicates that the system has no solution. The solution set is the empty set, $\varnothing$.

6. Substitute $4y - 8$ for x in the other equation:

$$5(\overbrace{4y - 8}^{x}) - 20y = -40$$
$$20y - 40 - 20y = -40$$
$$-40 = -40$$

The statement $-40 = -40$ is true which indicates that the system has infinitely many solutions. The solution set is $\{(x, y) | x = 4y - 8\}$ or $\{(x, y) | 5x - 20y = -40\}$.

7. a. $C(x) = 300,000 + 30x$

b. $R(x) = 80x$

c. $R(x) = C(x)$
$$80x = 300,000 + 30x$$
$$50x = 300,000$$
$$x = 6000$$
$$C(6000) = 300,000 + 30(6000) = 480,000$$
Break even point (6000, 480000)
The company will need to make 6000 pairs of shoes and earn \$480,000 to break even.

Exercise Set 3.1

1. $x + 3y = 11$
$$2 + 3(3) = 11$$
$$2 + 9 = 11$$
$$11 = 11 \text{ true}$$
$$x - 5y = -13$$
$$2 - 5(3) = -13$$
$$2 - 15 = -13$$
$$-13 = -13 \text{ true}$$
(2, 3) is a solution.

3. $2x + 3y = 17$
$$2(2) + 3(5) = 17$$
$$4 + 15 = 17$$
$$19 = 17 \text{ false}$$
(2, 5) is not a solution.

5. $x + y = 4$
$$y = 3x$$
Substitute the expression $3x$ for y in the first equation and solve for x.
$$x + 3x = 4$$
$$4x = 4$$
$$x = 1$$
Substitute 1 for x in the second equation.
$$y = 3(1) = 3$$
The solution set is $\{(1, 3)\}$.

7. $x + 3y = 8$
$$y = 2x - 9$$
Substitute the expression $2x - 9$ for y in the first equation and solve for x.
$$x + 3(2x - 9) = 8$$
$$x + 6x - 27 = 8$$
$$7x = 35$$
$$x = 5$$
Substitute 5 for x in the second equation.
$$y = 2(5) - 9 = 10 - 9 = 1$$
The solution set is $\{(5, 1)\}$.

9. $x = 4y - 2$
$$x = 6y + 8$$
Substitute the expression $4y - 2$ for x in the second equation and solve for y.
$$4y - 2 = 6y + 8$$
$$-10 = 2y$$
$$-5 = y$$
Substitute -5 for y in the equation $x = 4y - 2$.
$$x = 4(-5) - 2 = -22$$
The solution set is $\{(-22, -5)\}$.

11. $5x + 2y = 0$
$$x - 3y = 0$$
Solve the second equation for x.
$$x = 3y$$
Substitute the expression $3y$ for x in the first equation and solve for y.
$$5(3y) + 2y = 0$$
$$15y + 2y = 0$$
$$17y = 0$$
$$y = 0$$
Substitute 0 for y in the equation $x = 3y$
$$y = 3(0) = 0$$
The solution set is $\{(0, 0)\}$.

13. $2x + 5y = -4$
    $3x - y = 11$
Solve the second equation for y.
$-y = -3x + 11$
    $y = 3x - 11$
Substitute the expression $3x - 11$ for y in the first equation and solve for x.
$2x + 5(3x - 11) = -4$
$2x + 15x - 55 = -4$
        $17x = 51$
          $x = 3$
Substitute 3 for x in the equation $y = 3x - 11$.
$y = 3(3) - 11 = 9 - 11 = -2$
The solution set is $\{(3, -2)\}$.

15. $2x - 3y = 8 - 2x$
    $2x + 4y = x + 3y + 14$
Solve the second equation for y.
$y = -2x + 14$
Substitute the expression $-2x + 14$ for y in the first equation and solve for x.
$2x - 3(-2x + 14) = 8 - 2x$
$2x + 6x - 42 = 8 - 2x$
    $8x - 42 = 8 - 2x$
      $10x = 50$
        $x = 5$
Substitute 5 for x in the equation $y = -2x + 14$.
$y = -2(5) + 14 = -10 + 14 = 4$
The solution set is $\{(5, 4)\}$.

17. $y = \dfrac{1}{3}x + \dfrac{2}{3}$
    $y = \dfrac{5}{7}x - 2$

Substitute the expression $y = \dfrac{1}{3}x + \dfrac{2}{3}$ for y in the second equation and solve for x.
$\dfrac{1}{3}x + \dfrac{2}{3} = \dfrac{5}{7}x - 2$
$7x + 14 = 15x - 42$
    $56 = 8x$
    $7 = x$

Substitute 7 for x in the equation $y = \dfrac{1}{3}x + \dfrac{2}{3}$ and solve for y.
$y = \dfrac{1}{3}(7) + \dfrac{2}{3} = \dfrac{7}{3} + \dfrac{2}{3} = \dfrac{9}{3} = 3$
The solution set is $\{(7, 3)\}$.

19. Eliminate y by adding the equations.
$x + y = 1$
$\underline{x - y = 3}$
$2x = 4$
  $x = 2$
Substitute 2 for x in the first equation.
$2 + y = 1$
    $y = -1$
The solution set is $\{(2, -1)\}$.

21. Eliminate y by adding the equations.
$2x + 3y = 6$
$\underline{2x - 3y = 6}$
$4x = 12$
  $x = 3$
Substitute 3 for x in the first equation.
$2(3) + 3y = 6$
  $6 + 3y = 6$
      $3y = 0$
        $y = 0$
The solution set is $\{(3, 0)\}$.

23. $x + 2y = 2$
    $-4x + 3y = 25$
Eliminate x by multiplying the first equation by 4 and adding the resulting equations.
$4x + 8y = 8$
$\underline{-4x + 3y = 25}$
$11y = 33$
  $y = 3$
Substitute 3 for y in the first equation.
$x + 2(3) = 2$
  $x + 6 = 2$
      $x = -4$
The solution set is $\{(-4, 3)\}$.

25. $4x + 3y = 15$
    $2x - 5y = 1$
Eliminate x by multiplying the second equation by -2 and adding the resulting equations.
$4x + 3y = 15$
$\underline{-4x + 10y = -2}$
$13y = 13$
  $y = 1$
Substitute 1 for y in the second equation.
$2x - 5(1) = 1$
    $2x = 6$
      $x = 3$
The solution set is $\{(3, 1)\}$.

27. $3x - 4y = 11$
$2x + 3y = -4$
Eliminate x by multiplying the first equation by 2 and the second equation by –3. Add the resulting equations.
$6x - 8y = 22$
$\underline{-6x - 9y = 12}$
$-17y = 34$
$y = -2$
Substitute –2 for y in the second equation.
$2x + 3(-2) = -4$
$2x - 6 = -4$
$2x = 2$
$x = 1$
The solution set is $\{(1, -2)\}$.

29. $3x = 4y + 1$
$3y = 1 - 4x$
Arrange the system so that variable terms appear on the left and constants appear on the right.
$3x - 4y = 1$
$4x + 3y = 1$
Eliminate y by multiplying the first equation by 3 and the second equation by 4. Add the resulting equations.
$9x - 12y = 3$
$\underline{16x + 12y = 4}$
$25x = 7$
$x = \dfrac{7}{25}$
Substitute $\dfrac{7}{25}$ for x in the second equation.
$3y = 1 - 4\left(\dfrac{7}{25}\right)$
$3y = \dfrac{-3}{25}$
$y = \dfrac{-1}{25}$
The solution set is $\left\{\left(\dfrac{7}{25}, -\dfrac{1}{25}\right)\right\}$.

31. The substitution method is used here to solve the system.
$x = 9 - 2y$
$x + 2y = 13$
Substitute the expression $9 - 2y$ for x in the second equation and solve for y.
$9 - 2y + 2y = 13$
$9 = 13$
The false statement $9 = 13$ indicates that the system has no solution.
The solution set is the empty set, $\varnothing$.

33. The substitution method is used here to solve the system.
$y = 3x - 5$
$21x - 35 = 7y$
Substitute the expression $3x - 5$ for y in the second equation and solve for x.
$21x - 35 = 7(3x - 5)$
$21x - 35 = 21x - 35$
$-35 = -35$
This true statement indicates that the system has infinitely many solutions.
The solution set is $\left\{(x, y) \mid y = 3x - 5\right\}$.

35. The elimination method is used here to solve the system.
$3x - 2y = -5$
$4x + y = 8$
Eliminate y by multiplying the second equation by 2 and adding the resulting equations.
$3x - 2y = -5$
$\underline{8x + 2y = 16}$
$11x = 11$
$x = 1$
Substitute 1 for x in the second equation.
$4(1) + y = 8$
$y = 4$
The solution set is $\{(1, 4)\}$.

37. The elimination method is used here to solve the system.
$x + 3y = 2$
$3x + 9y = 6$
Eliminate x by multiplying the first equation by –3 and adding the resulting equations.
$-3x - 9y = -6$
$\underline{3x + 9y = 6}$
$0 = 0$
This true statement indicates that the system has infinitely many solutions.
The solution set is $\left\{(x, y) \mid x + 3y = 2\right\}$.

197

39. First multiply each term in the first equation by 4 to eliminate the fractions.

$$\frac{x}{4} - \frac{y}{4} = -1$$
$$x - y = -4$$

Multiply the first equation by -1 and add to the second equation and solve for y.

$$-x + y = 4$$
$$x + 4y = -9$$
$$5y = -5$$
$$y = -1$$

Substitute -1 for y in the equation $x - y = -4$ and solve for x.

$$x - (-1) = -4$$
$$x + 1 = -4$$
$$x = -5$$

The solution set is $\{(-5, -1)\}$.

41. Rearrange the equations to get in the standard form.

$$2x - 3y = 4$$
$$4x + 5y = 3$$

Multiply the first equation by -2 and add to the second equation. Solve for y.

$$-4x + 6y = -8$$
$$4x + 5y = 3$$
$$11y = -5$$
$$y = -\frac{5}{11}$$

Multiply the first equation by 5 and the second equation by 3 and add the equations. Solve for x.

$$10x - 15y = 20$$
$$12x + 15y = 9$$
$$22x = 29$$
$$x = \frac{29}{22}$$

The solution set is $\left\{\left(\frac{29}{22}, -\frac{5}{11}\right)\right\}$.

43. Add the equations to eliminate y.

$$x + y = 7$$
$$x - y = -1$$
$$2x = 6$$
$$x = 3$$

Substitute 3 for x in the first equation.

$$3 + y = 7$$
$$y = 4$$

The numbers are 3 and 4.

45.
$$3x - y = 1$$
$$x + 2y = 12$$

Eliminate y by multiplying the first equation by 2 and adding the resulting equations.

$$6x - 2y = 2$$
$$x + 2y = 12$$
$$7x = 14$$
$$x = 2$$

Substitute 2 for x in the first equation.

$$3(2) - y = 1$$
$$6 - y = 1$$
$$-y = -5$$
$$y = 5$$

The numbers are 2 and 5.

47.
$$\frac{x+2}{2} - \frac{y+4}{3} = 3$$
$$\frac{x+y}{5} = \frac{x-y}{2} - \frac{5}{2}$$

Start by multiplying each equation by its LCD and simplifying to clear the fractions.

$$\frac{x+2}{2} - \frac{y+4}{3} = 3$$
$$\frac{x+y}{5} = \frac{x-y}{2} - \frac{5}{2}$$

Start by multiplying each equation by its LCD and simplifying to clear the fractions.

$$6\left(\frac{x+2}{2} - \frac{y+4}{3}\right) = 6(3)$$
$$3(x+2) - 2(y+4) = 18$$
$$3x + 6 - 2y - 8 = 18$$
$$3x - 2y = 20$$

$$10\left(\frac{x+y}{5}\right) = 10\left(\frac{x-y}{2} - \frac{5}{2}\right)$$
$$2(x+y) = 5(x-y) - 5(5)$$
$$2x + 2y = 5x - 5y - 25$$
$$3x - 7y = 25$$

We now need to solve the equivalent system of equations:

$$3x - 2y = 20$$
$$3x - 7y = 25$$

Subtract the two equations:

$$3x - 2y = 20$$
$$-(3x - 7y = 25)$$
$$5y = -5$$
$$y = -1$$

Back-substitute this value for y and solve for x.

$$3x - 2y = 20$$
$$3x - 2(-1) = 20$$
$$3x + 2 = 20$$
$$3x = 18$$
$$x = 6$$

The solution is $(6, -1)$.

49. $5ax + 4y = 17$

$ax + 7y = 22$

Multiply the second equation by -5 and add the equations.

$$5ax + 4y = 17$$
$$\underline{-5ax - 35y = -110}$$
$$-31y = -93$$
$$y = 3$$

Back-substitute into one of the original equations to solve for x.

$$ax + 7y = 22$$
$$ax + 7(3) = 22$$
$$ax + 21 = 22$$
$$ax = 1$$
$$x = \frac{1}{a}$$

The solution is $\left(\frac{1}{a}, 3\right)$.

51. $f(-2) = 11 \rightarrow -2m + b = 11$

$f(3) = -9 \rightarrow 3m + b = -9$

We need to solve the resulting system of equations:

$-2m + b = 11$

$3m + b = -9$

Subtract the two equations:

$$-2m + b = 11$$
$$\underline{3m + b = -9}$$
$$-5m = 20$$
$$m = -4$$

Back-substitute into one of the original equations to solve for b.

$$-2m + b = 11$$
$$-2(-4) + b = 11$$
$$8 + b = 11$$
$$b = 3$$

Therefore, $m = -4$ and $b = 3$.

53. The solution to a system of linear equations is the point of intersection of the graphs of the equations in the system. If $(6, 2)$ is a solution, then we need to find the lines that intersect at that point. Looking at the graph, we see that the graphs of $x + 3y = 12$ and $x - y = 4$ intersect at the point $(6, 2)$. Therefore, the desired system of equations is

$x + 3y = 12$ or $y = -\frac{1}{3}x + 4$

$x - y = 4$ $\qquad$ $y = x - 4$

55. At the break-even point, $R(x) = C(x)$.

$$10000 + 30x = 50x$$
$$10000 = 20x$$
$$10000 = 20x$$
$$500 = x$$

Five hundred radios must be produced and sold to break-even.

57. $R(x) = 50x$

$R(200) = 50(200) = 10000$

$C(x) = 10000 + 30x$

$C(200) = 10000 + 30(200)$

$\qquad = 10000 + 6000 = 16000$

$R(200) - C(200) = 10000 - 16000$

$\qquad\qquad = -6000$

This means that if 200 radios are produced and sold the company will lose $6,000.

59. a. $P(x) = R(x) - C(x)$

$\qquad = 50x - (10000 + 30x)$

$\qquad = 50x - 10000 - 30x$

$\qquad = 20x - 10000$

$P(x) = 20x - 10000$

b. $P(10000) = 20(10000) - 10000$

$\qquad = 200000 - 10000 = 190000$

If 10,0000 radios are produced and sold the profit will be $190,000.

61. a. The cost function is:

$C(x) = 18,000 + 20x$

b. The revenue function is:

$R(x) = 80x$

c. At the break-even point, $R(x) = C(x)$.

$$80x = 18000 + 20x$$
$$60x = 18000$$
$$x = 300$$
$$R(x) = 80x$$
$$R(300) = 80(300)$$
$$= 24,000$$

When approximately 300 canoes are produced the company will break-even with cost and revenue at $24,000.

63. a. The cost function is:
$$C(x) = 30000 + 2500x$$

b. The revenue function is:
$$R(x) = 3125x$$

c. At the break-even point, $R(x) = C(x)$.
$$3125x = 30000 + 2500x$$
$$625x = 30000$$
$$x = 48$$

After 48 sold out performances, the investor will break-even. ($150,000)

65. a.
$$N_d = -5p + 750$$
$$= -5(120) + 750$$
$$= -600 + 750$$
$$= 150$$
$$N_s = 2.5(120) = 300$$

If the price of the televisions is $120, 150 sets can be sold and 300 sets can be supplied.

b. To find the price at which supply and demand are equal, we set the two equations equal to each other and solve for p.
$$-5p + 750 = 2.5p$$
$$750 = 7.5p$$
$$\frac{750}{7.5} = p$$
$$100 = p$$

$N = 2.5(100) = 250$.

Supply and demand will be equal if the price of the televisions is $100. At that price, 250 sets can be supplied and sold.

67. Solve $-x + y = 16$ for y

$$-x + y = 16$$
$$y = x + 16$$

Substitute for y in the other equation:

$$13x + 12\overbrace{(x+16)}^{y} = 992$$
$$13x + 12x + 192 = 992$$
$$25x = 800$$
$$x = 32$$

Substitute $x = 32$ into either equation to find y.

$$y = x + 16$$
$$y = 32 + 16$$
$$y = 48$$

The percentages will both be 48% 32 years after 1988, or 2020.

69. a. $y = 0.04x + 5.48$

b. $y = 0.17x + 1.84$

c. To find the year when the costs will be the same, we set the two equations equal to each other and solve for x.
$$0.04x + 5.48 = 0.17x + 1.84$$
$$-0.13x = -3.64$$
$$x = 28$$

The costs will be the same 28 years after 2000, or 2028.
$$y = 0.17x + 1.84$$
$$y = 0.17(28) + 1.84$$
$$y = 6.6$$

The cost of each program in 2028 will be 6.6% of the GDP. After that year, Medicare will have the greater cost.

71. a.
$$m = \frac{25.3 - 38}{17 - 0} = \frac{-12.7}{17} \approx -0.75$$

From the point $(0, 38)$ we have that the y-intercept is $b = 38$. Therefore, the equation of the line is $y = -0.75x + 38$.

b.
$$m = \frac{23 - 40}{17 - 0} = \frac{-17}{17} = -1$$

From the point $(0, 40)$ we have that the y-intercept is $b = 40$. Therefore, the equation of the line is $y = -x + 40$.

c. To find the year when cigarette use is the same, we set the two equations equal to each other and solve for x.

$$-0.75x + 38 = -x + 40$$
$$0.25x + 38 = 40$$
$$0.25x = 2$$
$$x = \frac{2}{0.25} = 8$$
$$y = -(8) + 40 = 32$$

Cigarette use was the same for African Americans and Hispanics in 1993 (8 years after 1985). At that time, 32% of each group used cigarettes.

73. $x + 2y = 1980$
$2x + y = 2670$
Multiply the first equation by -2 and add to the second equation. Solve for y.

$$-2x - 4y = -3960$$
$$2x + y = 2670$$
$$-3y = -1290$$
$$y = 430$$

Substitute 430 for y in the second equation and solve for x.

$2x + 430 = 2670$
$$2x = 2240$$
$$x = 1120$$

There are 1120 calories in a pan pizza and 430 calories in a beef burrito.

75. $x + y = 300 + 241$ or $x + y = 541$
$2x + 3y = 1257$
Multiply the first equation by -2 and add to the second equation. Solve for y.

$$-2x - 2y = -1082$$
$$2x + 3y = 1257$$
$$y = 175$$

Substitute 175 for y in the first equation and solve for x.

$x + 175 = 541$
$$x = 366$$

There are 366 mg in scrambled eggs and 175 mg in a Double Beef Whopper.

77. $x + y = 200$
$100x + 80y = 17000$
Multiply the first equation by -100 and add to the second equation. Solve for y.

$$-100x - 100y = -20000$$
$$100x + 80y = 17000$$
$$-20y = -3000$$
$$y = 150$$

Substitute 150 for y in the first equation and solve for x.

$x + 150 = 200$
$$x = 50$$

There are 50 rooms with kitchenettes and 150 rooms without.

79. $2x + 2y = 360$
$20x + 8(2y) = 3280$
Multiply the first equation by -10 and add to the second equation. Solve for y.

$$-20x - 20y = -3600$$
$$20x + 16y = 3280$$
$$-4y = -320$$
$$y = 80$$

Substitute 80 for y in the first equation and solve for x.

$2x + 2(80) = 360$
$$2x + 160 = 360$$
$$2x = 200$$
$$x = 100$$

The lot is 100 feet long and 80 feet wide.

81. $(x + y)2 = 16$
$(x - y)2 = 8$
Multiply to remove the parentheses and then add the two equations together. Solve for x.

$2x + 2y = 16$
$2x - 2y = 8$
$$4x = 24$$
$$x = 6$$

Substitute 6 for x in the first equation and solve for y.

$2(6) + 2y = 16$
$$12 + 2y = 16$$
$$2y = 4$$
$$y = 2$$

The crew rows 6 mph and the current is 2 mph.

83.
$$x + 2y = 180$$
$$(2x - 30) + y = 180$$
Rewrite the second equation in standard form.
$$x + 2y = 180$$
$$2x + y = 210$$
Multiply the first equation by -2 and add the equations.
$$-2x - 4y = -360$$
$$\underline{2x + y = 210}$$
$$-3y = -150$$
$$y = 50$$
Back-substitute to solve for x.
$$x + 2y = 180$$
$$x + 2(50) = 180$$
$$x + 100 = 180$$
$$x = 80$$
The three interior angles measure $80°$, $50°$, and $50°$.

97. x = first lucky number
y = second lucky number
$$3x + 6y = 12$$
$$x + 2y = 5$$
Eliminate x by multiplying the second equation by -3 and adding the resulting equations.
$$3x + 6y = 12$$
$$\underline{-3x - 6y = -15}$$
$$0 = -3$$

The false statement $0 = -3$ indicates that the system has no solution. Therefore, the twin who always lies is talking.

Section 3.2

Check Point Exercises

1.
$$x - 2y + 3z = 22$$
$$-1 - 2(-4) + 3(5) = 22$$
$$-1 + 8 + 15 = 22$$
$$22 = 22 \text{ true}$$
$$2x - 3y - z = 5$$
$$2(-1) - 3(-4) - 5 = 5$$
$$-2 + 12 - 5 = 5$$
$$5 = 5 \text{ true}$$
$$3x + y - 5z = -32$$
$$3(-1) - 4 - 5(5) = -32$$
$$-3 - 4 - 25 = -32$$
$$-32 = -32 \text{ true}$$
$(-1, -4, 5)$ is a solution of the system.

2.
$$x + 4y - z = 20$$
$$3x + 2y + z = 8$$
$$2x - 3y + 2z = -16$$
Eliminate z from Equations 1 and 2 by adding Equation 1 and Equation 2.
$$x + 4y - z = 20$$
$$\underline{3x + 2y + z = 8}$$
$$4x + 6y = 28 \text{ Equation 4}$$
Eliminate z from Equations 2 and 3 by multiplying Equation 2 by -2 and adding the resulting equation to Equation 3.
$$-6x - 4y - 2z = -16$$
$$\underline{2x - 3y + 2z = -16}$$
$$-4x - 7y = -32 \text{ Equation 5}$$
Solve Equations 4 and 5 for x and y by adding Equation 4 and Equation 5.
$$4x + 6y = 28$$
$$\underline{-4x - 7y = -32}$$
$$-y = -4$$
$$y = 4$$
Substitute 4 for y in Equation 4 and solve for x.
$$4x + 6(4) = 28$$
$$4x + 24 = 28$$
$$4x = 4$$
$$x = 1$$

Substitute 1 for x and 4 for y in Equation 2 and solve for z.

$$3(1) + 2(4) + z = 8$$
$$3 + 8 + z = 8$$
$$11 + z = 8$$
$$z = -3$$

The solution set is $\{(1, 4, -3)\}$.

3.
$$2y - z = 7$$
$$x + 2y + z = 17$$
$$2x - 3y + 2z = -1$$

Eliminate x and z from Equations 2 and 3 by multiplying Equation 2 by -2 and adding the resulting equation to Equation 3.

$$-2x - 4y - 2z = -34$$
$$\underline{2x - 3y + 2z = -1}$$
$$-7y = -35$$
$$y = 5$$

Substitute 5 for y in Equation 1 and solve for z.

$$2(5) - z = 7$$
$$10 - z = 7$$
$$-z = -3$$
$$z = 3$$

Substitute 5 for y and 3 for z in Equation 2 and solve for x.

$$x + 2(5) + 3 = 17$$
$$x + 10 + 3 = 17$$
$$x + 13 = 17$$
$$x = 4$$

The solution set is $\{(4, 5, 3)\}$.

4. $(1, 4), (2, 1), (3, 4)$

$$y = ax^2 + bx + c$$

Substitute 1 for x and 4 for y in

$y = ax^2 + bx + c$.

$$4 = a(1)^2 + b(1) + c$$
$$4 = a + b + c \quad \text{Equation 1}$$

Substitute 2 for x and 1 for y in

$y = ax^2 + bx + c$.

$$1 = a(2)^2 + b(2) + c$$
$$1 = 4a + 2b + c \quad \text{Equation 2}$$

Substitute 3 for x and 4 for y in

$y = ax^2 + bx + c$.

$$4 = a(3)^2 + b(3) + c$$
$$4 = 9a + 3b + c \quad \text{Equation 3}$$

Eliminate c from Equations 1 and 2 by multiplying Equation 2 by -1 and adding the

resulting equation to Equation 1.

$$4 = a + b + c$$
$$\underline{-1 = -4a - 2b - c}$$
$$3 = -3a - b \quad \text{Equation 4}$$

Eliminate c from Equation 2 and 3 by multiplying Equation 3 by -1 and adding the resulting equation to Equation 2.

$$1 = 4a + 2b + c$$
$$\underline{-4 = -9a - 3b - c}$$
$$-3 = -5a - b \quad \text{Equation 5}$$

Solve Equations 4 and 5 for a and b by multiplying Equation 5 by -1 and adding the resulting equation to Equation 4.

$$3 = -3a - b$$
$$\underline{3 = 5a + b}$$
$$6 = 2a$$
$$a = 3$$

Substitute 3 for a in Equation 4 and solve for b.

$$3 = -3(3) - b$$
$$3 = -9 - b$$
$$12 = -b$$
$$b = -12$$

Substitute 3 for a and -12 for b in Equation 1 and solve for c.

$$4 = 3 - 12 + c$$
$$4 = -9 + c$$
$$c = 13$$

Substituting 3 for a, -12 for b, and 13 for c in the quadratic equation $y = ax^2 + bx + c$ gives

$$y = 3x^2 - 12x + 13.$$

Exercise Set 3.2

1.
$$x + y + z = 4$$
$$2 - 1 + 3 = 4$$
$$4 = 4 \text{ true}$$
$$x - 2y - z = 1$$
$$2(2) - 2(-1) - 3 = 1$$
$$4 + 2 - 3 = 1$$
$$1 = 1 \text{ true}$$
$$2x - y - 2z = -1$$
$$2(2) - (-1) - 2(3) = -1$$
$$4 + 1 - 6 = -1$$
$$-1 = -1 \text{ false}$$

$(2, -1, 3)$ is a solution.

3. $x - 2y = 2$

       $4 - 2(1) = 2$

          $4 - 2 = 2$

            $2 = 2$ true

         $2x + 3y = 11$

       $2(4) + 3(1) = 11$

            $8 + 3 = 11$

             $11 = 11$ true

         $y - 4z = -7$

       $1 - 4(2) = -7$

          $1 - 8 = -7$

            $-7 = -7$ true

   $(4, 1, 2)$ is a solution.

5. $x + y + 2z = 11$

       $x + y + 3z = 14$

       $x + 2y - z = 5$

Eliminate x and y from Equations 1 and 2 by multiplying Equation 2 by -1 and adding the resulting equation to Equation 1.

     $-x - y - 3z = -14$

     $\underline{x + y + 2z = 11}$

           $-z = -3$

             $z = 3$

Substitute 3 for z in Equations 1 and 3.

$x + y + 2(3) = 11$

$x + 2y - (3) = 5$

Simplify:

  $x + y = 5$ Equation 4

$x + 2y = 8$ Equation 5

Solve Equations 4 and 5 for x and y by multiplying Equation 5 by -1 and adding the resulting equation to Equation 4.

      $x + y = 5$

    $\underline{-x - 2y = -8}$

        $-y = -3$

          $y = 3$

Substitute 3 for z and 3 for y in Equation 2 and solve for x.

$x + 3 + 3(3) = 14$

     $x + 12 = 14$

         $x = 2$

The solution set is $\{(2, 3, 3)\}$.

7. $4x - y + 2z = 11$

       $x + 2y - z = -1$

     $2x + 2y - 3z = -1$

Eliminate y from Equation 1 and 2 by multiplying Equation 1 by 2 and adding the resulting equation to Equation 2 and 3.

     $8x - 2y + 4z = 22$

     $\underline{x + 2y - z = -1}$

       $9x + 3z = 21$ Equation 4

Eliminate y from Equations 1 and 3 by multiplying Equation 1 by 2 and adding the resulting equation to Equation 3.

     $8x - 2y + 4z = 22$

     $\underline{2x + 2y - 3z = -1}$

      $10x + z = 21$ Equation 5

Solve Equations 4 and 5 for x and z by multiplying Equation 5 by -3 and adding the resulting equation to Equation 4.

      $9x + 3z = 21$

   $\underline{-30x - 3z = -63}$

      $-21x = -42$

         $x = 2$

Substitute 2 for x in Equation 5 and solve for z. $10(2) + z = 21$

       $20 + z = 21$

           $z = 1$

Substitute 2 for x and 1 for z in Equation 2 and solve for y.

$2 + 2y - 1 = -1$

    $2y + 1 = -1$

        $2y = -2$

          $y = -1$

The solution set is $\{(2, -1, 1)\}$.

9. $3x + 2y - 3z = -2$

     $2x - 5y + 2z = -2$

     $4x - 3y + 4z = 10$

Eliminate z from Equations 1 and 2 by multiplying Equation 1 by 2 and Equation 2 by 3. Add the resulting equations.

     $6x + 4y - 6z = -4$

    $\underline{6x - 15y + 6z = -6}$

     $12x - 11y = -10$ Equation 4

Eliminate z from Equations 2 and 3 by multiplying Equation 2 by -2.

   $-4x + 10y - 4z = 4$

    $\underline{4x - 3y + 4z = 10}$

          $7y = 14$ Equation 5

Solve Equation 5 for y

  $7y = 14$

    $y = 2$

Solve for x by substituting 7 for y in Equation 4.
$$12x - 11y = -10$$
$$12x - 11(2) = -10$$
$$12x - 22 = -10$$
$$12x = 12$$
$$x = 1$$

Substitute 2 for y and 1 for x in Equation 2 and solve for z.
$$2x - 5y + 2z = -2$$
$$2(1) - 5(2) + 2z = -2$$
$$2 - 10 + 2z = -2$$
$$2z = 6$$
$$z = 3$$
The solution set is $\{(1, 2, 3)\}$.

11. $2x - 4y + 3z = 17$
$x + 2y - z = 0$
$4x - y - z = 6$

Eliminate z from Equations 1 and 2 by multiplying Equation 2 by 3 and adding the resulting equation to Equation 1.
$$2x - 4y + 3z = 17$$
$$\underline{3x + 6y - 3z = 0}$$
$$5x + 2y = 17 \quad \text{Equation 4}$$

Eliminate z from Equations 2 and 3 by multiplying Equation 2 by -1 and adding the resulting equation to Equation 3.
$$-x - 2y + z = 0$$
$$\underline{4x - y - z = 6}$$
$$3x - 3y = 6 \quad \text{Equation 5}$$

Solve Equations 4 and 5 for x and y by multiplying Equation 5 by $\dfrac{2}{3}$ and adding the resulting equation to Equation 4.
$$5x + 2y = 17$$
$$\underline{2x - 2y = 4}$$
$$7x = 21$$
$$x = 3$$

Substitute 3 for x in Equation 4 and solve for y.
$$5(3) + 2y = 17$$
$$15 + 2y = 17$$
$$2y = 2$$
$$y = 1$$

Substitute 3 for x and 1 for y in Equation 2 and solve for z.
$$3 + 2(1) - z = 0$$
$$3 + 2 - z = 0$$
$$5 - z = 0$$
$$5 = z$$
The solution set is $\{(3, 1, 5)\}$.

13. $2x + y = 2$
$x + y - z = 4$
$3x + 2y + z = 0$

Eliminate z from Equations 2 and 3 by adding Equation 2 and Equation 3.
$$x + y - z = 4$$
$$\underline{3x + 2y + z = 0}$$
$$4x + 3y = 4 \quad \text{Equation 4}$$

Solve Equations 1 and 4 for x and y by multiplying Equation 1 by -3 and adding the resulting equation to Equation 4.
$$-6x - 3y = -6$$
$$\underline{4x + 3y = 4}$$
$$-2x = -2$$
$$x = 1$$

Substitute 1 for x in Equation 1 and solve for y.
$$2(1) + y = 2$$
$$2 + y = 2$$
$$y = 0$$

Substitute 1 for x and 0 for y in Equation 2 and solve for z.
$$1 + 0 - z = 4$$
$$1 - z = 4$$
$$-z = 3$$
$$z = -3$$
The solution set is $\{(1, 0, -3)\}$.

15. $x + y = -4$
$y - z = 1$
$2x + y + 3z = -21$

Eliminate y from Equations 1 and 2 by multiplying Equation 1 by -1 and adding the resulting equation to Equation 2.
$$-x - y = 4$$
$$\underline{y - z = 1}$$
$$-x - z = 5 \quad \text{Equation 4}$$

Eliminate y from Equations 2 and 3 by multiplying Equation 2 by -1 and adding the resulting equation to Equation 3.
$$-y + z = -1$$
$$\underline{2x + y + 3z = -21}$$
$$2x + 4z = -22 \quad \text{Equation 5}$$

Solve Equations 4 and 5 for x and z by multiplying Equation 4 by 2 and adding the resulting equation to Equation 5.

$-2x - 2z = 10$

$\underline{2x + 4z = -22}$

$2z = -12$

$z = -6$

Substitute -6 for z in Equation 2 and solve for y.

$y - (-6) = 1$

$y + 6 = 1$

$y = -5$

Substitute -5 for y in Equation 1 and solve for x

$x + (-5) = -4$

$x = 1$

The solution set is $\{(1, -5, -6)\}$.

17. $3(2x + y) + 5z = -1$

$2(x - 3y + 4z) = -9$

$4(1 + x) = -3(z - 3y)$

Simplify each equation.

$6x + 3y + 5z = -1$　　Equation 4

$2x - 6y + 8z = -9$　　Equation 5

$4 + 4x = -3z + 9y$

$4x - 9y + 3z = -4$　　Equation 6

Eliminate x from Equations 4 and 5 by multiplying Equation 5 by -3 and adding the resulting equation to Equation 4.

$-6x + 3y + 5z = -1$

$\underline{-6x + 18y - 24z = 27}$

$21y - 19z = 26$　　Equation 7

Eliminate x from Equations 5 and 6 by multiplying Equation 5 by -2 and adding the resulting equation to Equation 6.

$-4x + 12y - 16z = 18$

$\underline{4x - 9y + 3z = -4}$

$3y - 13z = 14$　　Equation 8

Solve Equations 7 and 8 for y and z by multiplying Equation 8 by -7 and adding the resulting equation to Equation 7.

$21y - 19z = 26$

$\underline{-21y + 91z = -98}$

$72z = -72$

$z = -1$

Substitute -1 for z in Equation 8 and solve for y.

$3y - 13(-1) = 14$

$3y + 13 = 14$

$3y = 1$

$y = \dfrac{1}{3}$

Substitute $\dfrac{1}{3}$ for y and -1 for z in Equation 5 and solve for x.

$2x - 6\left(\dfrac{1}{3}\right) + 8(-1) = -9$

$2x - 2 - 8 = -9$

$2x - 10 = -9$

$2x = 1$

$x = \dfrac{1}{2}$

The solution set is $\left\{\left(\dfrac{1}{2}, \dfrac{1}{3}, -1\right)\right\}$.

19. $(-1, 6), (1, 4), (2, 9)$

$y = ax^2 + bx + c$

Substitute -1 for x and 6 for y in $y = ax^2 + bx + c$.

$6 = a(-1)^2 + b(-1) + c$

$6 = a - b + c$　　　　Equation 1

Substitute 1 for x and 4 for y in $y = ax^2 + bx + c$.

$4 = a(1)^2 + b(1) + c$

$4 = a + b + c$　　　　Equation 2

Substitute 2 for x and 9 for y in $y = ax^2 + bx + c$.

$9 = a(2)^2 + b(2) + c$

$9 = 4a + 2b + c$　　　Equation 3

Eliminate b from Equations 1 and 2 by adding Equation 1 and Equation 2.

$6 = a - b + c$

$\underline{4 = a + b + c}$

$10 = 2a + 2c$　　Equation 4

Eliminate b from Equations 1 and 3 by multiplying Equation 1 by 2 and adding the resulting equation to Equation 3.

$12 = 2a - 2b + 2c$

$\underline{9 = 4a + 2b + c}$

$21 = 6a + 3c$　　Equation 5

Solve Equations 4 and 5 for a and c by multiplying Equation 4 by -3 and adding the resulting equation to Equation 5.

$-30 = -6a - 6c$

$\underline{21 = 6a + 3c}$

$-9 = -3c$

$c = 3$

Substitute 3 for c in Equation 4 and solve for a.

$10 = 2a + 2(3)$

$10 = 2a + 6$

$4 = 2a$

$a = 2$

Substitute 2 for a and 3 for c in Equation 2 and solve for b.

$4 = 2 + b + 3$

$4 = b + 5$

$b = -1$

Substituting 2 for a, -1 for b, and 3 for c in the quadratic equation $y = ax^2 + bx + c$ gives

$y = 2x^2 - x + 3$.

21. $(-1, -4), (1, -2), (2, 5)$

Substitute -1 for x and -4 for y in

$y = ax^2 + bx + c$.

$-4 = a(-1)^2 + b(-1) + c$

$-4 = a - b + c$ Equation 1

Substitute 1 for x and -2 for y in

$y = ax^2 + bx + c$.

$-2 = a(1)^2 + b(1) + c$

$-2 = a + b + c$ Equation 2

Substitute 2 for x and 5 for y in $y = ax^2 + bx + c$.

$5 = a(2)^2 + b(2) + c$

$5 = 4a + 2b + c$ Equation 3

Eliminate a and b from Equations 1 and 2 by multiplying Equation 1 by -1 and adding the resulting equation to Equation 2.

$4 = -a + b - c$

$\underline{-2 = a + b + c}$

$2 = 2b$

$b = 1$

Eliminate c from Equations 1 and 3 by multiplying Equation 1 by -1 and adding the resulting equation to Equation 3.

$4 = -a + b - c$

$\underline{5 = 4a + 2b + c}$

$9 = 3a + 3b$ Equation 4

Substitute 1 for b in Equation 4 and solve for a.

$9 = 3a + 3(1)$

$9 = 3a + 3$

$6 = 3a$

$a = 2$

Substitute 2 for a and 1 for b in Equation 2 and solve for c.

$-2 = 2 + 1 + c$

$-2 = c + 3$

$c = -5$

Substituting 2 for a, 1 for b, and -5 for c in quadratic equation $y = ax^2 + bx + c$ gives

$y = 2x^2 + x - 5$.

23. $x + y + z = 16$

$2x + 3y + 4z = 46$

$5x - y = 31$

Eliminate z from Equations 1 and 2 by multiplying Equation 1 by -4 and adding the resulting equation to Equation 2.

$-4x - 4y - 4z = -64$

$\underline{2x + 3y + 4z = 46}$

$-2x - y = -18$ Equation 4

Solve Equations 3 and 4 for x and y by multiplying Equation 4 by -1 and adding the resulting equation to Equation 3.

$5x - y = 31$

$\underline{2x + y = 18}$

$7x = 49$

$x = 7$

Substitute 7 for x in Equation 3 and solve for y.

$5(7) - y = 31$

$35 - y = 31$

$-y = -4$

$y = 4$

Substitute 7 for x and 4 for y in Equation 1 and solve for z.

$7 + 4 + z = 16$

$z + 11 = 16$

$z = 5$

The numbers are 7, 4 and 5.

207

25.

$$\frac{x+2}{6} - \frac{y+4}{3} + \frac{z}{2} = 0$$

$$6\left(\frac{x+2}{6} - \frac{y+4}{3} + \frac{z}{2}\right) = 6(0)$$

$$(x+2) - 2(y+4) + 3z = 0$$

$$x + 2 - 2y - 8 + 3z = 0$$

$$x - 2y + 3z = 6$$

$$\frac{x+1}{2} + \frac{y-1}{2} - \frac{z}{4} = \frac{9}{2}$$

$$4\left(\frac{x+1}{2} + \frac{y-1}{2} - \frac{z}{4}\right) = 4\left(\frac{9}{2}\right)$$

$$2(x+1) + 2(y-1) - z = 18$$

$$2x + 2 + 2y - 2 - z = 18$$

$$2x + 2y - z = 18$$

$$\frac{x-5}{4} + \frac{y+1}{3} + \frac{z-2}{2} = \frac{19}{4}$$

$$12\left(\frac{x-5}{4} + \frac{y+1}{3} + \frac{z-2}{2}\right) = 12\left(\frac{19}{4}\right)$$

$$3(x-5) + 4(y+1) + 6(z-2) = 57$$

$$3x - 15 + 4y + 4 + 6z - 12 = 57$$

$$3x + 4y + 6z = 80$$

We need to solve the equivalent system:

$$x - 2y + 3z = 6$$

$$2x + 2y - z = 18$$

$$3x + 4y + 6z = 80$$

Add the first two equations together.

$$x - 2y + 3z = 6$$

$$\underline{2x + 2y - z = 18}$$

$$3x + 2z = 24$$

Multiply the second equation by -2 and add it to the third equation.

$$-4x - 4y + 2z = -36$$

$$\underline{3x + 4y + 6z = 80}$$

$$-x + 8z = 44$$

Using the two reduced equations, we solve the system

$$3x + 2z = 24$$

$$-x + 8z = 44$$

Multiply the second equation by 3 and add the equations.

$$3x + 2z = 24$$

$$\underline{-3x + 24z = 132}$$

$$26z = 156$$

$$z = 6$$

Back-substitute to find x.

$$-x + 8(6) = 44$$

$$-x + 48 = 44$$

$$-x = -4$$

$$x = 4$$

Back-substitute to find y.

$$x - 2y + 3z = 6$$

$$4 - 2y + 3(6) = 6$$

$$-2y = -16$$

$$y = 8$$

The solution is $(4, 8, 6)$.

27. Selected points may vary, but the equation will be the same.

$$y = ax^2 + bx + c$$

Use the points $(2, -2)$, $(4, 1)$, and $(6, -2)$ to get the system

$$4a + 2b + c = -2$$

$$16a + 4b + c = 1$$

$$36a + 6b + c = -2$$

Multiply the first equation by -1 and add to the second equation.

$$-4a - 2b - c = 2$$

$$\underline{16a + 4b + c = 1}$$

$$12a + 2b = 3$$

Multiply the first equation by -1 and add to the third equation.

$$-4a - 2b - c = 2$$

$$\underline{36a + 6b + c = -2}$$

$$32a + 4b = 0$$

Using the two reduced equations, we get the system

$$12a + 2b = 3$$

$$32a + 4b = 0$$

Multiply the first equation by -2 and add to the second equation.

$$-24a - 4b = -6$$
$$\underline{32a + 4b = 0}$$
$$8a = -6$$
$$a = -\frac{3}{4}$$

Back-substitute to solve for b.
$$12a + 2b = 3$$
$$12\left(-\frac{3}{4}\right) + 2b = 3$$
$$-9 + 2b = 3$$
$$2b = 12$$
$$b = 6$$

Back-substitute to solve for c.
$$4a + 2b + c = -2$$
$$4\left(-\frac{3}{4}\right) + 2(6) + c = -2$$
$$-3 + 12 + c = -2$$
$$c = -11$$

The equation is:
$$y = -\frac{3}{4}x^2 + 6x - 11$$

29. $ax - by - 2cz = 21$
$ax + by + cz = 0$
$2ax - by + cz = 14$

Add the first two equations.
$$ax - by - 2cz = 21$$
$$\underline{ax + by + cz = 0}$$
$$2ax - cz = 21$$

Multiply the first equation by -1 and add to the third equation.
$$-ax + by + 2cz = -21$$
$$\underline{2ax - by + cz = 14}$$
$$ax + 3cz = -7$$

Use the two reduced equations to get the following system:
$$2ax - cz = 21$$
$$ax + 3cz = -7$$

Multiply the second equation by -2 and add the equations.
$$2ax - cz = 21$$
$$\underline{-2ax - 6cz = 14}$$
$$-7cz = 35$$
$$z = -\frac{5}{c}$$

Back-substitute to solve for x.

$$ax + 3cz = -7$$
$$ax + 3c\left(-\frac{5}{c}\right) = -7$$
$$ax - 15 = -7$$
$$ax = 8$$
$$x = \frac{8}{a}$$

Back-substitute to solve for y.
$$ax + by + cz = 0$$
$$a\left(\frac{8}{a}\right) + by + c\left(-\frac{5}{c}\right) = 0$$
$$8 + by - 5 = 0$$
$$by = -3$$
$$y = -\frac{3}{b}$$

The solution is $\left(\dfrac{8}{a}, -\dfrac{3}{b}, -\dfrac{5}{c}\right)$.

31.　a. 　2000: $(0, 2.5)$
　　　2002: $(2, 4.1)$
　　　2003: $(3, 3.5)$

b. 　$y = ax^2 + bx + c$
$$a(0)^2 + b(0) + c = 2.5$$
$$c = 2.5 \quad \text{Equation 1}$$
$$y = ax^2 + bx + c$$
$$a(2)^2 + b(2) + c = 4.1$$
$$4a + 2b + c = 4.1 \quad \text{Equation 2}$$
$$y = ax^2 + bx + c$$
$$a(3)^2 + b(3) + c = 3.5$$
$$9a + 3b + c = 3.5 \quad \text{Equation 3}$$
System:
$$c = 2.5$$
$$4a + 2b + c = 4.1$$
$$9a + 3b + c = 3.5$$

c. 　Substitute $c = 2.5$ into equation 2
$$4a + 2b + 2.5 = 4.1$$
$$4a + 2b = 1.6 \quad \text{Equation 4}$$
Substitute $c = 2.5$ into equation 2
$$9a + 3b + 2.5 = 3.5$$
$$9a + 3b = 1 \quad \text{Equation 5}$$
Solve the system of two equations using equations 4 and 5.

$4a + 2b = 1.6$ Mult. by 3 → $12a + 6b = 4.8$

$9a + 3b = 1$ Mult. by – 2 → $\underline{-18a - 6b = -2}$

$$-6a = 2.8$$
$$a \approx -0.4667$$
$$a \approx -0.47$$

Use back-substitution to find b.
$$4a + 2b = 1.6$$
$$4(-0.4667) + 2b = 1.6$$
$$b \approx 1.73$$

The equation that models steroid use by U.S. high school seniors x years after 2000 is $y = -0.47x^2 + 1.73x + 2.5$

33. **a.** Substitute the values for x and y into the quadratic form.
$$224 = a(1)^2 + b(1) + c$$
$$a + b + c = 224$$

$$176 = a(3)^2 + b(3) + c$$
$$9a + 3b + c = 176$$

$$104 = a(4)^2 + b(4) + c$$
$$16a + 4b + c = 104$$

Multiply the first equation by –1 and add to both the second and the third equations to obtain 2 new equations with 2 variables.
$$-a - b - c = -224$$
$$9a + 3b + c = 176$$
$$8a + 2b = -48$$

$$-a - b - c = -224$$
$$16a + 4b + c = 104$$
$$15a + 3b = -120$$

Use the two new equations to solve for a and b. Multiply the first equation by –3 and the second equation by 2 and add the results together. Solve for a. Substitute that value in $8a + 2b = -48$ and solve for b.

$$-24a - 6b = 144$$
$$30a + 6b = -240$$
$$6a = -96$$
$$a = -16$$

$$8(-16) + 2b = -48$$
$$-128 + 2b = -48$$
$$2b = 80$$
$$b = 40$$

Substitute –16 for a and 40 for b into the equation $a + b + c = 224$ and solve for c.
$$-16 + 40 + c = 224$$
$$c = 200$$

The equation is $y = -16x^2 + 40x + 200$.

b. $y = -16(5)^2 + 40(5) + 200 = 0$

The ball hit the ground after 5 seconds.

35. $x + y + z = 244$

$x - y = 4$

$y - z = 48$

Multiply the second equation by –1 and add to the first equation.
$$x + y + z = 244$$
$$\underline{-x + y = -4}$$
$$2y + z = 240$$

Add this new equation to equation to the third equation and solve for y.
$$y - z = 48$$
$$\underline{2y + z = 240}$$
$$3y = 288$$
$$y = 96$$

Substitute 96 for y in the equation $x - y = 4$ and solve for x.
$$x - 96 = 4$$
$$x = 100$$

Substitute 96 for y into the equation $y - z = 48$ and solve for z.
$$96 - z = 48$$
$$-z = -48$$
$$z = 48$$

Andrew Carnegie's fortune is worth \$100 billion in today's money. Cornelius Vanderbilt's fortune is worth \$96 billion and Bill Gates is worth \$48 billion.

37. x = number of \$8 tickets sold
y = number of \$10 tickets sold
z = number of \$12 tickets sold
From the given conditions we have the following system of equations.
$$x + y + z = 400$$
$$8x + 10y + 12z = 3700$$
$$x + y = 7z \text{ or } x + y - 7z = 0$$
Eliminate z from Equations 1 and 2 multiplying Equation 1 by -12 and adding the resulting equation to Equation 2.
$$-12x - 12y - 12z = -4800$$
$$\underline{8x + 10y + 12z = 3700}$$
$$-4x - 2y = -1100 \quad \text{Equation 4}$$

Eliminate z from Equations 1 and 3 by multiplying Equation 1 by 7 and adding the resulting equation to Equation 3.
$$7x + 7y + 7z = 2800$$
$$\underline{x + y - 7z = 0}$$
$$8x + 8y = 2800 \quad \text{Equation 5}$$

Solve Equations 4 and 5 for x and y by multiplying Equation 4 by 2 and adding the resulting equation to Equation 5.
$$-8x - 4y = -2200$$
$$\underline{8x + 8y = 2800}$$
$$4y = 600$$
$$y = 150$$
Substitute 150 for y in Equation 5 and solve for x.
$$8x + 8(150) = 2800$$
$$8x = 2800 - 1200$$
$$8x = 1600$$
$$x = 200$$
Substitute 200 for x and 150 for y in Equation 1 and solve for z.
$$200 + 150 + z = 400$$
$$350 + z = 400$$
$$z = 50$$
The number of \$8 tickets sold was 200.
The number of \$10 tickets sold was 150.
The number of \$12 tickets sold was 50.

39. x = amount of money invested at 10%
y = amount of money invested at 12%
z = amount of money invested at 15%
$$x + y + z = 6700$$
$$0.08x + 0.10y + 0.12z = 716$$
$$z = x + y + 300$$
Arrange Equation 3 so that variable terms appear on the left and constants appear on the right.
$$-x - y + z = 300 \quad \text{Equation 4}$$
Eliminate x and y from Equations 1 and 4 by adding Equations 1 and 4.
$$x + y + z = 6700$$
$$\underline{-x - y + z = 300}$$
$$2z = 7000$$
$$z = 3500$$
Substitute 3500 for z in Equation 1 and Equation 2 and simplify.
$$x + y + 3500 = 6700$$
$$x + y = 3200 \quad \text{Equation 5}$$
$$0.08x + 0.10y + 0.12(3500) = 716$$
$$0.08x + 0.10y + 420 = 716$$
$$0.08x + 10y = 296 \quad \text{Equation 6}$$
Solve Equations 5 and 6 for x and y by multiplying Equation 5 by -0.10 and adding the resulting equation to Equation 6.
$$-0.10x - 0.10y = -320$$
$$\underline{0.08x + 0.10y = 296}$$
$$-0.02x = 24$$
$$x = 1200$$
Substitute 1200 for x and 3,500 for z in Equation 1 and solve for y.
$$1200 + y + 3500 = 6700$$
$$y + 4700 = 6700$$
$$y = 2000$$
The person invested \$1200 at 8%, \$2000 at 10%, and \$3500 at 12%.

41. $x + y + z = 180$

$$2x - 5 + z = 180$$
$$2x + z = 185$$

$$2x + 5 + y = 180$$
$$2x + y = 175$$

Multiply the second equation by -1 and add to the first equation. Use the new equation and the third equation to solve for x and z.

$$-2x - z = -185$$
$$x + y + z = 180$$
$$-x + y = -5$$

Multiply the new equation by -1.

$$x - y = 5$$
$$2x + y = 175$$
$$3x = 180$$
$$x = 60$$

$$60 - y = 5$$
$$-y = -55$$
$$y = 55$$

Substitute 60 for x and 55 for y in the first equation and solve for z.

$$60 + 55 + z = 180$$
$$z = 65$$

49. $x = $ number of triangles
$y = $ number of rectangles
$z = $ number of pentagons

$$x + y + z = 40$$
$$3x + 4y + 5z = 153$$
$$2y + 5z = 72$$

Eliminate x from Equations 1 and 2 by multiplying Equation 1 by -3 and adding the resulting equation to Equation 2.

$$-3x - 3y - 3z = -120$$
$$\underline{3x + 4y + 5z = 153}$$
$$y + 2z = 33 \qquad \text{Equation 4}$$

Solve for z by multiplying Equation 4 by -2 and adding the resulting equation to Equation 3.

$$2y + 5z = 72$$
$$\underline{-2y - 4z = -66}$$
$$z = 6$$

Substitute 6 for z in Equation 4 and solve for y.

$$y + 2(6) = 33$$
$$y + 12 = 33$$
$$y = 21$$

Substitute 21 for y and 6 for z in Equation 1 and solve for x.

$$x + 21 + 6 = 40$$
$$x + 27 = 40$$
$$x = 13$$

The painting has 13 triangles, 21 rectangles, and 6 pentagons.

Section 3.3

Check Point Exercises

1. $\begin{bmatrix} 1 & -1 & 1 & | & 8 \\ 0 & 1 & -12 & | & -15 \\ 0 & 0 & 1 & | & 1 \end{bmatrix} \rightarrow \begin{matrix} 1x - 1y + 1z = 8 \\ 0x + 1y - 12z = -15 \\ 0x + 0y + 1z = 1 \end{matrix}$

    $x - y + z = 8$

    $y - 12z = -15$

    $z = 1$

    Solve for y by back-substitution.

    $y - 12(1) = -15$

    $y - 12 = -15$

    $y = -3$

    Use back substitution for x.

    $x - (-3) + 1 = 8$

    $x + 4 = 8$

    $x = 4$

    The solution set for the system is $\{(4, -3, 1)\}$.

2. **a.** The notation $R_1 \leftrightarrow R_2$ means to interchange the elements in row 1 and row 2. This results in the row-equivalent matrix

    $\begin{bmatrix} 1 & 6 & -3 & | & 7 \\ 4 & 12 & -20 & | & 8 \\ -3 & -2 & 1 & | & -9 \end{bmatrix}$.

    b. The notation $\frac{1}{4}R_1$ means to multiply each element in row 1 by $\frac{1}{4}$. This results in the row-equivalent matrix

    $\begin{bmatrix} \frac{1}{4}(4) & \frac{1}{4}(12) & \frac{1}{4}(-20) & | & \frac{1}{4}(8) \\ 1 & 6 & -3 & | & 7 \\ -3 & -2 & 1 & | & -9 \end{bmatrix} = \begin{bmatrix} 1 & 3 & -5 & | & 2 \\ 1 & 6 & -3 & | & 7 \\ -3 & -2 & 1 & | & -9 \end{bmatrix}$

    c. The notation $3R_2 + R_3$ means to add 3 times the elements in row 2 to the corresponding elements in row 3. Replace the elements in row 3 by these sums. First, we find 3 times the elements in row 2:
    $3(1) = 3, 3(6) = 18, 3(-3) = -9, 3(7) = 21$. Now we add these products to the corresponding elements in row 3. This results in the row equivalent matrix

    $\begin{bmatrix} 4 & 12 & -20 & | & 8 \\ 1 & 6 & -3 & | & 7 \\ -3+3=0 & -2+18=16 & 1-9=-8 & | & -9+21=12 \end{bmatrix} = \begin{bmatrix} 4 & 12 & -20 & | & 8 \\ 1 & 6 & -3 & | & 7 \\ 0 & 16 & -8 & | & 12 \end{bmatrix}$.

3. $\begin{aligned} 2x + y + 2z &= 18 \\ x - y + 2z &= 9 \\ x + 2y - z &= 6 \end{aligned} \rightarrow \begin{bmatrix} 2 & 1 & 2 & | & 18 \\ 1 & -1 & 2 & | & 9 \\ 1 & 2 & -1 & | & 6 \end{bmatrix}$

Interchange row 1 with row 2 to get 1 in the top position of the first column.

$\begin{bmatrix} 1 & -1 & 2 & | & 9 \\ 2 & 1 & 2 & | & 18 \\ 1 & 2 & -1 & | & 6 \end{bmatrix}$

Multiply the first row by –2 and add these products to row 2.

$\begin{bmatrix} 1 & -1 & 2 & | & 9 \\ 2+-2=0 & 1+2=3 & 2+-4=-2 & | & -18+18=0 \\ 1 & 2 & -1 & | & 6 \end{bmatrix} = \begin{bmatrix} 1 & -1 & 2 & | & 9 \\ 0 & 3 & -2 & | & 0 \\ 1 & 2 & -1 & | & 6 \end{bmatrix}$

Next, multiply the top row by –1 and add these products to row 3.

$\begin{bmatrix} 1 & -1 & 2 & | & 9 \\ 0 & 3 & -2 & | & 0 \\ 1+-1=0 & 2+1=3 & -1-2=-3 & | & 6-9=-3 \end{bmatrix} = \begin{bmatrix} 1 & -1 & 2 & | & 9 \\ 0 & 3 & -2 & | & 0 \\ 0 & 3 & -3 & | & -3 \end{bmatrix}$

Next, to obtain a 1 in the second row, second column, multiply 3 by its reciprocal, $\frac{1}{3}$. Therefore, we multiply

all the numbers in the second row by $\frac{1}{3}$ to get

$\begin{bmatrix} 1 & -1 & 2 & | & 9 \\ 0 & 1 & -\frac{2}{3} & | & 0 \\ 0 & 3 & -3 & | & -3 \end{bmatrix}$.

Next, to obtain a 0 in the third row, second column, multiply the second row by –3 and add the products to row three. The resulting matrix is

$\begin{bmatrix} 1 & -1 & 2 & | & 9 \\ 0 & 1 & -\frac{2}{3} & | & 0 \\ 0 & 0 & -1 & | & -3 \end{bmatrix}$.

To get 1 in the third row, third column, multiply –1 by its reciprocal, –1. Multiply all numbers in the third row by –1 to obtain the resulting matrix

$\begin{bmatrix} 1 & -1 & 2 & | & 9 \\ 0 & 1 & -\frac{2}{3} & | & 0 \\ 0 & 0 & 1 & | & 3 \end{bmatrix}$.

The system represented by this matrix is:

$x - y + 2z = 9$

$y - \dfrac{2}{3}z = 0$

$z = 3$

Use back substitution to find y and x.

$\begin{aligned} y - \frac{2}{3}(3) &= 0 & x - 2 + 6 &= 9 \\ y - 2 &= 0 & x + 4 &= 9 \\ y &= 2 & x &= 5 \end{aligned}$

The solution set for the original system is $\{(5, 2, 3)\}$.

4. $w - 3x - 2y + z = -3$

$2w - 7x - y + 2z = 1$

$3w - 7x - 3y + 3z = -5$

$5w + x + 4y - 2z = 18$

The augmented matrix is

$$\begin{bmatrix} 1 & -3 & -2 & 1 & | & -3 \\ 2 & -7 & -1 & 2 & | & 1 \\ 3 & -7 & -3 & 3 & | & -5 \\ 5 & 1 & 4 & -2 & | & 18 \end{bmatrix}.$$

Multiply the top row by –2 and add the products to the second row. Multiply the top row by –3 and add the products to the third row. Multiply the top row by –5 and add the products to the fourth row. The resulting matrix is

$$\begin{bmatrix} 1 & -3 & -2 & 1 & | & -3 \\ 0 & -1 & 3 & 0 & | & 7 \\ 0 & 2 & 3 & 0 & | & 4 \\ 0 & 16 & 14 & -7 & | & 33 \end{bmatrix}.$$

Next, multiply the second row by –1 to obtain a 1 in the second row, second column.

$$\begin{bmatrix} 1 & -3 & -2 & 1 & | & -3 \\ 0 & 1 & -3 & 0 & | & -7 \\ 0 & 2 & 3 & 0 & | & 4 \\ 0 & 16 & 14 & -7 & | & 33 \end{bmatrix}$$

Next, multiply the second row by –2 and add the products to the third row. Multiply the second row by –16 and add the products to the fourth row. The resulting matrix is

$$\begin{bmatrix} 1 & -3 & -2 & 1 & | & -3 \\ 0 & 1 & -3 & 0 & | & -7 \\ 0 & 0 & 9 & 0 & | & 18 \\ 0 & 0 & 62 & -7 & | & 145 \end{bmatrix}.$$

Next, multiply the third row by $\frac{1}{9}$ to obtain a 1 in the third row, third column. The resulting matrix is

$$\begin{bmatrix} 1 & -3 & -2 & 1 & | & -3 \\ 0 & 1 & -3 & 0 & | & -7 \\ 0 & 0 & 1 & 0 & | & 2 \\ 0 & 0 & 62 & -7 & | & 145 \end{bmatrix}.$$

Multiply the third row by –62 and add the products to the fourth row to obtain the resulting matrix

$$\begin{bmatrix} 1 & -3 & -2 & 1 & | & -3 \\ 0 & 1 & -3 & 0 & | & -7 \\ 0 & 0 & 1 & 0 & | & 2 \\ 0 & 0 & 0 & -7 & | & 21 \end{bmatrix}.$$

Multiply the fourth row by $-\frac{1}{7}$, the reciprocal of –7. The resulting matrix is

$$\begin{bmatrix} 1 & -3 & -2 & 1 & | & -3 \\ 0 & 1 & -3 & 0 & | & -7 \\ 0 & 0 & 1 & 0 & | & 2 \\ 0 & 0 & 0 & 1 & | & -3 \end{bmatrix}.$$

The system of linear equations corresponding to the resulting matrix is

$$w - 3x - 2y + z = -3$$
$$x - 3y = -7$$
$$y = 2$$
$$z = -3$$

Using back-substitution solve for x and w.
$$x - 3(2) = -7$$
$$x = -1$$

$$w - 3(-1) - 2(2) - 3 = -3$$
$$w - 4 = -3$$
$$w = 1$$

The solution set is $\{(1, -1, 2, -3)\}$.

5. The matrix obtained in 3 will be the starting point.

$$\begin{bmatrix} 1 & -1 & 2 & | & 9 \\ 0 & 1 & -\frac{2}{3} & | & 0 \\ 0 & 0 & 1 & | & 3 \end{bmatrix}$$

Next, multiply the third row by $\dfrac{2}{3}$ and add the products to the second row. Multiply the third row by 2 and add the products to the first row. The resulting matrix is

$$\begin{bmatrix} 1 & -1 & 0 & 3 \\ 0 & 1 & 0 & 2 \\ 0 & 0 & 1 & 3 \end{bmatrix}.$$

Add the second row to the first row and replace the first row.

$$\begin{bmatrix} 1 & 0 & 0 & 5 \\ 0 & 1 & 0 & 2 \\ 0 & 0 & 1 & 3 \end{bmatrix}$$

This matrix corresponds to $x = 5$, $y = 2$ and $z = 3$. The solution set is $\{(5, 2, 3)\}$.

Exercise Set 3.3

1. $\begin{bmatrix} 2 & 1 & 2 & | & 2 \\ 3 & -5 & -1 & | & 4 \\ 1 & -2 & -3 & | & -6 \end{bmatrix}$

3. $\begin{bmatrix} 1 & -1 & 1 & | & 8 \\ 0 & 1 & -12 & | & -15 \\ 0 & 0 & 1 & | & 1 \end{bmatrix}$

5. $\begin{bmatrix} 5 & -2 & -3 & | & 0 \\ 1 & 1 & 0 & | & 5 \\ 2 & 0 & -3 & | & 4 \end{bmatrix}$

7. $\begin{bmatrix} 2 & 5 & -3 & 1 & | & 2 \\ 0 & 3 & 1 & 0 & | & 4 \\ 1 & -1 & 5 & 0 & | & 9 \\ 5 & -5 & -2 & 0 & | & 1 \end{bmatrix}$

9. $5x + 3z = -11$
$$y - 4z = 12$$
$$7x + 2y = 3$$

11. $w + x + 4y + z = 3$
$$-w + x - y = 7$$
$$12w + 5z = 11$$
$$12y + 4z = 5$$

13. $x - 4z = 5$

$\quad\quad y - 12z = 13$

$\quad\quad\quad\quad z = -\dfrac{1}{2}$

$\quad y - 12\left(-\dfrac{1}{2}\right) = 13$

$\quad\quad\quad\quad y + 6 = 13$

$\quad\quad\quad\quad\quad y = 7$

$\quad x - 4\left(-\dfrac{1}{2}\right) = 5$

$\quad\quad\quad\quad x + 2 = 5$

$\quad\quad\quad\quad\quad x = 3$

The solution set is $\left\{\left(3,\ 7,\ -\dfrac{1}{2}\right)\right\}$.

15. $\begin{bmatrix} 1 & \frac{1}{2} & 1 & \Big| & \frac{11}{2} \\ 0 & 1 & \frac{3}{2} & \Big| & 7 \\ 0 & 0 & 1 & \Big| & 4 \end{bmatrix}$

$\quad x + \dfrac{1}{2}y + z = \dfrac{11}{2}$

$\quad\quad\quad y + \dfrac{3}{2}z = 7$

$\quad\quad\quad\quad\quad z = 4$

$\quad\quad y + \dfrac{3}{2}(4) = 7$

$\quad\quad\quad\quad y + 6 = 7$

$\quad\quad\quad\quad\quad y = 1$

$\quad x + \dfrac{1}{2}(1) + 4 = \dfrac{11}{2}$

$\quad\quad\quad x + \dfrac{9}{2} = \dfrac{11}{2}$

$\quad\quad\quad\quad x = \dfrac{11}{2} - \dfrac{9}{2}$

$\quad\quad\quad\quad x = 1$

The solution set is $\{(1,\ 1,\ 4)\}$.

17. $\begin{bmatrix} 1 & -1 & 1 & 1 & \Big| & 3 \\ 0 & 1 & -2 & -1 & \Big| & 0 \\ 0 & 0 & 1 & 6 & \Big| & 17 \\ 0 & 0 & 0 & 1 & \Big| & 3 \end{bmatrix}$

$\quad w - x + y + z = 3$

$\quad\quad x - 2y - z = 0$

$\quad\quad\quad y + 6z = 17$

$\quad\quad\quad\quad z = 3$

$\quad\quad y + 6(3) = 17$

$\quad\quad\quad y + 18 = 17$

$\quad\quad\quad\quad y = -1$

$\quad x - 2(-1) - 3 = 0$

$\quad\quad\quad\quad x - 1 = 0$

$\quad\quad\quad\quad\quad x = 1$

$\quad w - 1 + (-1) + 3 = 3$

$\quad\quad\quad w + 1 = 3$

$\quad\quad\quad\quad w = 2$

The solution set is $\{(2,\ 1,\ -1,\ 3)\}$.

19. $\begin{bmatrix} 2\left(\frac{1}{2}\right) & -6\left(\frac{1}{2}\right) & 4\left(\frac{1}{2}\right) & \Big| & 10\left(\frac{1}{2}\right) \\ 1 & 5 & -5 & \Big| & 0 \\ 3 & 0 & 4 & \Big| & 7 \end{bmatrix} \dfrac{1}{2}R_1$

$\begin{bmatrix} 1 & -3 & 2 & \Big| & 5 \\ 1 & 5 & -5 & \Big| & 0 \\ 3 & 0 & 4 & \Big| & 7 \end{bmatrix}$

21.
$$\begin{bmatrix} 1 & -3 & 2 & 0 \\ -3(1)+3 & -3(-3)+1 & -3(2)+-1 & -3(0)+7 \\ 2 & -2 & 1 & 3 \end{bmatrix} -3R_1 + R_2$$

$$\begin{bmatrix} 1 & -3 & 2 & 0 \\ 0 & 10 & -7 & 7 \\ 2 & -2 & 1 & 3 \end{bmatrix}$$

23.
$$\begin{bmatrix} 1 & -1 & 1 & 1 & 3 \\ 0 & 1 & -2 & -1 & 0 \\ 2 & 0 & 3 & 4 & 11 \\ 5 & 1 & 2 & 4 & 6 \end{bmatrix} \begin{matrix} \\ \\ -2R_1 + R_3 \\ -5R_1 + R_4 \end{matrix}$$

$$\begin{bmatrix} 1 & -1 & 1 & 1 & 3 \\ 0 & 1 & -2 & -1 & 0 \\ -2(1)+2 & -2(-1)+0 & -2(1)+3 & -2(1)+4 & -2(3)+11 \\ -5(1)+5 & -5(-1)+1 & -5(1)+2 & -5(1)+4 & -5(3)+6 \end{bmatrix} = \begin{bmatrix} 1 & -1 & 1 & 1 & 3 \\ 0 & 1 & -2 & -1 & 0 \\ 0 & 2 & 1 & 2 & 5 \\ 0 & 6 & -3 & -1 & -9 \end{bmatrix}$$

25.
$$\begin{bmatrix} 1 & -1 & 1 & 8 \\ 2 & 3 & -1 & -2 \\ 3 & -2 & -9 & 9 \end{bmatrix}$$

$$\begin{bmatrix} 1 & -1 & 1 & 8 \\ -2(1)+2 & -2(-1)+3 & -2(1)-1 & -2(8)-2 \\ -3(1)+3 & -3(-1)-2 & -3(1)-9 & -3(8)+9 \end{bmatrix}$$

$$\begin{bmatrix} 1 & -1 & 1 & 8 \\ 0 & 5 & \boxed{-3} & \boxed{-18} \\ 0 & 1 & \boxed{-12} & \boxed{-15} \end{bmatrix}$$

$$\begin{bmatrix} 1 & -1 & 1 & 8 \\ 0\left(\frac{1}{5}\right) & 1\left(\frac{1}{5}\right) & -3\left(\frac{1}{5}\right) & -18\left(\frac{1}{5}\right) \\ 0 & 1 & -12 & -15 \end{bmatrix}$$

$$\begin{bmatrix} 1 & -1 & 1 & 8 \\ 0 & 1 & \boxed{-\frac{3}{5}} & \boxed{-\frac{18}{5}} \\ 0 & 1 & \boxed{-12} & \boxed{-15} \end{bmatrix}$$

27.

$$x + y - z = -2$$
$$2x - y + z = 5$$
$$-x + 2y + 2z = 1$$

$$\begin{bmatrix} 1 & 1 & -1 & | & -2 \\ 2 & -1 & 1 & | & 5 \\ -1 & 2 & 2 & | & 1 \end{bmatrix} -2R_1 + R_2$$

$$\begin{bmatrix} 1 & 1 & -1 & | & -2 \\ 0 & -3 & 3 & | & 9 \\ -1 & 2 & 2 & | & 1 \end{bmatrix} 1R_1 + R_3$$

$$\begin{bmatrix} 1 & 1 & -1 & | & -2 \\ 0 & -3 & 3 & | & 9 \\ 0 & 3 & 1 & | & -1 \end{bmatrix} -\frac{1}{3}R_2$$

$$\begin{bmatrix} 1 & 1 & -1 & | & -2 \\ 0 & 1 & -1 & | & -3 \\ 0 & 3 & 1 & | & -1 \end{bmatrix} -3R_2 + R_3$$

$$= \begin{bmatrix} 1 & 1 & -1 & | & -2 \\ 0 & 1 & -1 & | & -3 \\ 0 & 0 & 4 & | & 8 \end{bmatrix}$$

$$4z = 8$$
$$z = 2$$
$$y - z = -3$$
$$y - 2 = -3$$
$$y = -1$$
$$x + y - z = -2$$
$$x - 1 - 2 = -2$$
$$x - 3 = -2$$
$$x = 1$$

The solution set is $\{(1, -1, 2)\}$.

29.

$$x + 3y = 0$$
$$x + y + z = 1$$
$$3x - y - z = 11$$

$$\begin{bmatrix} 1 & 3 & 0 & | & 0 \\ 1 & 1 & 1 & | & 1 \\ 3 & -1 & -1 & | & 11 \end{bmatrix} -1R_1 + R_2$$

$$\begin{bmatrix} 1 & 3 & 0 & | & 0 \\ 0 & -2 & 1 & | & 1 \\ 3 & -1 & -1 & | & 11 \end{bmatrix} -3R_1 + R_3$$

$$\begin{bmatrix} 1 & 3 & 0 & | & 0 \\ 0 & -2 & 1 & | & 1 \\ 0 & -10 & -1 & | & 11 \end{bmatrix} -\frac{1}{2}R_2$$

$$\begin{bmatrix} 1 & 3 & 0 & | & 0 \\ 0 & 1 & -\frac{1}{2} & | & -\frac{1}{2} \\ 0 & -10 & -1 & | & 11 \end{bmatrix} 10R_2 + R_3$$

$$\begin{bmatrix} 1 & 3 & 0 & | & 0 \\ 0 & 1 & -\frac{1}{2} & | & -\frac{1}{2} \\ 0 & 0 & -6 & | & 6 \end{bmatrix} -\frac{1}{6}R_3$$

$$\begin{bmatrix} 1 & 3 & 0 & | & 0 \\ 0 & 1 & -\frac{1}{2} & | & -\frac{1}{2} \\ 0 & 0 & 1 & | & -1 \end{bmatrix}$$

$$z = -1$$
$$y - \frac{1}{2}z = -\frac{1}{2}$$
$$y - \frac{1}{2}(-1) = -\frac{1}{2}$$
$$y + \frac{1}{2} = -\frac{1}{2}$$
$$y = -1$$

Interchange row one and row two.

$$x + 3y = 0$$
$$x + 3(-1) = 0$$
$$x = 3$$

The solution set is $\{(3, -1, -1)\}$.

31. $2x - y - z = 4$
            $x + y - 5z = -4$
            $x - 2y = 4$

$$\begin{bmatrix} 2 & -1 & -1 & 4 \\ 1 & 1 & -5 & -4 \\ 1 & -2 & 0 & 4 \end{bmatrix}$$

Interchange rows one and two.

$$\begin{bmatrix} 1 & 1 & -5 & -4 \\ 2 & -1 & -1 & 4 \\ 1 & -2 & 0 & 4 \end{bmatrix}$$

Replace row two with $-2R_1 + R_2$.
Replace row three with $-R_1 + R_3$.

$$\begin{bmatrix} 1 & 1 & -5 & -4 \\ 0 & -3 & 9 & 12 \\ 0 & -3 & 5 & 8 \end{bmatrix}$$

Replace row two with $-\dfrac{1}{3}R_2$.

$$\begin{bmatrix} 1 & 1 & -5 & -4 \\ 0 & 1 & -3 & -4 \\ 0 & -3 & 5 & 8 \end{bmatrix}$$

Replace row three with $3R_2 + R_3$.

$$\begin{bmatrix} 1 & 1 & -5 & -4 \\ 0 & 1 & -3 & -4 \\ 0 & 0 & -4 & -4 \end{bmatrix}$$

Replace row three with $-\dfrac{1}{4}R_3$.

$$\begin{bmatrix} 1 & 1 & -5 & -4 \\ 0 & 1 & -3 & -4 \\ 0 & 0 & 1 & 1 \end{bmatrix}$$

$z = 1$
        $y - 3z = -4$
        $y - 3(1) = -4$
             $y = -1$
    $x + y - 5z = -4$
    $x - 1 - 5(1) = -4$
          $x - 6 = -4$
             $x = 2$
The solution set is $\{(2, -1, 1)\}$.

33. $x + y + z = 4$
          $x - y - z = 0$
          $x - y + z = 2$

$$\begin{bmatrix} 1 & 1 & 1 & 4 \\ 1 & -1 & -1 & 0 \\ 1 & -1 & 1 & 2 \end{bmatrix}$$

Replace row two with $-R_1 + R_2$.
Replace row three with $-R_1 + R_3$.

$$\begin{bmatrix} 1 & 1 & 1 & 4 \\ 0 & -2 & -2 & -4 \\ 0 & -2 & 0 & -2 \end{bmatrix}$$

Replace row two with $-\dfrac{1}{2}R_2$.

$$\begin{bmatrix} 1 & 1 & 1 & 4 \\ 0 & 1 & 1 & 2 \\ 0 & -2 & 0 & -2 \end{bmatrix}$$

Replace row 3 with $2R_2 + R_3$.

$$\begin{bmatrix} 1 & 1 & 1 & 4 \\ 0 & 1 & 1 & 2 \\ 0 & 0 & 2 & 2 \end{bmatrix}$$

Replace row 3 with $\dfrac{1}{2}R_3$.

$$\begin{bmatrix} 1 & 1 & 1 & 4 \\ 0 & 1 & 1 & 2 \\ 0 & 0 & 1 & 1 \end{bmatrix}$$

$z = 1$
$y + 1 = 2$
     $y = 1$
$x + 1 + 1 = 4$
        $x = 2$
The solution set is $\{(2, 1, 1)\}$.

35. Write the equations in standard form.
        $x + 2y - z = -1$
        $x - y + z = 4$
        $x + y - 3z = -2$

$$\begin{bmatrix} 1 & 2 & -1 & -1 \\ 1 & -1 & 1 & 4 \\ 1 & 1 & -3 & -2 \end{bmatrix}$$

Replace row two with $-R_1 + R_2$.
Replace row three with $-R_1 + R_3$.

$$\begin{bmatrix} 1 & 2 & -1 & -1 \\ 0 & -3 & 2 & 5 \\ 0 & -1 & -2 & -1 \end{bmatrix}$$

Replace row two with $-R_3$.
Replace row three with R_2.

$$\begin{bmatrix} 1 & 2 & -1 & -1 \\ 0 & 1 & 2 & 1 \\ 0 & -3 & 2 & 5 \end{bmatrix}$$

Replace row 3 with $3R_2 + R_3$.

$$\begin{bmatrix} 1 & 2 & -1 & -1 \\ 0 & 1 & 2 & 1 \\ 0 & 0 & 8 & 8 \end{bmatrix}$$

Replace row 3 with $\frac{1}{8}R_3$.

$$\begin{bmatrix} 1 & 2 & -1 & -1 \\ 0 & 1 & 2 & 1 \\ 0 & 0 & 1 & 1 \end{bmatrix}$$

$z = 1$

$y + 2(1) = 1$

$\quad y = -1$

$x + 2(-1) - 1 = -1$

$\quad\quad x = 2$

The solution set is $\{(2, -1, 1)\}$.

37. $3a - b - 4c = 3$

$\quad 2a - b + 2c = -8$

$\quad a + 2b - 3c = 9$

Interchange equations 1 and 3.

$$\begin{bmatrix} 1 & 2 & -3 & 9 \\ 2 & -1 & 2 & -8 \\ 3 & -1 & -4 & 3 \end{bmatrix}$$

Replace row two with $-2R_1 + R_2$.
Replace row three with $-3R_1 + R_3$.

$$\begin{bmatrix} 1 & 2 & -3 & 9 \\ 0 & -5 & 8 & -26 \\ 0 & -7 & 5 & -24 \end{bmatrix}$$

Replace row two with $-\frac{1}{5}R_2$

$$\begin{bmatrix} 1 & 2 & -3 & 9 \\ 0 & 1 & -\frac{8}{5} & \frac{26}{5} \\ 0 & -7 & 5 & -24 \end{bmatrix}$$

Replace row three with $7R_2 + R_3$.

$$\begin{bmatrix} 1 & 2 & -3 & 9 \\ 0 & 1 & -\frac{8}{5} & \frac{26}{5} \\ 0 & 0 & -\frac{31}{5} & \frac{62}{5} \end{bmatrix}$$

Replace row 3 with $-\frac{5}{31}R_3$.

$$\begin{bmatrix} 1 & 2 & -3 & 9 \\ 0 & 1 & -\frac{8}{5} & \frac{26}{5} \\ 0 & 0 & 1 & -2 \end{bmatrix}$$

$z = -2$

$\quad y - \frac{8}{5}(-2) = \frac{26}{5}$

$\quad\quad y + \frac{16}{5} = \frac{26}{5}$

$\quad\quad\quad y = 2$

$x + 2(2) - 3(-2) = 9$

$\quad x + 4 + 6 = 9$

$\quad\quad x = -1$

The solution set is $\{(-1, 2, -2)\}$.

39. $2x + 2y + 7z = -1$

$\quad 2x + y + 2z = 2$

$\quad 4x + 6y + z = 15$

$$\begin{bmatrix} 2 & 2 & 7 & -1 \\ 2 & 1 & 2 & 2 \\ 4 & 6 & 1 & 15 \end{bmatrix} \frac{1}{2}R_1$$

$$\begin{bmatrix} 1 & 1 & \frac{7}{2} & -\frac{1}{2} \\ 2 & 1 & 2 & 2 \\ 4 & 6 & 1 & 15 \end{bmatrix} -2R_1 + R_2$$

$$\begin{bmatrix} 1 & 1 & \frac{7}{2} & -\frac{1}{2} \\ 0 & -1 & -5 & 3 \\ 4 & 6 & 1 & 15 \end{bmatrix} -4R_1 + R_3$$

$$\begin{bmatrix} 1 & 1 & \frac{7}{2} & -\frac{1}{2} \\ 0 & -1 & -5 & 3 \\ 0 & 2 & -13 & 17 \end{bmatrix} -1R_2$$

$$\begin{bmatrix} 1 & 1 & \frac{7}{2} & -\frac{1}{2} \\ 0 & 1 & 5 & -3 \\ 0 & 2 & -13 & 17 \end{bmatrix} -2R_2 + R_3$$

$$\begin{bmatrix} 1 & 1 & \frac{7}{2} & -\frac{1}{2} \\ 0 & 1 & 5 & -3 \\ 0 & 0 & -23 & 23 \end{bmatrix} -\frac{1}{23}R_3$$

$$\begin{bmatrix} 1 & 1 & \frac{7}{2} & -\frac{1}{2} \\ 0 & 1 & 5 & -3 \\ 0 & 0 & 1 & -1 \end{bmatrix}$$

$z = -1$

$$y + 5z = -3$$
$$y + 5(-1) = -3$$
$$y - 5 = -3$$
$$y = 2$$

$$x + y + \frac{7}{2}z = -\frac{1}{2}$$
$$x + 2 + \frac{7}{2}(-1) = -\frac{1}{2}$$
$$x - \frac{3}{2} = -\frac{1}{2}$$
$$x = 1$$

The solution set is $\{(1, 2, -1)\}$.

41.
$$w + x + y + z = 4$$
$$2w + x - 2y - z = 0$$
$$w - 2x - y - 2z = -2$$
$$3w + 2x + y + 3z = 4$$

$$\begin{bmatrix} 1 & 1 & 1 & 1 & | & 4 \\ 2 & 1 & -2 & -1 & | & 0 \\ 1 & -2 & -1 & -2 & | & -2 \\ 3 & 2 & 1 & 3 & | & 4 \end{bmatrix} -2R_1 + R_2$$

$$\begin{bmatrix} 1 & 1 & 1 & 1 & | & 4 \\ 0 & -1 & -4 & -3 & | & -8 \\ 1 & -2 & -1 & -2 & | & -2 \\ 3 & 2 & 1 & 3 & | & 4 \end{bmatrix} -1R_1 + R_3$$

$$\begin{bmatrix} 1 & 1 & 1 & 1 & | & 4 \\ 0 & -1 & -4 & -3 & | & -8 \\ 0 & -3 & -2 & -3 & | & -6 \\ 3 & 2 & 1 & 3 & | & 4 \end{bmatrix} -3R_1 + R_4$$

$$\begin{bmatrix} 1 & 1 & 1 & 1 & | & 4 \\ 0 & -1 & -4 & -3 & | & -8 \\ 0 & -3 & -2 & -3 & | & -6 \\ 0 & -1 & -2 & 0 & | & -8 \end{bmatrix} -1R_2$$

$$\begin{bmatrix} 1 & 1 & 1 & 1 & | & 4 \\ 0 & 1 & 4 & 3 & | & 8 \\ 0 & -3 & -2 & -3 & | & -6 \\ 0 & -1 & -2 & 0 & | & -8 \end{bmatrix} 3R_2 + R_3$$

$$\begin{bmatrix} 1 & 1 & 1 & 1 & | & 4 \\ 0 & 1 & 4 & 3 & | & 8 \\ 0 & 0 & 10 & 6 & | & 18 \\ 0 & -1 & -2 & 0 & | & -8 \end{bmatrix} 1R_2 + R_4$$

$$\begin{bmatrix} 1 & 1 & 1 & 1 & | & 4 \\ 0 & 1 & 4 & 3 & | & 8 \\ 0 & 0 & 10 & 6 & | & 18 \\ 0 & 0 & 2 & 3 & | & 0 \end{bmatrix} \frac{1}{10}R_3$$

$$\begin{bmatrix} 1 & 1 & 1 & 1 & | & 4 \\ 0 & 1 & 4 & 3 & | & 8 \\ 0 & 0 & 1 & \frac{3}{5} & | & \frac{9}{5} \\ 0 & 0 & 2 & 3 & | & 0 \end{bmatrix} -2R_3 + R_4$$

$$\begin{bmatrix} 1 & 1 & 1 & 1 & | & 4 \\ 0 & 1 & 4 & 3 & | & 8 \\ 0 & 0 & 1 & \frac{3}{5} & | & \frac{9}{5} \\ 0 & 0 & 0 & \frac{9}{5} & | & -\frac{18}{5} \end{bmatrix} \frac{5}{9}R_4$$

$$\begin{bmatrix} 1 & 1 & 1 & 1 & | & 4 \\ 0 & 1 & 4 & 3 & | & 8 \\ 0 & 0 & 1 & \frac{3}{5} & | & \frac{9}{5} \\ 0 & 0 & 0 & 1 & | & -2 \end{bmatrix}$$

$$z = -2$$
$$y + \frac{3}{5}z = \frac{9}{5}$$
$$y + \frac{3}{5}(-2) = \frac{9}{5}$$
$$y - \frac{6}{5} = \frac{9}{5}$$
$$y = 3$$
$$x + 4y + 3z = 8$$
$$x + 4(3) + 3(-2) = 8$$
$$x + 6 = 8$$
$$x = 2$$
$$w + x + y + z = 4$$
$$w + 2 + 3 - 2 = 4$$
$$w + 3 = 4$$
$$w = 1$$

The solution set is $\{(1, 2, 3, -2)\}$.

43. $3w - 4x + y + z = 9$

$w + x - y - z = 0$

$2w + x + 4y - 2z = 3$

$-w + 2x + y - 3z = 3$

$$\begin{bmatrix} 3 & -4 & 1 & 1 & | & 9 \\ 1 & 1 & -1 & -1 & | & 0 \\ 2 & 1 & 4 & -2 & | & 3 \\ -1 & 2 & 1 & -3 & | & 3 \end{bmatrix} R_1 \leftrightarrow R_2$$

$$\begin{bmatrix} 1 & 1 & -1 & -1 & | & 0 \\ 3 & -4 & 1 & 1 & | & 9 \\ 2 & 1 & 4 & -2 & | & 3 \\ -1 & 2 & 1 & -3 & | & 3 \end{bmatrix} -3R_1 + R_2$$

$$\begin{bmatrix} 1 & 1 & -1 & -1 & | & 0 \\ 0 & -7 & 4 & 4 & | & 9 \\ 2 & 1 & 4 & -2 & | & 3 \\ -1 & 2 & 1 & -3 & | & 3 \end{bmatrix} -2R_1 + R_3$$

$$\begin{bmatrix} 1 & 1 & -1 & -1 & | & 0 \\ 0 & -7 & 4 & 4 & | & 9 \\ 0 & -1 & 6 & 0 & | & 3 \\ -1 & 2 & 1 & -3 & | & 3 \end{bmatrix} 1R_1 + R_4$$

$$\begin{bmatrix} 1 & 1 & -1 & -1 & | & 0 \\ 0 & -7 & 4 & 4 & | & 9 \\ 0 & -1 & 6 & 0 & | & 3 \\ 0 & 3 & 0 & -4 & | & 3 \end{bmatrix} R_2 \leftrightarrow R_3$$

$$\begin{bmatrix} 1 & 1 & -1 & -1 & | & 0 \\ 0 & -1 & 6 & 0 & | & 3 \\ 0 & -7 & 4 & 4 & | & 9 \\ 0 & 3 & 0 & -4 & | & 3 \end{bmatrix} -R_2$$

$$\begin{bmatrix} 1 & 1 & -1 & -1 & | & 0 \\ 0 & 1 & -6 & 0 & | & -3 \\ 0 & -7 & 4 & 4 & | & 9 \\ 0 & 3 & 0 & -4 & | & 3 \end{bmatrix} 7R_2 + R_3$$

$$\begin{bmatrix} 1 & 1 & -1 & -1 & | & 0 \\ 0 & 1 & -6 & 0 & | & -3 \\ 0 & 0 & -38 & 4 & | & -12 \\ 0 & 3 & 0 & -4 & | & 3 \end{bmatrix} -3R_2 + R_4$$

$$\begin{bmatrix} 1 & 1 & -1 & -1 & | & 0 \\ 0 & 1 & -6 & 0 & | & -3 \\ 0 & 0 & -38 & 4 & | & -12 \\ 0 & 0 & 18 & -4 & | & 12 \end{bmatrix} -\frac{1}{38}R_3$$

$$\begin{bmatrix} 1 & 1 & -1 & -1 & | & 0 \\ 0 & 1 & -6 & 0 & | & -3 \\ 0 & 0 & 1 & -\frac{2}{19} & | & \frac{6}{19} \\ 0 & 0 & 18 & -4 & | & 12 \end{bmatrix} -18R_3 + R_4$$

$$\begin{bmatrix} 1 & 1 & -1 & -1 & | & 0 \\ 0 & 1 & -6 & 0 & | & -3 \\ 0 & 0 & 1 & -\frac{2}{19} & | & \frac{6}{19} \\ 0 & 0 & 0 & -\frac{40}{19} & | & \frac{120}{19} \end{bmatrix} -\frac{19}{40}R_4$$

$$\begin{bmatrix} 1 & 1 & -1 & -1 & | & 0 \\ 0 & 1 & -6 & 0 & | & -3 \\ 0 & 0 & 1 & -\frac{2}{19} & | & \frac{6}{19} \\ 0 & 0 & 0 & 1 & | & -3 \end{bmatrix}$$

$z = -3$

$$y - \frac{2}{19}z = \frac{6}{19}$$

$$y - \frac{2}{19}(-3) = \frac{6}{19}$$

$$y + \frac{6}{19} = \frac{6}{19}$$

$$y = 0$$

$x - 6y = -3$

$x - 6(0) = -3$

$x = -3$

$w + x - y - z = 0$

$w - 3 + 0 + 3 = 0$

$w = 0$

The solution set is $\{(0, -3, 0, -3)\}$.

45. $f(x) = ax^2 + bx + c$

Use the given function values to find three equations in terms of a, b, and c.

$f(-2) = a(-2)^2 + b(-2) + c = -4$

$4a - 2b + c = -4$

$f(1) = a(1)^2 + b(1) + c = 2$

$a + b + c = 2$

$f(2) = a(2)^2 + b(2) + c = 0$

$4a + 2b + c = 0$

System of equations:

$4a - 2b + c = -4$

$a + b + c = 2$

$4a + 2b + c = 0$

Matrix:

$$\begin{bmatrix} 4 & -2 & 1 & | & -4 \\ 1 & 1 & 1 & | & 2 \\ 4 & 2 & 1 & | & 0 \end{bmatrix}$$

This gives $a = -1$, $b = 1$, and $c = 2$.

Thus, $f(x) = -x^2 + x + 2$.

47. $f(x) = ax^3 + bx^2 + cx + d$

Use the given function values to find four equations in terms of a, b, c, and d.

$f(-1) = a(-1)^3 + b(-1)^2 + c(-1) + d = 0$

$-a + b - c + d = 0$

$f(1) = a(1)^3 + b(1)^2 + c(1) + d = 2$

$a + b + c + d = 2$

$f(2) = a(2)^3 + b(2)^2 + c(2) + d = 3$

$8a + 4b + 2c + d = 3$

$f(3) = a(3)^3 + b(3)^2 + c(3) + d = 12$

$27a + 9b + 3c + d = 12$

System of equations:

$-a + b - c + d = 0$

$a + b + c + d = 2$

$8a + 4b + 2c + d = 3$

$27a + 9b + 3c + d = 12$

Matrix:

$$\begin{bmatrix} -1 & 1 & -1 & 1 & | & 0 \\ 1 & 1 & 1 & 1 & | & 2 \\ 8 & 4 & 2 & 1 & | & 3 \\ 27 & 9 & 3 & 1 & | & 12 \end{bmatrix}$$

This gives $a = 1$, $b = -2$, $c = 0$, and $d = 3$.

Thus, $f(x) = x^3 - 2x^2 + 3$.

49. Let $A = \ln w$, $B = \ln x$, $C = \ln y$, and $D = \ln z$.

System of equations:

$2A + B + 3C - 2D = -6$

$4A + 3B + C - D = -2$

$A + B + C + D = -5$

$A + B - C - D = 5$

Matrix:

$$\begin{bmatrix} 2 & 1 & 3 & -2 & | & -6 \\ 4 & 3 & 1 & -1 & | & -2 \\ 1 & 1 & 1 & 1 & | & -5 \\ 1 & 1 & -1 & -1 & | & 5 \end{bmatrix}$$

This gives $A = -1$, $B = 1$, $C = -3$, and $D = -2$.

Substitute back to find w, x, y, and z.

$A = -1$ $\qquad\qquad$ $B = 1$

$\ln w = -1$ $\qquad\qquad$ $\ln x = 1$

$w = e^{-1}$ $\qquad\qquad$ $x = e^1$

$w \approx 0.37$ $\qquad\qquad$ $x \approx 2.72$

$C = -3$ $\qquad\qquad$ $D = -2$

$\ln y = -3$ $\qquad\qquad$ $\ln z = -2$

$y = e^{-3}$ $\qquad\qquad$ $z = e^{-2}$

$y \approx 0.05$ $\qquad\qquad$ $z \approx 0.14$

51. a. $s(t) = \dfrac{1}{2}at^2 + v_0 t + s_0$

Use the given function values to find three equations in terms of a, v_0, and s_0.

$s(1) = \dfrac{1}{2}a(1)^2 + v_0(1) + s_0 = 40$

$\dfrac{1}{2}a + v_0 + s_0 = 40$

$s(2) = \dfrac{1}{2}a(2)^2 + v_0(2) + s_0 = 48$

$2a + 2v_0 + s_0 = 48$

$s(3) = \dfrac{1}{2}a(3)^2 + v_0(3) + s_0 = 24$

$\dfrac{9}{2}a + 3v_0 + s_0 = 24$

System of equations:

$\dfrac{1}{2}a + v_0 + s_0 = 40$

$2a + 2v_0 + s_0 = 48$

$\dfrac{9}{2}a + 3v_0 + s_0 = 24$

Matrix:

$$\begin{bmatrix} \dfrac{1}{2} & 1 & 1 & \Big| & 40 \\ 2 & 2 & 1 & \Big| & 48 \\ \dfrac{9}{2} & 3 & 1 & \Big| & 24 \end{bmatrix}$$

This gives $a = -32$, $v_0 = 56$, and $s_0 = 0$.

Thus, $s(t) = \dfrac{1}{2}(-32)t^2 + (56)t + (0)$

$s(t) = -16t^2 + 56t$

b. $s(t) = -16t^2 + 56t$

$s(3.5) = -16(3.5)^2 + 56(3.5) = 0$

This is the point (3.5, 0).
The ball's height is 0 feet after 3.5
seconds. This is the point (3.5, 0).

c.   The maximum occurs when $x = -\dfrac{b}{2a}$.

$x = -\dfrac{b}{2a} = -\dfrac{v_0}{2a} = -\dfrac{56}{2(-16)} = 1.75$

$s(1.75) = -16(1.75)^2 + 56(1.75) = 49$

At 1.75 seconds the ball will reach its
maximum height of 49 feet.

53.   Let x = those who said yes
Let y = those who said no
Let z = those who are not sure
$x + y + z = 100$
$y = x + z + 22$
$2x = y + 7$

Write the equations in standard form.
$x + y + z = 100$
$-x + y - z = 22$
$2x - y = 7$

$$\begin{bmatrix} 1 & 1 & 1 & 100 \\ -1 & 1 & -1 & 22 \\ 2 & -1 & 0 & 7 \end{bmatrix}$$

Replace row two with $R_1 + R_2$.
Replace row three with $-2R_1 + R_3$.

$$\begin{bmatrix} 1 & 1 & 1 & 100 \\ 0 & 2 & 0 & 122 \\ 0 & -3 & -2 & -193 \end{bmatrix}$$

Replace row two with $\dfrac{1}{2}R_2$.

$$\begin{bmatrix} 1 & 1 & 1 & 100 \\ 0 & 1 & 0 & 61 \\ 0 & -3 & -2 & -193 \end{bmatrix}$$

Replace row three with $3R_2 + R_3$.

$$\begin{bmatrix} 1 & 1 & 1 & 100 \\ 0 & 1 & 0 & 61 \\ 0 & 0 & -2 & -10 \end{bmatrix}$$

Replace row three with $-\dfrac{1}{2}R_3$.

$$\begin{bmatrix} 1 & 1 & 1 & 100 \\ 0 & 1 & 0 & 61 \\ 0 & 0 & 1 & 5 \end{bmatrix}$$

$z = 5$
$y = 61$
$x + y + z = 100$
$x + 61 + 5 = 100$
$x = 34$

34% of single women said yes, 61% said no, 5%
did not know.

55.   Let x = Food A
Let y = Food B
Let z = Food C
$40x + 200y + 400z = 660$
$5x + 2y + 4z = 25$
$30x + 10y + 300z = 425$
$2x + 10y + 20z = 33$
$5x + 2y + 4z = 25$
$6x + 2y + 60z = 85$

$$\begin{bmatrix} 2 & 10 & 20 & 33 \\ 5 & 2 & 4 & 25 \\ 6 & 2 & 60 & 85 \end{bmatrix} \dfrac{1}{2}R_1$$

$$\begin{bmatrix} 1 & 5 & 10 & \frac{33}{2} \\ 5 & 2 & 4 & 25 \\ 6 & 2 & 60 & 85 \end{bmatrix} -5R_1 + R_2$$

$$\begin{bmatrix} 1 & 5 & 10 & \frac{33}{2} \\ 0 & -23 & -46 & -\frac{115}{2} \\ 6 & 2 & 60 & 85 \end{bmatrix} -6R_1 + R_3$$

$$\begin{bmatrix} 1 & 5 & 10 & \frac{33}{2} \\ 0 & -23 & -46 & -\frac{115}{2} \\ 0 & -28 & 0 & -14 \end{bmatrix} -\frac{1}{23}R_2$$

$$\begin{bmatrix} 1 & 5 & 10 & \frac{33}{2} \\ 0 & 1 & 2 & \frac{5}{2} \\ 0 & -28 & 0 & -14 \end{bmatrix} 28R_2 + R_3$$

$$\begin{bmatrix} 1 & 5 & 10 & | & \frac{33}{2} \\ 0 & 1 & 2 & | & \frac{5}{2} \\ 0 & 0 & 56 & | & 56 \end{bmatrix} \begin{array}{c} \\ \\ \frac{1}{56}R_3 \end{array}$$

$$\begin{bmatrix} 1 & 5 & 10 & | & \frac{33}{2} \\ 0 & 1 & 2 & | & \frac{5}{2} \\ 0 & 0 & 1 & | & 1 \end{bmatrix}$$

$$z = 1$$

$$y + 2z = \frac{5}{2}$$

$$y + 2 = \frac{5}{2}$$

$$2y + 4 = 5$$

$$2y = 1$$

$$y = \frac{1}{2}$$

$$x + 5y + 10z = \frac{33}{2}$$

$$x + \frac{5}{2} + 10 = \frac{33}{2}$$

$$2x + 5 + 20 = 33$$

$$2x + 25 = 33$$

$$2x = 8$$

$$x = 4$$

4 ounces of Food A

$\frac{1}{2}$ ounce of Food B

1 ounce of Food C

65. Statement **d.** is true.

Statement **a.** is false. Multiplying a row by a negative fraction is permitted.

Statement **b.** is false because there are three variables in the system. The augmented matrix should be:

$$\begin{bmatrix} 1 & -3 & 0 & | & 5 \\ 0 & 1 & -2 & | & 7 \\ 2 & 0 & 1 & | & 4 \end{bmatrix}$$

Statement **c.** is false. When solving a system of three equations in three variables, we use row operations to obtain ones along the diagonal and zeros below the ones.

Section 3.4

Check Point Exercises

1. **a.** $\begin{vmatrix} 10 & 9 \\ 6 & 5 \end{vmatrix} = 10 \cdot 5 - 6 \cdot 9 = 50 - 54 = -4$

b. $\begin{vmatrix} 4 & 3 \\ -5 & -8 \end{vmatrix} = 4 \cdot (-8) - (-5) \cdot (3)$

$$= -32 + 15 = -17$$

2. $5x + 4y = 12$

$3x - 6y = 24$

$$D = \begin{vmatrix} 5 & 4 \\ 3 & -6 \end{vmatrix} = 5 \cdot (-6) - 3 \cdot 4$$

$$= -30 - 12 = -42$$

$$D_x = \begin{vmatrix} 12 & 4 \\ 24 & -6 \end{vmatrix} = 12(-6) - 24(4)$$

$$= -72 - 96 = -168$$

$$D_y = \begin{vmatrix} 5 & 12 \\ 3 & 24 \end{vmatrix} = 5(24) - 3(12)$$

$$= 120 - 36 = 84$$

Thus, $x = \dfrac{D_x}{D} = \dfrac{-168}{-42} = 4$

$$y = \dfrac{D_y}{D} = \dfrac{84}{-42} = -2$$

The solution set is $\{(4, -2)\}$.

3. $\begin{bmatrix} 2 & 1 & 7 \\ -5 & 6 & 0 \\ -4 & 3 & 1 \end{bmatrix}$

The minor for 2 is $\begin{vmatrix} 6 & 0 \\ 3 & 1 \end{vmatrix}$.

The minor for -5 is $\begin{vmatrix} 1 & 7 \\ 3 & 1 \end{vmatrix}$.

The minor for -4 is $\begin{vmatrix} 1 & 7 \\ 6 & 0 \end{vmatrix}$.

$$\begin{bmatrix} 2 & 1 & 7 \\ -5 & 6 & 0 \\ -4 & 3 & 1 \end{bmatrix} = 2\begin{vmatrix} 6 & 0 \\ 3 & 1 \end{vmatrix} - (-5)\begin{vmatrix} 1 & 7 \\ 3 & 1 \end{vmatrix} - 4\begin{vmatrix} 1 & 7 \\ 6 & 0 \end{vmatrix}$$

$$= 2(6 \cdot 1 - 3 \cdot 0) + 5(1 \cdot 1 - 3 \cdot 7) - 4(1 \cdot 0 - 6 \cdot 7)$$
$$= 2(6 - 0) + 5(1 - 21) - 4(0 - 42)$$
$$= 12 - 100 + 168$$
$$= 80$$

4. $\begin{vmatrix} 6 & 4 & 0 \\ -3 & -5 & 3 \\ 1 & 2 & 0 \end{vmatrix} = 0\begin{vmatrix} -3 & -5 \\ 1 & 2 \end{vmatrix} - 3\begin{vmatrix} 6 & 4 \\ 1 & 2 \end{vmatrix} + 0\begin{vmatrix} 6 & 4 \\ -3 & -5 \end{vmatrix}$

$$= 0 - 3(6 \cdot 2 - 1 \cdot 4) + 0$$
$$= -3(12 - 4)$$
$$= -3(8)$$
$$= -24$$

5. $3x - 2y + z = 16$
$2x + 3y - z = -9$
$x + 4y + 3z = 2$

$$D = \begin{vmatrix} 3 & -2 & 1 \\ 2 & 3 & -1 \\ 1 & 4 & 3 \end{vmatrix}; \quad D_x = \begin{vmatrix} 16 & -2 & 1 \\ -9 & 3 & -1 \\ 2 & 4 & 3 \end{vmatrix}; \quad D_y = \begin{vmatrix} 3 & 16 & 1 \\ 2 & -9 & -1 \\ 1 & 2 & 3 \end{vmatrix}; \quad D_z = \begin{vmatrix} 3 & -2 & 16 \\ 2 & 3 & -9 \\ 1 & 4 & 2 \end{vmatrix}$$

$$D = \begin{vmatrix} 3 & -2 & 1 \\ 2 & 3 & -1 \\ 1 & 4 & 3 \end{vmatrix} = 3\begin{vmatrix} 3 & -1 \\ 4 & 3 \end{vmatrix} - 2\begin{vmatrix} -2 & 1 \\ 4 & 3 \end{vmatrix} + 1\begin{vmatrix} -2 & 1 \\ 3 & -1 \end{vmatrix}$$

$$= 3[(3) \cdot 3 - 4 \cdot (-1)] - 2[(-2) \cdot 3 - 4 \cdot 1] + 1[(-2) \cdot (-1) - (3) \cdot 1]$$
$$= 3(9 + 4) - 2(-6 - 4) + 1(2 - 3)$$
$$= 39 + 20 - 1$$
$$= 58$$

$$D_x = \begin{vmatrix} 16 & -2 & 1 \\ -9 & 3 & -1 \\ 2 & 4 & 3 \end{vmatrix} = 1\begin{vmatrix} -9 & 3 \\ 2 & 4 \end{vmatrix} - (-1)\begin{vmatrix} 16 & -2 \\ 2 & 4 \end{vmatrix} + 3\begin{vmatrix} 16 & -2 \\ -9 & 3 \end{vmatrix}$$

$$= 1[(-9)\cdot 4 - 2\cdot(3)] + 1[16\cdot 4 - 2(-2)] + 3[16\cdot(3) - (-9)\cdot(-2)]$$

$$= 1(-36 - 6) + 1(64 + 4) + 3(48 - 18)$$

$$= -42 + 68 + 90$$

$$= 116$$

$$D_y = \begin{vmatrix} 3 & 16 & 1 \\ 2 & -9 & -1 \\ 1 & 2 & 3 \end{vmatrix} = 3\begin{vmatrix} -9 & -1 \\ 2 & 3 \end{vmatrix} - 2\begin{vmatrix} 16 & 1 \\ 2 & 3 \end{vmatrix} + 1\begin{vmatrix} 16 & 1 \\ -9 & -1 \end{vmatrix}$$

$$= 3[(-9)\cdot 3 - 2\cdot(-1)] - 2[16\cdot 3 - 2\cdot 1] + 1[16(-1) - (-9)\cdot 1]$$

$$= 3(-27 + 2) - 2(48 - 2) + 1(-16 + 9)$$

$$= -75 - 92 - 7$$

$$= -174$$

$$D_z = \begin{vmatrix} 3 & -2 & 16 \\ 2 & 3 & -9 \\ 1 & 4 & 2 \end{vmatrix} = 3\begin{vmatrix} 3 & -9 \\ 4 & 2 \end{vmatrix} - 2\begin{vmatrix} -2 & 16 \\ 4 & 2 \end{vmatrix} + 1\begin{vmatrix} -2 & 16 \\ 3 & -9 \end{vmatrix}$$

$$= 3[(3)2 - 4(-9)] - 2[(-2)2 - 4\cdot 16] + 1[(-2)(-9) - (3)\cdot 16]$$

$$= 3(6 + 36) - 2(-4 - 64) + 1(18 - 48)$$

$$= 126 + 136 - 30$$

$$= 232$$

$$x = \frac{D_x}{D} = \frac{116}{58} = 2$$

$$y = \frac{D_y}{D} = \frac{-174}{58} = -3$$

$$z = \frac{D_z}{D} = \frac{232}{58} = 4$$

The solution to the system is $\{(2, -3, 4)\}$.

6. $|A| = \begin{vmatrix} 0 & 4 & 0 & -3 \\ -1 & 1 & 5 & 2 \\ 1 & -2 & 0 & 6 \\ 3 & 0 & 0 & 1 \end{vmatrix} = (-1)^{2+3}5\begin{vmatrix} 0 & 4 & -3 \\ 1 & -2 & 6 \\ 3 & 0 & 1 \end{vmatrix} = -5\begin{vmatrix} 0 & 4 & -3 \\ 1 & -2 & 6 \\ 3 & 0 & 1 \end{vmatrix}$

Evaluate the third-order determinant to get $|A| = -5(50) = -250$.

Exercise Set 3.4

1. $\begin{vmatrix} 5 & 7 \\ 2 & 3 \end{vmatrix} = 5\cdot 3 - 2\cdot 7 = 15 - 14 = 1$

3. $\begin{vmatrix} -4 & 1 \\ 5 & 6 \end{vmatrix} = (-4)6 - 5\cdot 1 = -24 - 5 = -29$

5. $\begin{vmatrix} -7 & 14 \\ 2 & -4 \end{vmatrix} = (-7)(-4) - 2(14) = 28 - 28 = 0$

7. $\begin{vmatrix} -5 & -1 \\ -2 & -7 \end{vmatrix} = (-5)(-7) - (-2)(-1) = 35 - 2 = 33$

9. $\begin{vmatrix} \frac{1}{2} & \frac{1}{2} \\ \frac{1}{8} & -\frac{3}{4} \end{vmatrix} = \frac{1}{2}\left(-\frac{3}{4}\right) - \frac{1}{8}\cdot\frac{1}{2} = -\frac{3}{8} - \frac{1}{16} = -\frac{7}{16}$

11. $D = \begin{vmatrix} 1 & 1 \\ 1 & -1 \end{vmatrix} = -1 - 1 = -2$

$D_x = \begin{vmatrix} 7 & 1 \\ 3 & -1 \end{vmatrix} = -7 - 3 = -10$

$D_y = \begin{vmatrix} 1 & 7 \\ 1 & 3 \end{vmatrix} = 3 - 7 = -4$

$x = \dfrac{D_x}{D} = \dfrac{-10}{-2} = 5$

$y = \dfrac{D_y}{D} = \dfrac{-4}{-2} = 2$

The solution set is $\{(5, 2)\}$.

13. $D = \begin{vmatrix} 12 & 3 \\ 2 & -3 \end{vmatrix} = -36 - 6 = -42$

$D_x = \begin{vmatrix} 15 & 3 \\ 13 & -3 \end{vmatrix} = -45 - 39 = -84$

$D_y = \begin{vmatrix} 12 & 15 \\ 2 & 13 \end{vmatrix} = 156 - 30 = 126$

$x = \dfrac{D_x}{D} = \dfrac{-84}{-42} = 2$

$y = \dfrac{D_y}{D} = \dfrac{126}{-42} = -3$

The solution set is $\{(2, -3)\}$.

15. $D = \begin{vmatrix} 4 & -5 \\ 2 & 3 \end{vmatrix} = 12 - (-10) = 22$

$D_x = \begin{vmatrix} 17 & -5 \\ 3 & 3 \end{vmatrix} = 51 - (-15) = 66$

$D_y = \begin{vmatrix} 4 & 17 \\ 2 & 3 \end{vmatrix} = 12 - 34 = -22$

$x = \dfrac{D_x}{D} = \dfrac{66}{22} = 3$

$y = \dfrac{D_y}{D} = \dfrac{-22}{22} = -1$

The solution set is $\{(3, -1)\}$.

17. $D = \begin{vmatrix} 1 & 2 \\ 5 & 10 \end{vmatrix} = 10 - 10 = 0$

$D_x = \begin{vmatrix} 3 & 2 \\ 15 & 10 \end{vmatrix} = 30 - 30 = 0$

$D_y = \begin{vmatrix} 1 & 3 \\ 5 & 15 \end{vmatrix} = 15 - 15 = 0$

Because all 3 determinants equal zero, the system is dependent.

19. $D = \begin{vmatrix} 3 & -4 \\ 2 & 2 \end{vmatrix} = 6 - (-8) = 14$

$D_x = \begin{vmatrix} 4 & -4 \\ 12 & 2 \end{vmatrix} = 8 - (-48) = 56$

$D_y = \begin{vmatrix} 3 & 4 \\ 2 & 12 \end{vmatrix} = 36 - 8 = 28$

$x = \dfrac{D_x}{D} = \dfrac{56}{14} = 4$

$y = \dfrac{D_y}{D} = \dfrac{28}{14} = 2$

The solution set is $\{(4, 2)\}$.

21. $D = \begin{vmatrix} 2 & -3 \\ 5 & 4 \end{vmatrix} = 8 - (-15) = 23$

$D_x = \begin{vmatrix} 2 & -3 \\ 51 & 4 \end{vmatrix} = 8 - (-153) = 161$

$D_y = \begin{vmatrix} 2 & 2 \\ 5 & 51 \end{vmatrix} = 102 - 10 = 92$

$x = \dfrac{D_x}{D} = \dfrac{161}{23} = 7$

$y = \dfrac{D_y}{D} = \dfrac{92}{23} = 4$

The solution set is $\{(7, 4)\}$.

23. $D = \begin{vmatrix} 3 & 3 \\ 2 & 2 \end{vmatrix} = 6 - 6 = 0$

$D_x = \begin{vmatrix} 2 & 3 \\ 3 & 2 \end{vmatrix} = 4 - 9 = -5$

$D_y = \begin{vmatrix} 3 & 2 \\ 2 & 3 \end{vmatrix} = 9 - 4 = 5$

Because $D = 0$ but D_x or $D_y \neq 0$, the system is inconsistent.

25. Write the equations in standard form.

$3x + 4y = 16$

$6x + 8y = 32$

$D = \begin{bmatrix} 3 & 4 \\ 6 & 8 \end{bmatrix} = 24 - 24 = 0$

$D_x = \begin{bmatrix} 16 & 4 \\ 32 & 8 \end{bmatrix} = 128 - 128 = 0$

$D_y = \begin{bmatrix} 3 & 16 \\ 6 & 32 \end{bmatrix} = 96 - 69 = 0$

Since all determinants are zero, the system is dependent.

27. $\begin{vmatrix} 3 & 0 & 0 \\ 2 & 1 & -5 \\ -2 & 5 & -1 \end{vmatrix} = 3\begin{vmatrix} 1 & -5 \\ 5 & -1 \end{vmatrix} - 0\begin{vmatrix} 2 & -5 \\ -2 & -1 \end{vmatrix} + 0\begin{vmatrix} 2 & 1 \\ -2 & 5 \end{vmatrix}$

$= 3[(1)(-1) - (5)(-5)]$
$= 3(-1 + 25) = 3(24)$
$= 72$

29. $\begin{vmatrix} 3 & 1 & 0 \\ -3 & 4 & 0 \\ -1 & 3 & -5 \end{vmatrix} = 0\begin{vmatrix} -3 & 4 \\ -1 & 3 \end{vmatrix} - 0\begin{vmatrix} 3 & 1 \\ -1 & 3 \end{vmatrix} + (-5)\begin{vmatrix} 3 & 1 \\ -3 & 4 \end{vmatrix}$

$= -5[3 \cdot 4 - (-3)(1)]$
$= -5(12 + 3) = -5(15)$
$= -75$

31. $\begin{vmatrix} 1 & 1 & 1 \\ 2 & 2 & 2 \\ -3 & 4 & -5 \end{vmatrix} -2R_1 + R_2$

$\begin{vmatrix} 1 & 1 & 1 \\ 0 & 0 & 0 \\ -3 & 4 & -5 \end{vmatrix} = 0$

33. $D = \begin{vmatrix} 1 & 1 & 1 \\ 2 & -1 & 1 \\ -1 & 3 & -1 \end{vmatrix}$

$= \begin{vmatrix} -1 & 1 \\ 3 & -1 \end{vmatrix} - \begin{vmatrix} 2 & 1 \\ -1 & -1 \end{vmatrix} + \begin{vmatrix} 2 & -1 \\ -1 & 3 \end{vmatrix}$

$= (1 - 3) - [-2 - (-1)] + (6 - 1)$
$= -2 - (-1) + 5 = -2 + 1 + 5 = 4$

$D_x = \begin{vmatrix} 0 & 1 & 1 \\ -1 & -1 & 1 \\ -8 & 3 & -1 \end{vmatrix} = (-1)\begin{vmatrix} -1 & 1 \\ -8 & -1 \end{vmatrix} + \begin{vmatrix} -1 & -1 \\ -8 & 3 \end{vmatrix}$

$= (-1)[1 - (-8)] + (-3 - 8) = (-1)(9) - 11$
$= -20$

$D_y = \begin{vmatrix} 1 & 0 & 1 \\ 2 & -1 & 1 \\ -1 & -8 & -1 \end{vmatrix} = \begin{vmatrix} -1 & 1 \\ -8 & -1 \end{vmatrix} + \begin{vmatrix} 2 & -1 \\ -1 & -8 \end{vmatrix}$

$= 1 - (-8) + (-16 - 1) = 1 + 8 - 17 = -8$

$D_z = \begin{vmatrix} 1 & 1 & 0 \\ 2 & -1 & -1 \\ -1 & 3 & -8 \end{vmatrix} = 1\begin{vmatrix} -1 & -1 \\ 3 & -8 \end{vmatrix} - 1\begin{vmatrix} 2 & -1 \\ -1 & -8 \end{vmatrix}$

$= 8 - (-3) - 1(-16 - 1) = 11 + 17 = 28$

$x = \dfrac{D_x}{D} = \dfrac{-20}{4} = -5$

$y = \dfrac{D_y}{D} = \dfrac{-8}{4} = -2$

$z = \dfrac{D_z}{D} = \dfrac{28}{4} = 7$

The solution to the system is $\{(-5, -2, 7)\}$.

35. $D = \begin{vmatrix} 4 & -5 & -6 \\ 1 & -2 & -5 \\ 2 & -1 & 0 \end{vmatrix} = 2\begin{vmatrix} -5 & -6 \\ -2 & -5 \end{vmatrix} - (-1)\begin{vmatrix} 4 & -6 \\ 1 & -5 \end{vmatrix}$

$= 2(25 - 12) + [-20 - (-6)] = 2(13) + (-14)$
$= 26 - 14 = 12$

$D_x = \begin{vmatrix} -1 & -5 & -6 \\ -12 & -2 & -5 \\ 7 & -1 & 0 \end{vmatrix}$

$= 7\begin{vmatrix} -5 & -6 \\ -2 & -5 \end{vmatrix} - (-1)\begin{vmatrix} -1 & -6 \\ -12 & -5 \end{vmatrix}$

$= 7(25 - 12) + (5 - 72) = 7(13) - 67$
$= 91 - 67 = 24$

$D_y = \begin{vmatrix} 4 & -1 & -6 \\ 1 & -12 & -5 \\ 2 & 7 & 0 \end{vmatrix} = 2\begin{vmatrix} -1 & -6 \\ -12 & -5 \end{vmatrix} - 7\begin{vmatrix} 4 & -6 \\ 1 & -5 \end{vmatrix}$

$= 2(5 - 72) - 7[-20 - (-6)]$
$= 2(-67) - 7(-14) = -134 + 98 = -36$

230

$$D_z = \begin{vmatrix} 4 & -5 & -1 \\ 1 & -2 & -12 \\ 2 & -1 & 7 \end{vmatrix}$$

$$= 4\begin{vmatrix} -2 & -12 \\ -1 & 7 \end{vmatrix} - (-5)\begin{vmatrix} 1 & -12 \\ 2 & 7 \end{vmatrix} + (-1)\begin{vmatrix} 1 & -2 \\ 2 & -1 \end{vmatrix}$$

$$= 4(-14 - 12) + 5[7 - (-24)] - [-1 - (-4)]$$

$$= 4(-26) + 5(31) - (3) = -104 + 155 - 3 = 48$$

$$x = \frac{D_x}{D} = \frac{24}{12} = 2, \; y = \frac{D_y}{D} = \frac{-36}{12} = -3,$$

$$z = \frac{D_z}{D} = \frac{48}{12} = 4$$

The solution set is $\{(2, -3, 4)\}$.

37. $$D = \begin{vmatrix} 1 & 1 & 1 \\ 1 & -2 & 1 \\ 1 & 3 & 2 \end{vmatrix} = 1\begin{vmatrix} -2 & 1 \\ 3 & 2 \end{vmatrix} - 1\begin{vmatrix} 1 & 1 \\ 1 & 2 \end{vmatrix} + 1\begin{vmatrix} 1 & -2 \\ 1 & 3 \end{vmatrix}$$

$$= -4 - 3 - (2 - 1) + [3 - (-2)]$$

$$= -7 - 1 + 5 = -3$$

$$D_x = \begin{vmatrix} 4 & 1 & 1 \\ 7 & -2 & 1 \\ 4 & 3 & 2 \end{vmatrix} = 4\begin{vmatrix} -2 & 1 \\ 3 & 2 \end{vmatrix} - 1\begin{vmatrix} 7 & 1 \\ 4 & 2 \end{vmatrix} + 1\begin{vmatrix} 7 & -2 \\ 4 & 3 \end{vmatrix}$$

$$= 4(-4 - 3) - (14 - 4) + [21 - (-8)]$$

$$= 4(-7) - 10 + 29 = -28 + 19 = -9$$

$$D_y = \begin{vmatrix} 1 & 4 & 1 \\ 1 & 7 & 1 \\ 1 & 4 & 2 \end{vmatrix} = 1\begin{vmatrix} 7 & 1 \\ 4 & 2 \end{vmatrix} - 1\begin{vmatrix} 4 & 1 \\ 4 & 2 \end{vmatrix} + 1\begin{vmatrix} 4 & 1 \\ 7 & 1 \end{vmatrix}$$

$$= 14 - 4 - (8 - 4) + (4 - 7) = 10 - 4 - 3 = 3$$

$$D_z = \begin{vmatrix} 1 & 1 & 4 \\ 1 & -2 & 7 \\ 1 & 3 & 4 \end{vmatrix} = 1\begin{vmatrix} -2 & 7 \\ 3 & 4 \end{vmatrix} - 1\begin{vmatrix} 1 & 4 \\ 3 & 4 \end{vmatrix} + 1\begin{vmatrix} 1 & 4 \\ -2 & 7 \end{vmatrix}$$

$$= -8 - 21 - (4 - 12) + [7 - (-8)]$$

$$= -29 + 8 + 15 = -6$$

$$x = \frac{D_x}{D} = \frac{-9}{-3} = 3, \; y = \frac{D_y}{D} = \frac{3}{-3} = -1,$$

$$z = \frac{D_z}{D} = \frac{-6}{-3} = 2$$

The solution set is $\{3, -1, 2\}$.

39. $$D = \begin{vmatrix} 1 & 0 & 2 \\ 0 & 2 & -1 \\ 2 & 3 & 0 \end{vmatrix} = \begin{vmatrix} 2 & -1 \\ 3 & 0 \end{vmatrix} + 2\begin{vmatrix} 0 & 2 \\ 2 & 3 \end{vmatrix}$$

$$= 0 - (-3) + 2(0 - 4) = 3 - 8 = -5$$

$$D_x = \begin{vmatrix} 4 & 0 & 2 \\ 5 & 2 & -1 \\ 13 & 3 & 0 \end{vmatrix} = 4\begin{vmatrix} 2 & -1 \\ 3 & 0 \end{vmatrix} + 2\begin{vmatrix} 5 & 2 \\ 13 & 3 \end{vmatrix}$$

$$= 4[0 - (-3)] + 2(15 - 26)$$

$$= 4(3) + 2(-11) = 12 - 22 = -10$$

$$D_y = \begin{vmatrix} 1 & 4 & 2 \\ 0 & 5 & -1 \\ 2 & 13 & 0 \end{vmatrix} = \begin{vmatrix} 5 & -1 \\ 13 & 0 \end{vmatrix} + 2\begin{vmatrix} 4 & 2 \\ 5 & -1 \end{vmatrix}$$

$$= 0 - (-13) + 2(-4 - 10)$$

$$= 13 + 2(-14) = 13 - 28 = -15$$

$$D_z = \begin{vmatrix} 1 & 0 & 4 \\ 0 & 2 & 5 \\ 2 & 3 & 13 \end{vmatrix} = \begin{vmatrix} 2 & 5 \\ 3 & 13 \end{vmatrix} + 4\begin{vmatrix} 0 & 2 \\ 2 & 3 \end{vmatrix}$$

$$= 26 - 15 + 4(0 - 4) = 11 + 4(-4)$$

$$= 11 - 16 = -5$$

$$x = \frac{D_x}{D} = \frac{-10}{-5} = 2, \; y = \frac{D_y}{D} = \frac{-15}{-5} = 3,$$

$$z = \frac{D_z}{D} = \frac{-5}{-5} = 1$$

The solution set is $\{(2, 3, 1)\}$.

41.

$$\begin{vmatrix} 4 & 2 & 8 & -7 \\ -2 & 0 & 4 & 1 \\ 5 & 0 & 0 & 5 \\ 4 & 0 & 0 & -1 \end{vmatrix} = -2\begin{vmatrix} -2 & 4 & 1 \\ 5 & 0 & 5 \\ 4 & 0 & -1 \end{vmatrix} + 0\begin{vmatrix} 4 & 8 & -7 \\ 5 & 0 & 5 \\ 4 & 0 & -1 \end{vmatrix} - 0\begin{vmatrix} 4 & 8 & -7 \\ -2 & 4 & 1 \\ 4 & 0 & -1 \end{vmatrix} + 0\begin{vmatrix} 4 & 8 & -7 \\ -2 & 4 & 1 \\ 5 & 0 & 5 \end{vmatrix}$$

$$= (-2)\left[(-4)\begin{vmatrix} 5 & 5 \\ 4 & -1 \end{vmatrix} + 0\begin{vmatrix} -2 & 1 \\ 4 & -1 \end{vmatrix} - 0\begin{vmatrix} -2 & 1 \\ 5 & 5 \end{vmatrix} \right] = (-2)(-4)[5(-1) - 4 \cdot 5] = 8(-5 - 20) = 8(-25) = -200$$

43.

$$\begin{vmatrix} -2 & -3 & 3 & 5 \\ 1 & -4 & 0 & 0 \\ 1 & 2 & 2 & -3 \\ 2 & 0 & 1 & 1 \end{vmatrix} = -1\begin{vmatrix} -3 & 3 & 5 \\ 2 & 2 & -3 \\ 0 & 1 & 1 \end{vmatrix} + (-4)\begin{vmatrix} -2 & 3 & 5 \\ 1 & 2 & -3 \\ 2 & 1 & 1 \end{vmatrix} - 0\begin{vmatrix} -2 & -3 & 5 \\ 1 & 2 & -3 \\ 2 & 0 & 1 \end{vmatrix} + 0\begin{vmatrix} -2 & -3 & 3 \\ 1 & 2 & 2 \\ 2 & 0 & 1 \end{vmatrix}$$

$$= (-1)\left[0\begin{vmatrix} 3 & 5 \\ 2 & -3 \end{vmatrix} - 1\begin{vmatrix} -3 & 5 \\ 2 & -3 \end{vmatrix} + 1\begin{vmatrix} -3 & 3 \\ 2 & 2 \end{vmatrix} \right] - 4\left[2\begin{vmatrix} 3 & 5 \\ 2 & -3 \end{vmatrix} - 1\begin{vmatrix} -2 & 5 \\ 1 & -3 \end{vmatrix} + 1\begin{vmatrix} -2 & 3 \\ 1 & 2 \end{vmatrix} \right]$$

$$= (-1)\{(-1)[(-3)(-3) - 2\cdot5] + [(-3)(2) - 2\cdot3]\} - 4\{2[3(-3) - 2\cdot5] - [(-2)(-3) - 1\cdot5] + [(-2)(2) - 1\cdot3]\} = 195$$

45.

$$\begin{vmatrix} \begin{vmatrix} 3 & 1 \\ -2 & 3 \end{vmatrix} & \begin{vmatrix} 7 & 0 \\ 1 & 5 \end{vmatrix} \\ \begin{vmatrix} 3 & 0 \\ 0 & 7 \end{vmatrix} & \begin{vmatrix} 9 & -6 \\ 3 & 5 \end{vmatrix} \end{vmatrix} = \begin{vmatrix} 3(3)-(-2)(1) & 7(5)-1(0) \\ 3(7)-0(0) & 9(5)-3(-6) \end{vmatrix} = \begin{vmatrix} 9+2 & 35-0 \\ 21-0 & 45+18 \end{vmatrix} = \begin{vmatrix} 11 & 35 \\ 21 & 63 \end{vmatrix}$$

$$= 11(63) - 21(35) = 693 - 735 = -42$$

47.

From $D = \begin{vmatrix} 2 & -4 \\ 3 & 5 \end{vmatrix}$ we obtain the coefficients of the variables in our equations:

$$2x - 4y = c_1$$
$$3x + 5y = c_2$$

From $D_x = \begin{vmatrix} 8 & -4 \\ -10 & 5 \end{vmatrix}$ we obtain the constant coefficients: 8 and -10

$$2x - 4y = 8$$
$$3x + 5y = -10$$

49.

$$\begin{vmatrix} -2 & x \\ 4 & 6 \end{vmatrix} = 32$$

$$-2(6) - 4(x) = 32$$
$$-12 - 4x = 32$$
$$-4x = 44$$
$$x = -11$$

The solution is -11.

51.

$$\begin{vmatrix} 1 & x & -2 \\ 3 & 1 & 1 \\ 0 & -2 & 2 \end{vmatrix} = -8$$

$$0\begin{vmatrix} x & -2 \\ 1 & 1 \end{vmatrix} - (-2)\begin{vmatrix} 1 & -2 \\ 3 & 1 \end{vmatrix} + 2\begin{vmatrix} 1 & x \\ 3 & 1 \end{vmatrix} = -8$$

$$2[1(1)-3(-2)]+2[1(1)-3(x)] = -8$$

$$2(1+6)+2(1-3x) = -8$$

$$2(7)+2(1-3x) = -8$$

$$14+2-6x = -8$$

$$-6x = -24$$

$$x = 4$$

The solution is 4.

53. $\text{Area} = \pm\dfrac{1}{2}\begin{vmatrix} 3 & -5 & 1 \\ 2 & 6 & 1 \\ -3 & 5 & 1 \end{vmatrix} = \pm\dfrac{1}{2}\begin{vmatrix} 3 & -5 & 1 \\ -1 & 11 & 0 \\ -6 & 10 & 0 \end{vmatrix} = \pm\dfrac{1}{2}\begin{vmatrix} -1 & 11 \\ -6 & 10 \end{vmatrix} = \pm\dfrac{1}{2}[-10-(-66)] = \pm\dfrac{1}{2}(56) = 28$

The area is 28 square units.

The slope of the line through (3, –5) and (–3, 5) is $m = \dfrac{5-(-5)}{-3-3} = \dfrac{10}{-6} = -\dfrac{5}{3}$.

The equation of the line is $y-(-5) = -\dfrac{5}{3}(x-3)$ or $y = -\dfrac{5}{3}x$.

The line perpendicular to $y = -\dfrac{5}{3}x$ through (2, 6) has equation $y-6 = \dfrac{3}{5}(x-2)$ or $y = \dfrac{3}{5}x+\dfrac{24}{5}$.

These lines intersect where $-\dfrac{5}{3}x = \dfrac{3}{5}x+\dfrac{24}{5}$.

$-\dfrac{36}{17} = x$ and $-\dfrac{24}{5} = \dfrac{34}{15}x$ $y = -\dfrac{5}{3}\left(-\dfrac{36}{17}\right) = \dfrac{60}{17}$

Using the side connecting (3, –5) and

(–3, 5) as the base, the height is the distance from (2, 6) to $\left(-\dfrac{36}{17}, \dfrac{60}{17}\right)$.

$b = \sqrt{[3-(-3)]^2+(-5-5)^2}$

$= \sqrt{36+100} = \sqrt{136} = 2\sqrt{34}$

$h = \sqrt{\left[2-\left(-\dfrac{36}{17}\right)\right]^2+\left(6-\dfrac{60}{17}\right)^2}$

$= \sqrt{\dfrac{4900}{289}+\dfrac{1764}{289}} = \dfrac{14\sqrt{34}}{17}$

$\dfrac{1}{2}bh = \dfrac{1}{2}(2\sqrt{34})\left(\dfrac{14\sqrt{34}}{17}\right) = \dfrac{14(34)}{17}$

$= 14(2) = 28$ square units

55. $\begin{vmatrix} 3 & -1 & 1 \\ 0 & -3 & 1 \\ 12 & 5 & 1 \end{vmatrix} = \begin{vmatrix} 3 & -1 & 1 \\ -3 & -2 & 0 \\ 9 & 6 & 0 \end{vmatrix} = \begin{vmatrix} -3 & -2 \\ 9 & 6 \end{vmatrix}$

$= -18 - (-18) = 0$

Yes, the points are collinear.

57. $\begin{vmatrix} x & y & 1 \\ 3 & -5 & 1 \\ -2 & 6 & 1 \end{vmatrix} = x\begin{vmatrix} -5 & 1 \\ 6 & 1 \end{vmatrix} - y\begin{vmatrix} 3 & 1 \\ -2 & 1 \end{vmatrix} + \begin{vmatrix} 3 & -5 \\ -2 & 6 \end{vmatrix} = x(-5-6) - y[3-(-2)] + (18-10)$

$= -11x - 5y + 8$

The equation of the line is $-11x - 5y + 8 = 0$. The equation of the line in slope-intercept form is $y = -\dfrac{11}{5}x + \dfrac{8}{5}$.

69. Input the matrix as $[A]$, then use $\det[A]$ to find the determinant.

$\begin{vmatrix} 8 & 2 & 6 & -1 & 0 \\ 2 & 0 & -3 & 4 & 7 \\ 2 & 1 & -3 & 6 & -5 \\ -1 & 2 & 1 & 5 & -1 \\ 4 & 5 & -2 & 3 & -8 \end{vmatrix} = 13,200$

In exercise 71, expansions are all done about the first column of the matrix and the resulting products of 0 and a determinant are not shown.

71. **a.** $\begin{vmatrix} a & a \\ 0 & a \end{vmatrix} = a^2 - 0 = a^2$

b. $\begin{vmatrix} a & a & a \\ 0 & a & a \\ 0 & 0 & a \end{vmatrix} = a\begin{vmatrix} a & a \\ 0 & a \end{vmatrix} - 0 + 0$

$= a(a^2) = a^3$

c. $\begin{vmatrix} a & a & a & a \\ 0 & a & a & a \\ 0 & 0 & a & a \\ 0 & 0 & 0 & a \end{vmatrix} = a\begin{vmatrix} a & a & a \\ 0 & a & a \\ 0 & 0 & a \end{vmatrix} - 0 + 0 - 0$

$= a(a^3) = a^4$

d. Each determinant has zeros below the main diagonal and a's everywhere else.

e. Each determinant equals a raised to the power equal to the order of the determinant.

73. The sign of the value is changed when 2 columns are interchanged in a 2nd order determinant.

75. Evaluate the determinate and write the equation in slope intercept form.

$$\begin{vmatrix} x & y & 1 \\ x_1 & y_1 & 1 \\ x_2 & y_2 & 1 \end{vmatrix} = 0$$

$$x\begin{vmatrix} y_1 & 1 \\ y_2 & 1 \end{vmatrix} - y\begin{vmatrix} x_1 & 1 \\ x_2 & 1 \end{vmatrix} + 1\begin{vmatrix} x_1 & y_1 \\ x_2 & y_2 \end{vmatrix} = 0$$

$$x(y_1 - y_2) - y(x_1 - x_2) + x_1 y_2 - x_2 y_1 = 0$$

$$-y(x_1 - x_2) = -x(y_1 - y_2) + x_2 y_1 - x_1 y_2$$

$$y(x_2 - x_1) = x(y_2 - y_1) + x_2 y_1 - x_1 y_2$$

$$y = \frac{y_2 - y_1}{x_2 - x_1} x + \frac{x_2 y_1 - x_1 y_2}{x_2 - x_1}$$

$$m = \frac{y_2 - y_1}{x_2 - x_1} \qquad b = \frac{x_2 y_1 - x_1 y_2}{x_2 - x_1}$$

Write the slope-point equation of the line the in point slope form.

$$y - y_1 = \frac{y_2 - y_1}{x_2 - x_1}(x - x_1)$$

$$y - y_1 = \frac{y_2 - y_1}{x_2 - x_1} x + \frac{-x_1 y_2 + x_1 y_1}{x_2 - x_1}$$

$$y = \frac{y_2 - y_1}{x_2 - x_1} x + \frac{-x_1 y_2 + x_1 y_1}{x_2 - x_1} + y_1$$

$$y = \frac{y_2 - y_1}{x_2 - x_1} x + \frac{-x_1 y_2 + x_1 y_1}{x_2 - x_1} + \frac{x_2 y_1 - x_1 y_1}{x_2 - x_1}$$

$$y = \frac{y_2 - y_1}{x_2 - x_1} x + \frac{x_2 y_1 - x_1 y_2}{x_2 - x_1}$$

$$m = \frac{y_2 - y_1}{x_2 - x_1} \qquad b = \frac{x_2 y_1 - x_1 y_2}{x_2 - x_1}$$

Since both forms give the same slope and y-intercept, the determinant does give the equation of the line.

Chapter 3 Review Exercises

1.
$$y = 4x + 1$$
$$3x + 2y = 13$$
Substitute $4x + 1$ for y in the second equation:
$$3x + 2(4x + 1) = 13$$
$$3x + 8x + 2 = 13$$
$$11x = 11$$
$$x = 1$$
$$y = 4(1) + 1 = 5$$
The solution set is $\{(1,5)\}$.

2. $\quad x + 4y = 14$
$$2x - y = 1$$
Multiply the second equation by 4 and add to the first equation.
$$x + 4y = 14$$
$$\underline{8x - 4y = 4}$$
$$9x = 18$$
$$x = 2$$
$$2(2) - y = 1$$
$$-y = -3$$
$$y = 3$$
The solution set is $\{(2,3)\}$.

3. $5x + 3y = 1$

$3x + 4y = -6$

Multiply the first equation by 4 and the second equation by –3.
Then add.

$20x + 12y = 4$

$\underline{-9x - 12y = 18}$

$11x = 22$

$x = 2$

$5(2) + 3y = 1$

$3y = -9$

$y = -3$

The solution set is $\{(2, -3)\}$.

4. $2y - 6x = 7$

$3x - y = 9$

The second equation can be written as $y = 3x - 9$.
Substitute:

$2(3x - 9) - 6x = 7$

$6x - 18 - 6x = 7$

$-18 = 7$

Since this is false, the system has no solution.
The solution set is the empty set, $\varnothing$.

5. $4x - 8y = 16$

$3x - 6y = 12$

Divide the first equation by 4 and the second equation by 3.

$x - 2y = 4$

$x - 2y = 4$

Since these equations are identical, the system has an infinite number of solutions.
The solution set is $\{(x, y) \mid 3x - 6y = 12\}$.

6. a. $C(x) = 60,000 + 200x$

b. $R(x) = 450x$

c. $450x = 60000 + 200x$

$250x = 60000$

$x = 240$

$450(240) = 108,000$

The company must make 240 desks at a cost of \$108,000 to break even.

7. Let x = the number of years of healthy life expectancy of people in Japan.
Let y = the number of years of healthy life expectancy of people in Switzerland.

The system to solve is

$x + y = 146.4$

$x - y = 0.8$

Add the two equations:

$x + y = 146.4$

$\underline{x - y = 0.8}$

$2x = 147.2$

$x = 73.6$

Back substitute to find y:

$x + y = 146.4$

$73.6 + y = 146.4$

$y = 72.8$

The number of years of healthy life expectancy in Japan is 73.6 years and in Switzerland is 72.8 years.

8. Let l = the length of the table
Let w = the width of the table

$2l + 2w = 34$

$4l - 3w = 33$

Multiply the first equation by –2 and solve by addition.

$-4l - 4w = -68$

$\underline{4l - 3w = 33}$

$-7w = -35$

$w = 5$

Back-substitute 5 for w to find l.

$2l + 2w = 34$

$2l + 2(5) = 34$

$2l + 10 = 34$

$2l = 24$

$l = 12$

The dimensions of the table are 12 feet by 5 feet.

9. Let x = the cost of the hotel
y = the cost of the car

$3x + 2y = 360$

$4x + 3y = 500$

Solve the system.

$12x + 8y = 1440$

$\underline{-12x - 9y = -1500}$

$-y = -60$

$y = 60$

$3x + 2(60) = 360$

$3x = 240$

$x = 80$

The room costs \$80 a day and the car rents for \$60 a day.

10. x = number of apples
y = number of avocados

$$100x + 350y = 1000$$
$$24x + 14y = 100$$
$$100x + 350y = 1000$$
$$\underline{-600x - 350y = -2500}$$
$$-500x = -1500$$
$$x = 3$$
$$100(3) + 350y = 1000$$
$$350y = 700$$
$$y = 2$$

3 apples and 2 avocados supply 1000 calories and 100 grams of carbohydrates.

11.
$$2x - y + z = 1 \,(1)$$
$$3x - 3y + 4z = 5 \,(2)$$
$$4x - 2y + 3z = 4 \,(3)$$
Eliminate y from (1) and (2) by multiplying (1) by -3 and adding the result to (2).
$$-6x + 3y - 3z = -3$$
$$\underline{3x - 3y + 4z = 5}$$
$$-3x + z = 2 \,\,(4)$$
Eliminate y from (1) and (3) by multiplying (1) by -2 and adding the result to (3).
$$-4x + 2y - 2z = -2$$
$$\underline{4x - 2y + 3z = 4}$$
$$z = 2$$
Substituting $z = 2$ into (4), we get:
$$-3x + 2 = 2$$
$$-3x = 0$$
$$x = 0$$
Substituting $x = 0$ and $z = 2$ into (1), we have:
$$2(0) - y + 2 = 1$$
$$-y = -1$$
$$y = 1$$
The solution set is $\{(0, 1, 2)\}$.

12. $x + 2y - z = 5 \,\,(1)$
$2x - y + 3z = 0 \,\,(2)$
$2y + z = 1 \,\,(3)$
Eliminate x from (1) and (2) by multiplying (1) by -2 and adding the result to (2).
$$-2x - 4y + 2z = -10$$
$$\underline{2x - y + 3z = 0}$$
$$-5y + 5z = -10$$
$$y - z = 2 \,\,\,(4)$$

Adding (3) and (4), we get:
$$2y + z = 1$$
$$\underline{y - z = 2}$$
$$3y = 3$$
$$y = 1$$
Substituting $y = 1$ into (3), we have:
$$2(1) + z = 1$$
$$z = -1$$
Substituting $y = 1$ and $z = -1$ into (1), we obtain:
$$x + 2(1) - (-1) = 5$$
$$x + 3 = 5$$
$$x = 2$$
The solution set is $\{(2, 1, -1)\}$.

13. $y = ax^2 + bx + c$
$$(1,4) : 4 = a + b + c \qquad\qquad (1)$$
$$(3,20) : 20 = 9a + 3b + c \qquad (2)$$
$$(-2,25) : 25 = 4a - 2b + c \quad (3)$$
Multiply (1) by -1 and add to (2).
$$20 = 9a + 3b + c$$
$$\underline{-4 = -a - b - c}$$
$$16 = 8a + 2b$$
$$8 = 4a + b$$
$$8 = 4a + b \qquad\qquad (4)$$
Multiply (1) by -1 and add to (3).
$$25 = 4a - 2b + c$$
$$\underline{-4 = -a - b - c}$$
$$21 = 3a - 3b$$
$$7 = a - b \qquad\qquad (5)$$
Add (4) and (5).
$$8 = 4a + b$$
$$\underline{7 = a - b}$$
$$15 = 5a$$
$$a = 3$$

$$8 = 4(3) + b$$
$$b = -4$$
$$3 - 4 + c = 4$$
$$c = 5$$
Hence, the quadratic function is
$$y = 3x^2 - 4x + 5 \,.$$

14. a. $(0, 3.5)$ $(15, 5.0)$ $(33, 3.8)$

    b. Substitute point values into the equation
$$y = ax^2 + bx + c \,.$$

$$3.5 = a(0)^2 + b(0) + c$$
$$3.5 = c$$

$$5.0 = a(15)^2 + b(15) + c$$
$$5.0 = 225a + 15b + c$$

$$3.8 = a(33)^2 + b(33) + c$$
$$3.8 = 1089a + 33b + c$$

15. Model the given information as a system of equations.
$$x - (y + z) = 48$$
or $x - y - z = 48$ Equation 1
$$x - 3z = 9$$ Equation 2
$$x + y + z = 246$$ Equation 3
Add equation 1 and 3 and solve for x.
$$x - y - z = 48$$
$$\underline{x + y + z = 246}$$
$$2x = 294$$
$$x = 147$$
Back-substitute into equation 2 to find z.
$$x - 3z = 9$$
$$147 - 3z = 9$$
$$-3z = -138$$
$$z = 46$$
Back-substitute into equation 3 to find y.
$$147 + y + 46 = 246$$
$$y = 53$$

The registrations for Labs was 147 thousand, for Golden retrievers 53 thousand, and for German shepherds 46 thousand.

16. $x + y + 3z = 12$
$$y - 2z = -4$$
$$z = 3$$

$$y - 2(3) = -4$$
$$y - 6 = -4$$
$$y = 2$$

$$x + 2 + 3(3) = 12$$
$$x + 11 = 12$$
$$x = 1$$
The solution to the system is $\{(1, 2, 3)\}$.

17. $w - 2y + 2z = 1$
$$x + y - z = 0$$
$$y - \frac{7}{3}x = -\frac{1}{3}$$
$$z = 1$$
$$y - \frac{7}{3}(1) = -\frac{1}{3}$$
$$y - \frac{7}{3} = -\frac{1}{3}$$
$$y = \frac{6}{3}$$
$$y = 2$$
$$x + 2 - 1 = 0$$
$$x + 1 = 0$$
$$x = -1$$
$$w - 2(2) + 2(1) = 1$$
$$w - 2 = 1$$
$$w = 3$$
The solution to the system is $\{(3, -1, 2, 1)\}$.

18. $\begin{bmatrix} 1 & 2 & 2 & | & 2 \\ 0 & 1 & -1 & | & 2 \\ 0 & 5 & 4 & | & 1 \end{bmatrix} -5R_2 + R_3$

$\begin{bmatrix} 1 & 2 & 2 & | & 2 \\ 0 & 1 & -1 & | & 2 \\ 0 & 0 & 9 & | & -9 \end{bmatrix}$

19. $\begin{bmatrix} 2 & -2 & 1 & | & -1 \\ 1 & 2 & -1 & | & 2 \\ 6 & 4 & 3 & | & 5 \end{bmatrix} \frac{1}{2}R_1$

$\begin{bmatrix} 1 & -1 & \frac{1}{2} & | & -\frac{1}{2} \\ 1 & 2 & -1 & | & 2 \\ 6 & 4 & 3 & | & 5 \end{bmatrix}$

20. $\begin{bmatrix} 1 & 2 & 3 & | & -5 \\ 2 & 1 & 1 & | & 1 \\ 1 & 1 & -1 & | & 8 \end{bmatrix} \begin{matrix} -2R_1 + R_2 \\ -1R_1 + R_3 \end{matrix}$

$\begin{bmatrix} 1 & 2 & 3 & | & -5 \\ 0 & -3 & -5 & | & 11 \\ 0 & -1 & -4 & | & 13 \end{bmatrix} R_2 \leftrightarrow R_3$

$\begin{bmatrix} 1 & 2 & 3 & | & -5 \\ 0 & -1 & -4 & | & 13 \\ 0 & -3 & -5 & | & 11 \end{bmatrix} -1R_2$

$\begin{bmatrix} 1 & 2 & 3 & | & -5 \\ 0 & 1 & 4 & | & -13 \\ 0 & -3 & -5 & | & 11 \end{bmatrix} 3R_2 + R_3$

$\begin{bmatrix} 1 & 2 & 3 & | & -5 \\ 0 & 1 & 4 & | & -13 \\ 0 & 0 & 7 & | & -28 \end{bmatrix} \frac{1}{7}R_3$

$\begin{bmatrix} 1 & 2 & 3 & | & -5 \\ 0 & 1 & 4 & | & -13 \\ 0 & 0 & 1 & | & -4 \end{bmatrix} -2R_2 + R_1$

$\begin{bmatrix} 1 & 0 & -5 & | & 21 \\ 0 & 1 & 4 & | & -13 \\ 0 & 0 & 1 & | & -4 \end{bmatrix} \begin{matrix} 5R_3 + R_1 \\ -4R_3 + R_2 \end{matrix}$

$\begin{bmatrix} 1 & 0 & 0 & | & 1 \\ 0 & 1 & 0 & | & 3 \\ 0 & 0 & 1 & | & -4 \end{bmatrix}$

The solution set is $\{(1, 3, -4)\}$.

21. $\begin{bmatrix} 1 & -2 & 1 & | & 0 \\ 0 & 1 & -3 & | & -1 \\ 0 & 2 & 5 & | & -2 \end{bmatrix} -2R_2 + R_3$

$\begin{bmatrix} 1 & -2 & 1 & | & 0 \\ 0 & 1 & -3 & | & -1 \\ 0 & 0 & 11 & | & 0 \end{bmatrix} \frac{1}{11}R_3$

$\begin{bmatrix} 1 & -2 & 1 & | & 0 \\ 0 & 1 & -3 & | & -1 \\ 0 & 0 & 1 & | & 0 \end{bmatrix} 2R_2 + R_1$

$\begin{bmatrix} 1 & 0 & -5 & | & -2 \\ 0 & 1 & -3 & | & -1 \\ 0 & 0 & 1 & | & 0 \end{bmatrix} \begin{matrix} 3R_3 + R_2 \\ 5R_3 + R_1 \end{matrix}$

$\begin{bmatrix} 1 & 0 & 0 & | & -2 \\ 0 & 1 & 0 & | & -1 \\ 0 & 0 & 1 & | & 0 \end{bmatrix}$

$x = -2; y = -1; z = 0$
The solution set is $\{(-2, -1, 0)\}$.

22. $\begin{bmatrix} 3 & 5 & -8 & 5 & | & -8 \\ 1 & 2 & -3 & 1 & | & -7 \\ 2 & 3 & -7 & 3 & | & -11 \\ 4 & 8 & -10 & 7 & | & -10 \end{bmatrix} R_1 \leftrightarrow R_2$

$\begin{bmatrix} 1 & 2 & -3 & 1 & | & -7 \\ 3 & 5 & -8 & 5 & | & -8 \\ 2 & 3 & -7 & 3 & | & -11 \\ 4 & 8 & -10 & 7 & | & -10 \end{bmatrix} \begin{matrix} -3R_1 + R_2 \\ -2R_1 + R_3 \\ -4R_1 + R_4 \end{matrix}$

$\begin{bmatrix} 1 & 2 & -3 & 1 & | & -7 \\ 0 & -1 & 1 & 2 & | & 13 \\ 0 & -1 & -1 & 1 & | & 3 \\ 0 & 0 & 2 & 3 & | & 18 \end{bmatrix} -1R_2$

$\begin{bmatrix} 1 & 2 & -3 & 1 & | & -7 \\ 0 & 1 & -1 & -2 & | & -13 \\ 0 & -1 & -1 & 1 & | & 3 \\ 0 & 0 & 2 & 3 & | & 18 \end{bmatrix} \begin{matrix} -2R_2 + R_1 \\ 1R_2 + R_3 \end{matrix}$

$\begin{bmatrix} 1 & 0 & -1 & 5 & | & 19 \\ 0 & 1 & -1 & -2 & | & -13 \\ 0 & 0 & -2 & -1 & | & -10 \\ 0 & 0 & 2 & 3 & | & 18 \end{bmatrix} -\frac{1}{2}R_3$

$\begin{bmatrix} 1 & 0 & -1 & 5 & | & 19 \\ 0 & 1 & -1 & -2 & | & -13 \\ 0 & 0 & 1 & \frac{1}{2} & | & 5 \\ 0 & 0 & 2 & 3 & | & 18 \end{bmatrix} \begin{matrix} 1R_3 + R_1 \\ 1R_3 + R_2 \\ -2R_3 + R_4 \end{matrix}$

$\begin{bmatrix} 1 & 0 & 0 & \frac{11}{2} & | & 24 \\ 0 & 1 & 0 & -\frac{3}{2} & | & -8 \\ 0 & 0 & 1 & \frac{1}{2} & | & 5 \\ 0 & 0 & 0 & 2 & | & 8 \end{bmatrix} \frac{1}{2}R_4$

$\begin{bmatrix} 1 & 0 & 0 & \frac{11}{2} & | & 24 \\ 0 & 1 & 0 & -\frac{3}{2} & | & -8 \\ 0 & 0 & 1 & \frac{1}{2} & | & 5 \\ 0 & 0 & 0 & 1 & | & 4 \end{bmatrix} \begin{matrix} -\frac{11}{2}R_4 + R_1 \\ \frac{3}{2}R_4 + R_2 \\ -\frac{1}{2}R_4 + R_3 \end{matrix}$

$\begin{bmatrix} 1 & 0 & 0 & 0 & | & 2 \\ 0 & 1 & 0 & 0 & | & -2 \\ 0 & 0 & 1 & 0 & | & 3 \\ 0 & 0 & 0 & 1 & | & 4 \end{bmatrix}$

The solution set is $\{(2, -2, 3, 4)\}$.

23. a. The function must satisfy:
$98 = 4a = 2b + c$
$138 = 16a + 4b + c$
$162 = 100a + 10b + c.$

239

$$\begin{bmatrix} 4 & 2 & 1 & \vline & 98 \\ 16 & 4 & 1 & \vline & 138 \\ 100 & 10 & 1 & \vline & 162 \end{bmatrix} \frac{1}{4}R_1$$

$$\begin{bmatrix} 1 & \frac{1}{2} & \frac{1}{4} & \vline & \frac{49}{2} \\ 16 & 4 & 1 & \vline & 138 \\ 100 & 10 & 1 & \vline & 162 \end{bmatrix} \begin{matrix} -16R_1 + R_2 \\ -100R_1 + R_3 \end{matrix}$$

$$\begin{bmatrix} 1 & \frac{1}{2} & \frac{1}{4} & \vline & \frac{49}{2} \\ 0 & -4 & -3 & \vline & -254 \\ 0 & -40 & -24 & \vline & -2288 \end{bmatrix} -\frac{1}{4}R_2$$

$$\begin{bmatrix} 1 & \frac{1}{2} & \frac{1}{4} & \vline & \frac{49}{2} \\ 0 & 1 & \frac{3}{4} & \vline & \frac{127}{2} \\ 0 & -40 & -24 & \vline & -2288 \end{bmatrix} 40R_2 + R_3$$

$$\begin{bmatrix} 1 & \frac{1}{2} & \frac{1}{4} & \vline & \frac{49}{2} \\ 0 & 1 & \frac{3}{4} & \vline & \frac{127}{2} \\ 0 & 0 & 6 & \vline & 252 \end{bmatrix} \frac{1}{6}R_3$$

$$\begin{bmatrix} 1 & \frac{1}{2} & \frac{1}{4} & \vline & \frac{49}{2} \\ 0 & 1 & \frac{3}{4} & \vline & \frac{127}{2} \\ 0 & 0 & 1 & \vline & 42 \end{bmatrix} \begin{matrix} -\frac{1}{4}R_3 + R_1 \\ -\frac{3}{4}R_3 + R_2 \end{matrix}$$

$$\begin{bmatrix} 1 & \frac{1}{2} & 0 & \vline & 14 \\ 0 & 1 & 0 & \vline & 32 \\ 0 & 0 & 1 & \vline & 42 \end{bmatrix} -\frac{1}{2}R_3 + R_1$$

$$\begin{bmatrix} 1 & 0 & 0 & \vline & -2 \\ 0 & 1 & 0 & \vline & 32 \\ 0 & 0 & 1 & \vline & 42 \end{bmatrix}$$

The function is $y = -2x^2 + 32x + 42$ and $a = -2$, $b = 32$ and $c = 42$.

b. $y = -2x^2 + 32x + 42$ is a parabola.

The maximum occurs when

$$x = \frac{-32}{2(-2)} = \frac{-32}{-4} = 8.$$

The air pollution level is a maximum 8 hours after 6 A.M., which is 2 P.M.
When $x = 8$, $y = -2(64) + 32(8) + 42$
$$= -128 + 256 + 42.$$
$$= 170.$$
The maximum level is 170 parts per million at 2 P.M.

24. $\begin{vmatrix} 3 & 2 \\ -1 & 5 \end{vmatrix} = 15 - (-2) = 17$

25. $\begin{vmatrix} -2 & -3 \\ -4 & -8 \end{vmatrix} = 16 - 12 = 4$

26. $\begin{vmatrix} 2 & 4 & -3 \\ 1 & -1 & 5 \\ -2 & 4 & 0 \end{vmatrix} = -2\begin{vmatrix} 4 & -3 \\ -1 & 5 \end{vmatrix} - 4\begin{vmatrix} 2 & -3 \\ 1 & 5 \end{vmatrix} + 0\begin{vmatrix} 2 & 4 \\ 1 & -1 \end{vmatrix}$

$$= -2(20 - 3) - 4[10 - (-3)] + 0$$
$$= -2(17) - 4(13)$$
$$= -34 - 52$$
$$= -86$$

27. $\begin{vmatrix} 4 & 7 & 0 \\ -5 & 6 & 0 \\ 3 & 2 & -4 \end{vmatrix} = 4\begin{vmatrix} 6 & 0 \\ 2 & -4 \end{vmatrix} + 5\begin{vmatrix} 7 & 0 \\ 2 & -4 \end{vmatrix} + 3\begin{vmatrix} 7 & 0 \\ 6 & 0 \end{vmatrix}$

$$= 4(-24 - 0) + 5(-28 - 0) + 3(0 - 0)$$
$$= 4(-24) + 5(-28) + 0$$
$$= -236$$

28. $\begin{vmatrix} 1 & 1 & 0 & 2 \\ 0 & 3 & 2 & 1 \\ 0 & -2 & 4 & 0 \\ 0 & 3 & 0 & 1 \end{vmatrix} = \begin{vmatrix} 3 & 2 & 1 \\ -2 & 4 & 0 \\ 3 & 0 & 1 \end{vmatrix}$

$$= 3\begin{vmatrix} 2 & 1 \\ 4 & 0 \end{vmatrix} + \begin{vmatrix} 3 & 2 \\ -2 & 4 \end{vmatrix}$$
$$= 3(0 - 4) + [12 - (-4)]$$
$$= 3(-4) + 16$$
$$= -12 + 16$$
$$= 4$$

29. $\begin{vmatrix} 2 & 2 & 2 & 2 \\ 0 & 2 & 2 & 2 \\ 0 & 0 & 2 & 2 \\ 0 & 0 & 0 & 2 \end{vmatrix} = 2\begin{vmatrix} 2 & 2 & 2 \\ 0 & 2 & 2 \\ 0 & 0 & 2 \end{vmatrix}$

$$= 2(2)\begin{vmatrix} 2 & 2 \\ 0 & 2 \end{vmatrix}$$
$$= 2(2)(4)$$
$$= 16$$

30. $D = \begin{vmatrix} 1 & -2 \\ 3 & 2 \end{vmatrix} = 2 - (-6) = 2 + 6 = 8$

$$D_x = \begin{vmatrix} 8 & -2 \\ -1 & 2 \end{vmatrix} = 16 - 2 = 14$$

$$D_y = \begin{vmatrix} 1 & 8 \\ 3 & -1 \end{vmatrix} = -1 - 24 = -25$$

$x = \dfrac{D_x}{D} = \dfrac{14}{8} = \dfrac{7}{4},\ y = \dfrac{D_y}{D} = \dfrac{-25}{8} = -\dfrac{25}{8}$

The solution to the system is $\left\{\left(\dfrac{7}{4},\ -\dfrac{25}{8}\right)\right\}$.

31. $D = \begin{vmatrix} 7 & 2 \\ 2 & 1 \end{vmatrix} = 7 - 4 = 3$

$D = \begin{vmatrix} 7 & 2 \\ 2 & 1 \end{vmatrix} = 7 - 4 = 3$

$D_x = \begin{vmatrix} 0 & 2 \\ -3 & 1 \end{vmatrix} = 0 - (-6) = 6$

$D_y = \begin{vmatrix} 7 & 0 \\ 2 & -3 \end{vmatrix} = -21 - 0 = -21$

$x = \dfrac{D_x}{D} = \dfrac{6}{3} = 2$

$y = \dfrac{D_y}{D} = \dfrac{-21}{3} = -7$

The solution to the system is $\{(2,\ -7)\}$.

32. $D = \begin{vmatrix} 1 & 2 & 2 \\ 2 & 4 & 7 \\ -2 & -5 & -2 \end{vmatrix}$

$= \begin{vmatrix} 1 & 2 & 2 \\ 0 & 0 & 3 \\ 0 & -1 & 2 \end{vmatrix}$

$= \begin{vmatrix} 0 & 3 \\ -1 & 2 \end{vmatrix}$

$= 0 - (-3)$

$= 3$

$D_x = \begin{vmatrix} 5 & 2 & 2 \\ 19 & 4 & 7 \\ 8 & -5 & -2 \end{vmatrix}$

$= 5 \begin{vmatrix} 4 & 7 \\ -5 & -2 \end{vmatrix} - 2 \begin{vmatrix} 19 & 7 \\ 8 & -2 \end{vmatrix} + 2 \begin{vmatrix} 19 & 4 \\ 8 & -5 \end{vmatrix}$

$= 5[-8 - (-35)] - 2(-38 - 56) + 2(-95 - 32)$

$= 5(27) - 2(-94) - 2(127)$

$= 135 + 188 - 254$

$= 69$

$D_y = \begin{vmatrix} 1 & 5 & 2 \\ 2 & 19 & 7 \\ -2 & 8 & -2 \end{vmatrix}$

$= \begin{vmatrix} 1 & 5 & 2 \\ 0 & 9 & 3 \\ 0 & 18 & 2 \end{vmatrix}$

$= \begin{vmatrix} 9 & 3 \\ 18 & 2 \end{vmatrix}$

$= 18 - 54$

$= -36$

$D_z = \begin{vmatrix} 1 & 2 & 5 \\ 2 & 4 & 19 \\ -2 & -5 & 8 \end{vmatrix}$

$= \begin{vmatrix} 1 & 2 & 5 \\ 0 & 0 & 9 \\ 0 & -1 & 18 \end{vmatrix}$

$= \begin{vmatrix} 0 & 9 \\ -1 & 18 \end{vmatrix}$

$= 0 - (-9)$

$= 9$

$x = \dfrac{D_x}{D} = \dfrac{69}{3} = 23,\ y = \dfrac{D_y}{D} = \dfrac{-36}{3} = -12,$

$z = \dfrac{D_z}{D} = \dfrac{9}{3} = 3$

The solution to the system is $\{(23,\ -12,\ 3)\}$.

33. $D = \begin{vmatrix} 2 & 1 & 0 \\ 0 & 1 & -2 \\ 3 & 0 & -2 \end{vmatrix}$

$= 2\begin{vmatrix} 1 & -2 \\ 0 & -2 \end{vmatrix} + 3\begin{vmatrix} 1 & 0 \\ 1 & -2 \end{vmatrix}$

$= 2(-2-0) + 3(-2-0)$

$= 2(-2) + 3(-2)$

$= -4 - 6$

$= -10$

$D_x = \begin{vmatrix} -4 & 1 & 0 \\ 0 & 1 & -2 \\ -11 & 0 & -2 \end{vmatrix}$

$= -1\begin{vmatrix} 0 & -2 \\ -11 & -2 \end{vmatrix} + 1\begin{vmatrix} -4 & 0 \\ -11 & -2 \end{vmatrix}$

$= -1(0-22) + 1(8-0)$

$= 22 + 8$

$= 30$

$D_y = \begin{vmatrix} 2 & -4 & 0 \\ 0 & 0 & -2 \\ 3 & -11 & -2 \end{vmatrix}$

$= 2\begin{vmatrix} 0 & -2 \\ -11 & -2 \end{vmatrix} + 3\begin{vmatrix} -4 & 0 \\ 0 & -2 \end{vmatrix}$

$= 2(0-22) + 3(8-0)$

$= 2(-22) + 3(8)$

$= -44 + 24$

$= -20$

$D_z = \begin{vmatrix} 2 & 1 & -4 \\ 0 & 1 & 0 \\ 3 & 0 & -11 \end{vmatrix}$

$= 2\begin{vmatrix} 1 & 0 \\ 0 & -11 \end{vmatrix} + 3\begin{vmatrix} 1 & -4 \\ 1 & 0 \end{vmatrix}$

$= 2(-11-0) + 3(0+4)$

$= 2(-11) + 3(+4) = -22 + 12$

$= -10$

$x = \dfrac{D_x}{D} = \dfrac{30}{-10} = -3$

$y = \dfrac{D_y}{D} = \dfrac{-20}{-10} = 2$

$z = \dfrac{D_z}{D} = \dfrac{-10}{-10} = 1$

The solution to the system is $\{(-3, 2, 1)\}$.

34. The quadratic function must satisfy
$f(20) = 400 = 400a + 20b + c$
$f(40) = 150 = 1600a + 40b + c$
$f(60) = 400 = 3600a + 60b + c$

$D = \begin{vmatrix} 400 & 20 & 1 \\ 1600 & 40 & 1 \\ 3600 & 60 & 1 \end{vmatrix}$

$= (400)(20)\begin{vmatrix} 1 & 1 & 1 \\ 4 & 2 & 1 \\ 9 & 3 & 1 \end{vmatrix}$

$= 8000\begin{vmatrix} 1 & 1 & 1 \\ 3 & 1 & 0 \\ 8 & 2 & 0 \end{vmatrix} = 8000\begin{vmatrix} 3 & 1 \\ 8 & 2 \end{vmatrix}$

$= 8000(6-8)$

$= 8000(-2)$

$= -16,000$

$D_a = \begin{vmatrix} 400 & 20 & 1 \\ 150 & 40 & 1 \\ 400 & 60 & 1 \end{vmatrix}$

$= (50)(20)\begin{vmatrix} 8 & 1 & 1 \\ 3 & 2 & 1 \\ 8 & 3 & 1 \end{vmatrix}$

$= 1000\begin{vmatrix} 8 & 1 & 1 \\ -5 & 1 & 0 \\ 0 & 2 & 0 \end{vmatrix}$

$= 1000\begin{vmatrix} -5 & 1 \\ 0 & 2 \end{vmatrix}$

$= 1000(-10-0)$

$= -10,000$

$D_b = \begin{vmatrix} 400 & 400 & 1 \\ 1600 & 150 & 1 \\ 3600 & 400 & 1 \end{vmatrix}$

$= (400)(50)\begin{vmatrix} 1 & 8 & 1 \\ 4 & 3 & 1 \\ 9 & 8 & 1 \end{vmatrix}$

$= 20,000\begin{vmatrix} 1 & 8 & 1 \\ 3 & -5 & 0 \\ 8 & 0 & 0 \end{vmatrix}$

$= 20,000\begin{vmatrix} 3 & -5 \\ 8 & 0 \end{vmatrix}$

242

$$= 20,000[0 - (-40)]$$
$$= 20,000(40)$$
$$= 800,000$$

$$D_c = \begin{vmatrix} 400 & 20 & 400 \\ 1600 & 40 & 150 \\ 3600 & 60 & 400 \end{vmatrix}$$

$$= (400)(20)(50)\begin{vmatrix} 1 & 1 & 8 \\ 4 & 2 & 3 \\ 9 & 3 & 8 \end{vmatrix}$$

$$= 400,000\begin{vmatrix} 1 & 0 & 0 \\ 4 & -2 & -29 \\ 2 & -6 & -64 \end{vmatrix}$$

$$= 400,000\begin{vmatrix} -2 & -29 \\ -6 & -64 \end{vmatrix}$$

$$= 400,000(128 - 174)$$
$$= 400,000(-46)$$
$$= -18,400,000$$

$$a = \frac{D_a}{D} = \frac{-10,000}{-16,000} = \frac{5}{8},$$

$$b = \frac{D_b}{D} = \frac{800,000}{-16,000} = -50,$$

$$c = \frac{D_c}{D} = \frac{-18,400,000}{-16,000} = 1150$$

The model is $f(x) = \frac{5}{8}x^2 - 50x + 1150$.

$$f(30) = \frac{5}{8}(900) - 50(30) + 1150$$
$$= 562.5 - 1500 + 1150$$
$$= 212.5$$

$$f(50) = \frac{5}{8}(2500) - 50(50) + 1150$$
$$= 1562.8 - 2500 + 1150$$
$$= 212.5$$

30- and 50-year-olds are involved in an average of 212.5 automobile accidents per day.

Chapter 3 Test

1. $x = y + 4$

$3x + 7y = -18$

Substitute $y + 4$ for x into second equation.

$3(y + 4) + 7y = -18$

$3y + 12 + 7y = -18$

$10y = -30$

$y = -3$

$x = -3 + 4 = 1$

The solution set to the system is $\{(1, -3)\}$.

2. $2x + 5y = -2$

$3x - 4y = 20$

Multiply the first equation by 3 and the second equation by -2 and add the result.

$6 + 15y = -6$

$\underline{-6x + 8y = -40}$

$23y = -46$

$y = -2$

Substitute $y = -2$ into the first equation:

$2x + 5(-2) = -2$

$2x - 10 = -2$

$2x = 8$

$x = 4$

The solution to the system is $\{(4, -2)\}$.

3. $x + y + z = 6 \,(1)$

$3x + 4y - 7z = 1 \,(2)$

$2x - y + 3z = 5 \,(3)$

Eliminate x by multiplying (1) by -3 and adding the result to (2) and by multiplying (1) by -2 and adding the result to (3).

$-3x - 3y - 3z = -18$

$\underline{3x + 4y - 7z = 1}$

$y - 10z = -17 \,(4)$

$-2x - 2y - 2z = -12$

$\underline{2x - y + 3z = 5}$

$-3y + z = -7 \,(5)$

Multiply (4) by 3 and add the result to (5) to eliminate y.

$3y - 30z = -51$

$\underline{-3y + z = -7}$

$-29z = -58$

$z = 2$

Substitute $z = 2$ into (5).

$-3y + 2 = -7$

$-3y = -9$

$y = 3$

Substitute $z = 2$ and $y = 3$ into (1).

$x + 3 + 2 = 6$

$x = 1$

The solution to the system is $\{(1, 3, 2)\}$.

4.   **a.** $C(x) = 360,000 + 850x$

    b. $R(x) = 1150x$

    c. $1150x = 360000 + 850x$

        $300x = 360000$

          $x = 1200$

243

$1150(1200) = 1,380,000$
1200 computers need to be sold to make
$1,380,00 for the company to break even.

5. $y = ax^2 + bx + c$

$(-1, -2): -2 = a - b + c$

$(2, 1): 1 = 4a + 2b + c$

$(-2, 1): 1 = 4a - 2b + c$

$4a + 2b + c = 1$

$\underline{-4a + 2b - c = -1}$

$4b = 0$

$b = 0$

$a + c = -2$

$4a + c = 1$

$\underline{-a - c = 2}$

$3a = 3$

$a = 1$

$a + c = -2$

$c = -3$

The quadratic function is $y = x^2 - 3$.

6. $\begin{bmatrix} 1 & 2 & -1 & | & -3 \\ 2 & -4 & 1 & | & -7 \\ -2 & 2 & -3 & | & 4 \end{bmatrix} \begin{matrix} \\ -2R_1 + R_2 \\ 2R_1 + R_3 \end{matrix}$

$\begin{bmatrix} 1 & 2 & -1 & | & -3 \\ 0 & -8 & 3 & | & -1 \\ 0 & 6 & -5 & | & -2 \end{bmatrix} -\tfrac{1}{8}R_2$

$\begin{bmatrix} 1 & 2 & -1 & | & -3 \\ 0 & 1 & -\tfrac{3}{8} & | & \tfrac{1}{8} \\ 0 & 6 & -5 & | & -2 \end{bmatrix} -6R_2 + R_3$

$\begin{bmatrix} 1 & 2 & -1 & | & -3 \\ 0 & 1 & -\tfrac{3}{8} & | & \tfrac{1}{8} \\ 0 & 0 & -\tfrac{11}{4} & | & -\tfrac{11}{4} \end{bmatrix} -\tfrac{4}{11}R_3$

$\begin{bmatrix} 1 & 2 & -1 & | & -3 \\ 0 & 1 & -\tfrac{3}{8} & | & \tfrac{1}{8} \\ 0 & 0 & 1 & | & 1 \end{bmatrix}$

$x + 2y - z = -3$

$y - \dfrac{3}{8}z = \dfrac{1}{8}$

$z = 1$

Using back substitution,

$y - \dfrac{3}{8}(1) = \dfrac{1}{8}$ and $x + 2\left(\dfrac{1}{2}\right) - 1 = -3$.

$y = \dfrac{1}{2}$ $x + 1 - 1 = -3$

$x = -3$

The solution to the system is $\left\{ \left(-3, \dfrac{1}{2}, 1 \right) \right\}$.

7. $\begin{vmatrix} 4 & -1 & 3 \\ 0 & 5 & -1 \\ 5 & 2 & 4 \end{vmatrix} = 4 \begin{vmatrix} 5 & -1 \\ 2 & 4 \end{vmatrix} + 5 \begin{vmatrix} -1 & 3 \\ 5 & -1 \end{vmatrix}$

$ = 4[20 - (-2)] + 5(1 - 15)$

$ = 4(22) + 5(-14)$

$ = 88 - 70$

$ = 18$

8. $D = \begin{vmatrix} 3 & 1 & -2 \\ 2 & 7 & 3 \\ 4 & -3 & -1 \end{vmatrix} = 3 \begin{vmatrix} 7 & 3 \\ -3 & -1 \end{vmatrix} - 1 \begin{vmatrix} 2 & 3 \\ 4 & -1 \end{vmatrix} - 2 \begin{vmatrix} 2 & 7 \\ 4 & -3 \end{vmatrix}$

$ = 3[-7 - (-9)] - 1(-2 - 12) - 2(-6 - 28)$

$ = 3(2) - 1(-14) - 2(-34)$

$ = 6 + 14 + 68$

$ = 88$

$D_x = \begin{vmatrix} -3 & 1 & -2 \\ 9 & 7 & 3 \\ 7 & -3 & -1 \end{vmatrix} = -3 \begin{vmatrix} 7 & 3 \\ -3 & -1 \end{vmatrix} - 1 \begin{vmatrix} 9 & 3 \\ 7 & -1 \end{vmatrix} - 2 \begin{vmatrix} 9 & 7 \\ 7 & -3 \end{vmatrix}$

$ = -3[-7 - (-9)] - 1(-9 - 21) - 2(-27 - 49)$

$ = -3(2) - 1(-30) - 2(-76)$

$ = -6 + 30 + 152$

$ = 176$

$x = \dfrac{D_x}{D} = \dfrac{176}{88} = 2$

Cumulative Review Exercises (Chapters 1–3)

1.   Domain: $(-\infty, \infty)$ Range: $[-\infty, 3)$

2. -1 and 1 are both zeros with a minimum multiplicity of 1.

3.   The relative maximum is $y = 3$ and it occurs at $x = 0$.

4. $f(x)$ is decreasing on the interval $(0, 2)$.

5. At $x = -0.7$, the curve is above the x-axis and thus $f(x)$ is positive.

6. $(f \circ f)(-1) = f(f(-1)) = f(0) = 3$

7. $f(-x) = f(x)$ thus the function is even.

8. The graph of $g(x) = f(x+2) - 1$ can be obtained by shifting $f(x)$ 2 units left and 1 unit down.

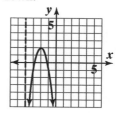

$g(x) = f(x+2) - 1$

9. The graph of $h(x) = \frac{1}{2}f\left(\frac{1}{2}x\right)$ can be obtained by shrinking the graph of $f(x)$ horizontally by a factor of $\frac{1}{2}$ and vertically by a factor of $\frac{1}{2}$.

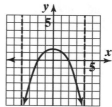

$h(x) = \frac{1}{2}f\left(\frac{1}{2}x\right)$

10.
$$\sqrt{x^2 - 3x} = 2x - 6$$
$$x^2 - 3x = 4x^2 - 24x + 36$$
$$3x^2 - 21x + 36 = 0$$
$$x^2 - 7x + 12 = 0$$
$$(x - 3)(x - 4) = 0$$
$$x = 3, 4$$
The solution set is $\{3, 4\}$.

11.
$$4x^2 = 8x - 7$$
$$4x^2 - 8x + 7 = 0$$
$$x = \frac{8 \pm \sqrt{64 - 112}}{8} = \frac{8 \pm \sqrt{-48}}{8}$$
$$= \frac{8 \pm 4\sqrt{3}i}{8} = \frac{2 \pm \sqrt{3}i}{2}$$
The solution set is $\left\{\frac{2 + i\sqrt{3}}{2}, \frac{2 - i\sqrt{3}}{2}\right\}$.

12. $\left|\dfrac{x}{3} + 2\right| < 4$

$$-4 < \frac{x}{3} + 2 < 4$$
$$-6 < \frac{x}{3} < 2$$
$$-18 < x < 6$$
The solution is $\{x \mid -18 < x < 6\}$ or $(-18, 6)$.

13.
$$6x - 3(5x + 2) = 4(1 - x)$$
$$6x - 15x - 6 = 4 - 4x$$
$$-9x - 6 = 4 - 4x$$
$$-5x = 10$$
$$x = -2$$
The solution set is $\{-2\}$.

14.
$$x^{\frac{1}{2}} - 2x^{\frac{1}{4}} - 15 = 0$$
$$\sqrt[4]{x^2} - 2\sqrt[4]{x} - 15 = 0$$
$$\left(\sqrt[4]{x} + 3\right)\left(\sqrt[4]{x} - 5\right) = 0$$

$\sqrt[4]{x} + 3 = 0$ $\sqrt[4]{x} - 5 = 0$

$\sqrt[4]{x} = -3$ or $\sqrt[4]{x} = 5$

$x = (-3)^4$ $x = 5^4$

$x = 81$ $x = 625$

81 does not check. The solution set is $\{625\}$.

15.
$$x + 2y + 3z = -2$$
$$3x + 3y + 10z = -2$$
$$2y - 5z = 6$$
Multiply equation 1 by -3 and add to equation 2.
$$-3x - 6y - 9z = 6$$
$$\underline{3x + 3y + 10z = -2}$$
$$-3y + z = 4 \quad \text{Equation 4}$$
Multiply equation 4 by 5 and add to equation 3 and solve for y.
$$-15y + 5z = 20$$
$$\underline{2y - 5z = 6}$$
$$-13y = 26$$
$$y = -2$$
Back-substitute to find z.
$$-3y + z = 4$$
$$-3(-2) + z = 4$$
$$z = -2$$

Back-substitute to find x.
$$x + 2y + 3z = -2$$
$$x + 2(-2) + 3(-2) = -2$$
$$x = 8$$
The solution set is $\{8, -2, -2\}$.

16. vertex: $(-2, -4)$
y-intercept:
$$f(0) = (0 + 2)^2 - 4 = 0$$
x-intercepts:
$$(x + 2)^2 - 4 = 0$$
$$x^2 + 4x + 4 - 4 = 0$$
$$x^2 + 4x = 0$$
$$x(x + 4) = 0$$
$$x = 0, x - 4$$

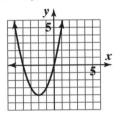

$$f(x) = (x + 2)^2 - 4$$

17.

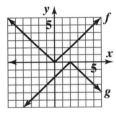

$$f(x) = |x|$$
$$g(x) = -|x - 2|$$

18. $(f \circ g)(x) = f(g(x))$
$$= 2(1 - x)^2 - (1 - x) - 1$$
$$= 2x^2 - 3x$$
$(g \circ f) = g(f(x))$
$$= 1 - (2x^2 - x - 1)$$
$$= 1 - 2x^2 + x + 1$$
$$= -2x^2 + x + 2$$

19. $\dfrac{f(x + h) - f(x)}{h}$

$$= \frac{\left[2(x + h)^2 - (x + h) - 1\right] - \left[2x^2 - x - 1\right]}{h}$$

$$= \frac{2x^2 + 4hx + 2h^2 - x - h - 1 - 2x^2 + x + 1}{h}$$

$$= \frac{4hx + 2h^2 - h}{h}$$

$$= 4x + 2h - 1$$

20. Find slope: $m = \dfrac{4 - (-2)}{2 - 4} = \dfrac{6}{-2} = -3$
Use point slope form to find an equation.
$$y - y_1 = m(x - x_1)$$
$$y - 4 = -3(x - 2)$$
Put in slope-intercept form.
$$y - 4 = -3(x - 2)$$
$$y - 4 = -3x + 6$$
$$y = -3x + 10$$

21. Find the slope of the perpendicular line by putting in slope-intercept form.
$$x + 3y - 6 = 0$$
$$3y = -x + 6$$
$$y = -\frac{1}{3}x + 2$$

The slope of the perpendicular line is $-\dfrac{1}{3}$ so the slope of the desired line is the negative reciprocal, or 3.
Use point slope form to find an equation.
$$y - y_1 = m(x - x_1)$$
$$y - 0 = 3(x + 1)$$
Put in slope-intercept form.
$$y - 0 = 3(x + 1)$$
$$y = 3x + 3$$

22. Let x = the amount invested at 12%
Let $4000 - x$ = the amount invested at 14%
$$0.12x + 0.14(4000 - x) = 508$$
$$0.12x + 560 - 0.14x = 508$$
$$-0.02x = -52$$
$$x = \frac{-52}{-0.02}$$
$$x = 2600$$

$4000 - x = 4000 - 2600 = 1400$
Thus, \$2600 was invested at 12% and \$1400 was invested at 14%.

23.
$$L = 2W + 1$$
$$LW = 36$$
$$W(2W+1) = 36$$
$$2W^2 + W - 36 = 0$$
$$(2W+9)(W-4) = 0$$
$$W = -\frac{9}{2} \text{ or } 4$$

Length cannot be negative. If $W = 4$, $4L = 36$, $L = 9$. The dimensions are 4 m by 9 m.

24.
$$2x^2 = 4 - x$$
$$2x^2 + x - 4 = 0$$
$$x = \frac{-1 \pm \sqrt{1^2 - 4(2)(-4)}}{2(2)}$$
$$x = \frac{-1 \pm \sqrt{1-32}}{4}$$
$$x = \frac{-1 \pm \sqrt{33}}{4}$$

The solution set is $\left\{\frac{-1+\sqrt{33}}{4}, \frac{-1-\sqrt{33}}{4}\right\}$.

25.
$$5x + 8 \le 7(1+x)$$
$$5x + 8 \le 7 + 7x$$
$$-2x \le -1$$
$$x \ge \frac{1}{2}$$

The solution set is $\left\{x \,\middle|\, x \ge \frac{1}{2}\right\}$ or $\left[\frac{1}{2}, \infty\right)$.

26.
$$\sqrt{2x+4} - \sqrt{x+3} - 1 = 0$$
$$\sqrt{2x+4} = \sqrt{x+3} + 1$$
$$2x + 4 = x + 3 + 2\sqrt{x+3} + 1$$
$$x = 2\sqrt{x+3}$$
$$x^2 = 4(x+3)$$
$$x^2 = 4x + 12$$
$$x^2 - 4x - 12 = 0$$
$$(x-6)(x+2) = 0$$
$$x = 6 \text{ or } x = -2$$

$x = -2$ does not check. The solution set is $\{6\}$.

27.
$$\left[\begin{array}{rrr|r} 1 & -1 & 1 & 17 \\ 2 & 3 & 1 & 8 \\ -4 & 1 & 5 & -2 \end{array}\right] \begin{array}{l} \\ -2R_1 + R_2 \\ 4R_1 + R_3 \end{array}$$

$$\left[\begin{array}{rrr|r} 1 & -1 & 1 & 17 \\ 0 & 5 & -1 & -26 \\ 0 & -3 & 9 & 66 \end{array}\right] \begin{array}{l} \\ -\frac{1}{3}R_3 \\ \\ \end{array}$$

$$\left[\begin{array}{rrr|r} 1 & -1 & 1 & 17 \\ 0 & 1 & -3 & -22 \\ 0 & 5 & -1 & -26 \end{array}\right] \begin{array}{l} \\ -5R_2 + R_3 \\ 1R_2 + R_1 \end{array}$$

$$\left[\begin{array}{rrr|r} 1 & 0 & -2 & -5 \\ 0 & 1 & -3 & -22 \\ 0 & 0 & 14 & 84 \end{array}\right] \begin{array}{l} \\ \frac{1}{14}R_3 \\ \\ \end{array}$$

$$\left[\begin{array}{rrrr} 1 & 0 & -2 & -5 \\ 0 & 1 & -3 & -22 \\ 0 & 0 & 1 & 6 \end{array}\right] \begin{array}{l} \\ 3R_3 + R_2 \\ 2R_3 + R_1 \end{array}$$

$$\left[\begin{array}{rrrr} 1 & 0 & 0 & 7 \\ 0 & 1 & 0 & -4 \\ 0 & 0 & 1 & 6 \end{array}\right]$$

$x = 7$ $y = -4$ $z = 6$
The solution set is $\{(7, -4, 6)\}$.

28.
$$D = \begin{vmatrix} 1 & -2 & 1 \\ 2 & 1 & -1 \\ 3 & 2 & -2 \end{vmatrix}$$
$$= 1\begin{vmatrix} 1 & -1 \\ 2 & -2 \end{vmatrix} - 2\begin{vmatrix} -2 & 1 \\ 2 & -2 \end{vmatrix} + 3\begin{vmatrix} -2 & 1 \\ 1 & 1 \end{vmatrix}$$
$$= 1(-2+2) - 2(4-2) + 3(2-1)$$
$$= 0 - 4 + 3$$
$$= -1$$

$$D_y = \begin{vmatrix} 1 & 7 & 1 \\ 2 & 0 & -1 \\ 3 & -2 & -2 \end{vmatrix} = 7\begin{vmatrix} 2 & -1 \\ 3 & -2 \end{vmatrix} - 2\begin{vmatrix} 1 & 1 \\ 2 & -1 \end{vmatrix}$$
$$= 7(-4+3) - 2(-1-2)$$
$$= -7 + 6 = 1$$

$$y = \frac{D_y}{D} = \frac{1}{-1} = -1$$
$$y = -1$$

29. $y = -\dfrac{2}{3}x - 1$

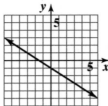

x	y
0	−1
3	−3
−3	1

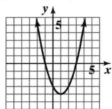

$$y = -\frac{2}{3}x - 1$$

30. $f(x) = x^2 - 2x - 3$

$\qquad f(x) = (x^2 - 2x + 1) - 3 - 1$

$\qquad f(x) = (x-1)^2 - 4$

$$f(x) = x^2 - 2x - 3$$

31. $(x-1)^2 + (y+1)^2 = 9$

$\qquad$ center $(1, -1)$

$\qquad$ radius $= 3$

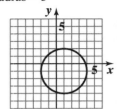

$$(x-1)^2 + (y+1)^2 = 9$$

Chapter 4

Section 4.1

Check Point Exercises

1. The radian measure of a central angle is the length of the intercepted arc, *s*, divided by the circle's radius, *r*. The length of the intercepted arc is 42 feet: *s* = 42 feet. The circle's radius is 12 feet: *r* = 12 feet. Now use the formula for radian measure to find the radian measure of θ.

    $$\theta = \frac{s}{r} = \frac{42 \text{ feet}}{12 \text{ feet}} = 3.5$$

    Thus, the radian measure of θ is 3.5

2. **a.** $60° = 60° \cdot \frac{\pi \text{ radians}}{180°} = \frac{60\pi}{180} \text{ radians}$

    $\quad = \frac{\pi}{3} \text{ radians}$

    b. $270° = 270° \cdot \frac{\pi \text{ radians}}{180°} = \frac{270\pi}{180} \text{ radians}$

    $\quad = \frac{3\pi}{2} \text{ radians}$

    c. $-300° = -300° \cdot \frac{\pi \text{ radians}}{180°} = \frac{-300\pi}{180} \text{ radians}$

    $\quad = -\frac{5\pi}{3} \text{ radians}$

3. **a.** $\frac{\pi}{4} \text{ radians} = \frac{\pi \text{ radians}}{4} \cdot \frac{180°}{\pi \text{ radians}}$

    $\quad = \frac{180°}{4} = 45°$

    b. $-\frac{4\pi}{3} \text{ radians} = -\frac{4\pi \text{ radians}}{3} \cdot \frac{180°}{\pi}$

    $\quad = -\frac{4 \cdot 180°}{3} = -240°$

    c. $6 \text{ radians} = 6 \text{ radians} \cdot \frac{180°}{\pi \text{ radians}}$

    $\quad = \frac{6 \cdot 180°}{\pi} \approx 343.8°$

4. **a.**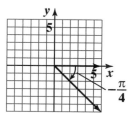

    b.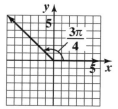

    c.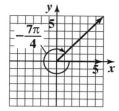

    d.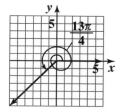

5. **a.** For a 400° angle, subtract 360° to find a positive coterminal angle.
    $400° - 360° = 40°$

    b. For a −135° angle, add 360° to find a positive coterminal angle.
    $-135° + 360° = 225°$

6. **a.** $\frac{13\pi}{5} - 2\pi = \frac{13\pi}{5} - \frac{10\pi}{5} = \frac{3\pi}{5}$

    b. $-\frac{\pi}{15} + 2\pi = -\frac{\pi}{15} + \frac{30\pi}{15} = \frac{29\pi}{15}$

7. **a.** $855° - 360° \cdot 2 = 855° - 720° = 135°$

    b. $\frac{17\pi}{3} - 2\pi \cdot 2 = \frac{17\pi}{3} - 4\pi$

    $\quad = \frac{17\pi}{3} - \frac{12\pi}{3} = \frac{5\pi}{3}$

249

c. $\quad -\dfrac{25\pi}{6} + 2\pi \cdot 3 = -\dfrac{25\pi}{6} + 6\pi$

$\qquad = -\dfrac{25\pi}{6} + \dfrac{36\pi}{6} = \dfrac{11\pi}{6}$

8. The formula $s = r\theta$ can only be used when θ is expressed in radians. Thus, we begin by converting $45°$ to radians. Multiply by

$\dfrac{\pi \text{ radians}}{180°} \cdot$

$45° = 45° \cdot \dfrac{\pi \text{ radians}}{180°} = \dfrac{45}{180}\pi \text{ radians}$

$\qquad = \dfrac{\pi}{4} \text{ radians}$

Now we can use the formula $s = r\theta$ to find the length of the arc. The circle's radius is 6 inches : $r = 6$ inches. The measure of the central angle in radians is $\dfrac{\pi}{4} : \theta = \dfrac{\pi}{4}$. The length of the arc intercepted by this central angle is

$s = r\theta = (6 \text{ inches})\left(\dfrac{\pi}{4}\right) = \dfrac{6\pi}{4} \text{ inches} \approx 4.71 \text{ inches.}$

9. We are given ω, the angular speed.
$\omega = 45$ revolutions per minute
We use the formula $v = r\omega$ to find v, the linear speed. Before applying the formula, we must express ω in radians per minute.

$\omega = \dfrac{45 \text{ revolutions}}{1 \text{ minute}} \cdot \dfrac{2\pi \text{ radians}}{1 \text{ revolution}}$

$\quad = \dfrac{90\pi \text{ radians}}{1 \text{ minute}}$

The angular speed of the propeller is 90π radians per minute. The linear speed is

$v = r\omega = 1.5 \text{ inches} \cdot \dfrac{90\pi}{1 \text{ minute}} = \dfrac{135\pi \text{ inches}}{\text{minute}}$

The linear speed is 135π inches per minute, which is approximately 424 inches per minute.

Exercise Set 4.1

1. obtuse

3. acute

5. straight

7. $\theta = \dfrac{s}{r} = \dfrac{40 \text{ inches}}{10 \text{ inches}} = 4 \text{ radians}$

9. $\theta = \dfrac{s}{r} = \dfrac{8 \text{ yards}}{6 \text{ yards}} = \dfrac{4}{3} \text{ radians}$

11. $\theta = \dfrac{s}{r} = \dfrac{400 \text{ centimeters}}{100 \text{ centimeters}} = 4 \text{ radians}$

13. $45° = 45° \cdot \dfrac{\pi \text{ radians}}{180°}$

$\qquad = \dfrac{45\pi}{180} \text{ radians}$

$\qquad = \dfrac{\pi}{4} \text{ radians}$

15. $135° = 135° \cdot \dfrac{\pi \text{ radians}}{180°}$

$\qquad = \dfrac{135\pi}{180} \text{ radians}$

$\qquad = \dfrac{3\pi}{4} \text{ radians}$

17. $300° = 300° \cdot \dfrac{\pi \text{ radians}}{180°}$

$\qquad = \dfrac{300\pi}{180} \text{ radians}$

$\qquad = \dfrac{5\pi}{3} \text{ radians}$

19. $-225° = -225° \cdot \dfrac{\pi \text{ radians}}{180°}$

$\qquad = -\dfrac{225\pi}{180} \text{ radians}$

$\qquad = -\dfrac{5\pi}{4} \text{ radians}$

21. $\dfrac{\pi}{2} \text{ radians} = \dfrac{\pi \text{ radians}}{2} \cdot \dfrac{180°}{\pi \text{ radians}}$

$\qquad = \dfrac{180°}{2}$

$\qquad = 90°$

23. $\dfrac{2\pi}{3} \text{ radians} = \dfrac{2\pi \text{ radians}}{3} \cdot \dfrac{180°}{\pi \text{ radians}}$

$\qquad = \dfrac{2 \cdot 180°}{3}$

$\qquad = 120°$

250

25. $\dfrac{7\pi}{6}$ radians $= \dfrac{7\pi \text{ radians}}{6} \cdot \dfrac{180°}{\pi \text{ radians}}$

$\qquad\qquad = \dfrac{7 \cdot 180°}{6}$

$\qquad\qquad = 210°$

27. -3π radians $= -3\pi$ radians $\cdot \dfrac{180°}{\pi \text{ radians}}$

$\qquad\qquad = -3 \cdot 180°$

$\qquad\qquad = -540°$

29. $18° = 18° \cdot \dfrac{\pi \text{ radians}}{180°}$

$\qquad = \dfrac{18\pi}{180}$ radians

$\qquad \approx 0.31$ radians

31. $-40° = -40° \cdot \dfrac{\pi \text{ radians}}{180°}$

$\qquad = -\dfrac{40\pi}{180}$ radians

$\qquad \approx -0.70$ radians

33. $200° = 200° \cdot \dfrac{\pi \text{ radians}}{180°}$

$\qquad = \dfrac{200\pi}{180}$ radians

$\qquad \approx 3.49$ radians

35. 2 radians $= 2$ radians $\cdot \dfrac{180°}{\pi \text{ radians}}$

$\qquad\qquad = \dfrac{2 \cdot 180°}{\pi}$

$\qquad\qquad \approx 114.59°$

37. $\dfrac{\pi}{13}$ radians $= \dfrac{\pi \text{ radians}}{13} \cdot \dfrac{180°}{\pi \text{ radians}}$

$\qquad\qquad = \dfrac{180°}{13}$

$\qquad\qquad \approx 13.85°$

39. -4.8 radians $= -4.8$ radians $\cdot \dfrac{180°}{\pi \text{ radians}}$

$\qquad\qquad = \dfrac{-4.8 \cdot 180°}{\pi}$

$\qquad\qquad \approx -275.02°$

41.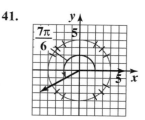

43.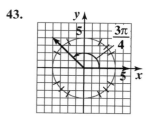

45.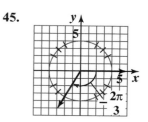

47.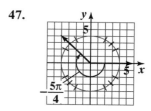

49.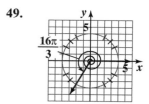

51.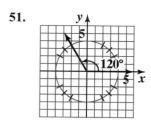

53.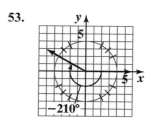

251

55.

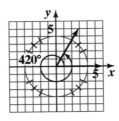

57. $395° - 360° = 35°$

59. $-150° + 360° = 210°$

61. $-765° + 360° \cdot 3 = -765° + 1080° = 315°$

63. $\dfrac{19\pi}{6} - 2\pi = \dfrac{19\pi}{6} - \dfrac{12\pi}{6} = \dfrac{7\pi}{6}$

65. $\dfrac{23\pi}{5} - 2\pi \cdot 2 = \dfrac{23\pi}{5} - 4\pi = \dfrac{23\pi}{5} - \dfrac{20\pi}{5} = \dfrac{3\pi}{5}$

67. $-\dfrac{\pi}{50} + 2\pi = -\dfrac{\pi}{50} + \dfrac{100\pi}{50} = \dfrac{99\pi}{50}$

69. $-\dfrac{31\pi}{7} + 2\pi \cdot 3 = -\dfrac{31\pi}{7} + 6\pi$

$= -\dfrac{31\pi}{7} + \dfrac{42\pi}{7} = \dfrac{11\pi}{7}$

71. $r = 12$ inches, $\theta = 45°$

Begin by converting $45°$ to radians, in order to use the formula $s = r\theta$.

$45° = 45° \cdot \dfrac{\pi \text{ radians}}{180°} = \dfrac{\pi}{4}$ radians

Now use the formula $s = r\theta$.

$s = r\theta = 12 \cdot \dfrac{\pi}{4} = 3\pi$ inches ≈ 9.42 inches

73. $r = 8$ feet, $\theta = 225°$

Begin by converting $225°$ to radians, in order to use the formula $s = r\theta$.

$225° = 225° \cdot \dfrac{\pi \text{ radians}}{180°} = \dfrac{5\pi}{4}$ radians

Now use the formula $s = r\theta$.

$s = r\theta = 8 \cdot \dfrac{5\pi}{4} = 10\pi$ feet ≈ 31.42 feet

75. 6 revolutions per second

$= \dfrac{6 \text{ revolutions}}{1 \text{ second}} \cdot \dfrac{2\pi \text{ radians}}{1 \text{ revolutions}} = \dfrac{12\pi \text{ radians}}{1 \text{ seconds}}$

$= 12\pi$ radians per second

77. $-\dfrac{4\pi}{3}$ and $\dfrac{2\pi}{3}$

79. $-\dfrac{3\pi}{4}$ and $\dfrac{5\pi}{4}$

81. $-\dfrac{\pi}{2}$ and $\dfrac{3\pi}{2}$

83. $\dfrac{55}{60} \cdot 2\pi = \dfrac{11\pi}{6}$

85. 3 minutes and 40 seconds equals 220 seconds.

$\dfrac{220}{60} \cdot 2\pi = \dfrac{22\pi}{3}$

87. First, convert to degrees.

$\dfrac{1}{6}$ revolution $= \dfrac{1}{6}$ revolution $\cdot \dfrac{360°}{1 \text{ revolution}}$

$= \dfrac{1}{6} \cdot 360° = 60°$

Now, convert $60°$ to radians.

$60° = 60° \cdot \dfrac{\pi \text{ radians}}{180°} = \dfrac{60\pi}{180}$ radians

$= \dfrac{\pi}{3}$ radians

Therefore, $\dfrac{1}{6}$ revolution is equivalent to $60°$ or

$\dfrac{\pi}{3}$ radians.

89. The distance that the tip of the minute hand moves is given by its arc length, s. Since $s = r\theta$, we begin by finding r and θ. We are given that $r = 8$ inches. The minute hand moves from 12 to 2 o'clock, or $\dfrac{1}{6}$ of a complete revolution. The formula $s = r\theta$ can only be used when θ is expressed in radians. We must convert $\dfrac{1}{6}$ revolution to radians.

$\dfrac{1}{6}$ revolution $= \dfrac{1}{6}$ revolution $\cdot \dfrac{2\pi \text{ radians}}{1 \text{ revolution}}$

$= \dfrac{\pi}{3}$ radians

The distance the tip of the minute hand moves is

$s = r\theta = (8 \text{ inches})\left(\dfrac{\pi}{3}\right) = \dfrac{8\pi}{3}$ inches

≈ 8.38 inches.

252

91. The length of each arc is given by $s = r\theta$. We are given that $r = 24$ inches and $\theta = 90°$. The formula $s = r\theta$ can only be used when θ is expressed in radians.

$$90° = 90° \cdot \frac{\pi \text{ radians}}{180°} = \frac{90\pi}{180} \text{ radians}$$

$$= \frac{\pi}{2} \text{ radians}$$

The length of each arc is

$$s = r\theta = (24 \text{ inches})\left(\frac{\pi}{2}\right) = 12\pi \text{ inches}$$

$$\approx 37.70 \text{ inches.}$$

93. Recall that $\theta = \frac{s}{r}$. We are given that $s = 8000$ miles and $r = 4000$ miles.

$$\theta = \frac{s}{r} = \frac{8000 \text{ miles}}{4000 \text{ miles}} = 2 \text{ radians}$$

Now, convert 2 radians to degrees.

$$2 \text{ radians} = 2 \text{ radians} \cdot \frac{180°}{\pi \text{ radians}} \approx 114.59°$$

95. Recall that $s = r\theta$. We are given that $r = 4000$ miles and $\theta = 30°$. The formula $s = r\theta$ can only be used when θ is expressed in radians.

$$30° = 30° \cdot \frac{\pi \text{ radians}}{180°} = \frac{30\pi}{180} \text{ radians}$$

$$= \frac{\pi}{6} \text{ radians}$$

$$s = r\theta = (4000 \text{ miles})\left(\frac{\pi}{6}\right) \approx 2094 \text{ miles}$$

To the nearest mile, the distance from A to B is 2094 miles.

97. Linear speed is given by $\nu = r\omega$. We are given that $\omega = \frac{\pi}{12}$ radians per hour and $r = 4000$ miles. Therefore,

$$\nu = r\omega = (4000 \text{ miles})\left(\frac{\pi}{12}\right)$$

$$= \frac{4000\pi}{12} \text{ miles per hour}$$

$$\approx 1047 \text{ miles per hour}$$

The linear speed is about 1047 miles per hour.

99. Linear speed is given by $\nu = r\omega$. We are given that $r = 12$ feet and the wheel rotates at 20 revolutions per minute.
20 revolutions per minute

$$= 20 \text{ revolutions per minute} \cdot \frac{2\pi \text{ radians}}{1 \text{ revolution}}$$

$$= 40\pi \text{ radians per minute}$$

$$\nu = r\omega = (12 \text{ feet})(40\pi)$$

$$\approx 1508 \text{ feet per minute}$$

The linear speed of the wheel is about 1508 feet per minute.

113.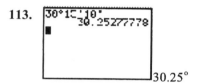

30.25°

115.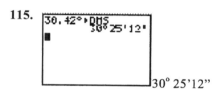

30° 25'12"

117. A right angle measures 90° and

$$90° = \frac{\pi}{2} \text{ radians} \approx 1.57 \text{ radians.}$$

If $\theta = \frac{3}{2}$ radians $= 1.5$ radians, θ is smaller than a right angle.

119. $s = r\theta$

Begin by changing $\theta = 26°$ to radians.

$$26° = 26° \cdot \frac{\pi}{180°} = \frac{13\pi}{90} \text{ radians}$$

$$s = 4000 \cdot \frac{13\pi}{90}$$

$$\approx 1815 \text{ miles}$$

To the nearest mile, Miami, Florida is 1815 miles north of the equator.

Section 4.2

Checkpoint Exercises

1. Use the Pythagorean Theorem, $c^2 = a^2 + b^2$, to find c.

   $a = 3, \ b = 4$

   $c^2 = a^2 + b^2 = 3^2 + 4^2 = 9 + 16 = 25$

   $c = \sqrt{25} = 5$

   Referring to these lengths as opposite, adjacent, and hypotenuse, we have

   $\sin\theta = \dfrac{\text{opposite}}{\text{hypotenuse}} = \dfrac{3}{5}$

   $\cos\theta = \dfrac{\text{adjacent}}{\text{hypotenuse}} = \dfrac{4}{5}$

   $\tan\theta = \dfrac{\text{opposite}}{\text{adjacent}} = \dfrac{3}{4}$

   $\csc\theta = \dfrac{\text{hypotenuse}}{\text{opposite}} = \dfrac{5}{3}$

   $\sec\theta = \dfrac{\text{hypotenuse}}{\text{adjacent}} = \dfrac{5}{4}$

   $\cot\theta = \dfrac{\text{adjacent}}{\text{opposite}} = \dfrac{4}{3}$

2. Use the Pythagorean Theorem, $c^2 = a^2 + b^2$, to find b.

   $a^2 + b^2 = c^2$

   $1^2 + b^2 = 5^2$

   $1 + b^2 = 25$

   $b^2 = 24$

   $b = \sqrt{24} = 2\sqrt{6}$

   Note that side a is opposite θ and side b is adjacent to θ.

   $\sin\theta = \dfrac{\text{opposite}}{\text{hypotenuse}} = \dfrac{1}{5}$

   $\cos\theta = \dfrac{\text{adjacent}}{\text{hypotenuse}} = \dfrac{2\sqrt{6}}{5}$

   $\tan\theta = \dfrac{\text{opposite}}{\text{adjacent}} = \dfrac{1}{2\sqrt{6}} = \dfrac{\sqrt{6}}{12}$

   $\csc\theta = \dfrac{\text{hypotenuse}}{\text{opposite}} = \dfrac{5}{1} = 5$

   $\sec\theta = \dfrac{\text{hypotenuse}}{\text{adjacent}} = \dfrac{5}{2\sqrt{6}} = \dfrac{5\sqrt{6}}{12}$

   $\cot\theta = \dfrac{\text{adjacent}}{\text{opposite}} = \dfrac{2\sqrt{6}}{1} = 2\sqrt{6}$

3. Apply the definitions of these three trigonometric functions.

   $\csc 45° = \dfrac{\text{length of hypotenuse}}{\text{length of side opposite } 45°}$

   $= \dfrac{\sqrt{2}}{1} = \sqrt{2}$

   $\sec 45° = \dfrac{\text{length of hypotenuse}}{\text{length of side adjacent to } 45°}$

   $= \dfrac{\sqrt{2}}{1} = \sqrt{2}$

   $\cot 45° = \dfrac{\text{length of side adjacent to } 45°}{\text{length of side opposite } 45°}$

   $= \dfrac{1}{1} = 1$

4. $\tan 60° = \dfrac{\text{length of side opposite } 60°}{\text{length of side adjacent to } 60°}$

   $= \dfrac{\sqrt{3}}{1} = \sqrt{3}$

   $\tan 30° = \dfrac{\text{length of side opposite } 30°}{\text{length of side adjacent to } 30°}$

   $= \dfrac{1}{\sqrt{3}} = \dfrac{1}{\sqrt{3}} \cdot \dfrac{\sqrt{3}}{3} = \dfrac{\sqrt{3}}{3}$

5. $\tan\theta = \dfrac{\sin\theta}{\cos\theta} = \dfrac{\frac{2}{3}}{\frac{\sqrt{5}}{3}}$

   $= \dfrac{2}{3} \cdot \dfrac{3}{\sqrt{5}} = \dfrac{2}{\sqrt{5}}$

   $= \dfrac{2}{\sqrt{5}} \cdot \dfrac{\sqrt{5}}{\sqrt{5}} = \dfrac{2\sqrt{5}}{5}$

   $\csc\theta = \dfrac{1}{\sin\theta} = \dfrac{1}{\frac{2}{3}} = \dfrac{3}{2}$

   $\sec\theta = \dfrac{1}{\cos\theta} = \dfrac{1}{\frac{\sqrt{5}}{3}} = \dfrac{3}{\sqrt{5}}$

   $= \dfrac{3}{\sqrt{5}} \cdot \dfrac{\sqrt{5}}{\sqrt{5}} = \dfrac{3\sqrt{5}}{5}$

   $\cot\theta = \dfrac{1}{\tan\theta} = \dfrac{1}{\frac{2}{\sqrt{5}}} = \dfrac{\sqrt{5}}{2}$

6. We can find the value of $\cos\theta$ by using the Pythagorean identity.

$$\sin^2\theta + \cos^2\theta = 1$$

$$\left(\frac{1}{2}\right)^2 + \cos^2\theta = 1$$

$$\frac{1}{4} + \cos^2\theta = 1$$

$$\cos^2\theta = 1 - \frac{1}{4}$$

$$\cos^2\theta = \frac{3}{4}$$

$$\cos\theta = \sqrt{\frac{3}{4}} = \frac{\sqrt{3}}{2}$$

b.
$$\cot\frac{\pi}{12} = \tan\left(\frac{\pi}{2} - \frac{\pi}{12}\right)$$

$$= \tan\left(\frac{6\pi}{12} - \frac{\pi}{12}\right)$$

$$= \tan\frac{5\pi}{12}$$

7. a. $\sin 46° = \cos(90° - 46°) = \cos 44°$

8.

Many Scientific Calculators			
Function	**Mode**	**Keystrokes**	**Display** (rounded to four places)
a. sin 72.8°	Degree	72.8 SIN	0.9553
b. csc 1.5	Radian	1.5 SIN 1/x	1.0025

Many Graphing Calculators			
Function	**Mode**	**Keystrokes**	**Display** (rounded to four places)
a. sin 72.8°	Degree	SIN 72.8 ENTER	0.9553
b. csc 1.5	Radian	(SIN 1.5) x^{-1} ENTER	1.0025

9. Because we have a known angle, an unknown opposite side, and a known adjacent side, we select the tangent function.

$$\tan 24° = \frac{a}{750}$$

$$a = 750\tan 24°$$

$$a \approx 750(0.4452) \approx 334$$

The distance across the lake is approximately 334 yards.

10.　$\tan\theta = \dfrac{\text{side opposite}}{\text{side adjacent}} = \dfrac{14}{10}$

Use a calculator in degree mode to find θ.

Many Scientific Calculators	Many Graphing Calculators
$\boxed{\text{TAN}^{-1}}\ \boxed{(}\ \boxed{14}\ \boxed{\div}\ \boxed{10}\ \boxed{)}\ \boxed{\text{ENTER}}$	$\boxed{\text{TAN}}\boxed{(}\ \boxed{14}\ \boxed{\div}\ \boxed{10}\ \boxed{)}\boxed{\text{ENTER}}$

The display should show approximately 54. Thus, the angle of elevation of the sun is approximately $54°$.

Exercise Set 4.2

1.　$c^2 = 9^2 + 12^2 = 225$

$c = \sqrt{225} = 15$

$\sin\theta = \dfrac{\text{opposite}}{\text{hypotenuse}} = \dfrac{9}{15} = \dfrac{3}{5}$

$\cos\theta = \dfrac{\text{adjacent}}{\text{hypotenuse}} = \dfrac{12}{15} = \dfrac{4}{5}$

$\tan\theta = \dfrac{\text{opposite}}{\text{adjacent}} = \dfrac{9}{12} = \dfrac{3}{4}$

$\csc\theta = \dfrac{\text{hypotenuse}}{\text{opposite}} = \dfrac{15}{9} = \dfrac{5}{3}$

$\sec\theta = \dfrac{\text{hypotenuse}}{\text{adjacent}} = \dfrac{15}{12} = \dfrac{5}{4}$

$\cot\theta = \dfrac{\text{adjacent}}{\text{opposite}} = \dfrac{12}{9} = \dfrac{4}{3}$

3.　$a^2 + 21^2 = 29^2$

$a^2 = 841 - 441 = 400$

$a = \sqrt{400} = 20$

$\sin\theta = \dfrac{\text{opposite}}{\text{hypotenuse}} = \dfrac{20}{29}$

$\cos\theta = \dfrac{\text{adjacent}}{\text{hypotenuse}} = \dfrac{21}{29}$

$\tan\theta = \dfrac{\text{opposite}}{\text{adjacent}} = \dfrac{20}{21}$

$\csc\theta = \dfrac{\text{hypotenuse}}{\text{opposite}} = \dfrac{29}{20}$

$\sec\theta = \dfrac{\text{hypotenuse}}{\text{adjacent}} = \dfrac{29}{21}$

$\cot\theta = \dfrac{\text{adjacent}}{\text{opposite}} = \dfrac{21}{20}$

5.　$10^2 + b^2 = 26^2$

$b^2 = 676 - 100 = 576$

$b = \sqrt{576} = 24$

$\sin\theta = \dfrac{\text{opposite}}{\text{hypotenuse}} = \dfrac{10}{26} = \dfrac{5}{13}$

$\cos\theta = \dfrac{\text{adjacent}}{\text{hypotenuse}} = \dfrac{24}{26} = \dfrac{12}{13}$

$\tan\theta = \dfrac{\text{opposite}}{\text{adjacent}} = \dfrac{10}{24} = \dfrac{5}{12}$

$\csc\theta = \dfrac{\text{hypotenuse}}{\text{opposite}} = \dfrac{26}{10} = \dfrac{13}{5}$

$\sec\theta = \dfrac{\text{hypotenuse}}{\text{adjacent}} = \dfrac{26}{24} = \dfrac{13}{12}$

$\cot\theta = \dfrac{\text{adjacent}}{\text{opposite}} = \dfrac{24}{10} = \dfrac{12}{5}$

7.　$21^2 + b^2 = 35^2$

$b^2 = 1225 - 441 = 784$

$b = \sqrt{784} = 28$

$\sin\theta = \dfrac{\text{opposite}}{\text{hypotenuse}} = \dfrac{28}{35} = \dfrac{4}{5}$

$\cos\theta = \dfrac{\text{adjacent}}{\text{hypotenuse}} = \dfrac{21}{35} = \dfrac{3}{5}$

$\tan\theta = \dfrac{\text{opposite}}{\text{adjacent}} = \dfrac{28}{21} = \dfrac{4}{3}$

$\csc\theta = \dfrac{\text{hypotenuse}}{\text{opposite}} = \dfrac{35}{28} = \dfrac{5}{4}$

$\sec\theta = \dfrac{\text{hypotenuse}}{\text{adjacent}} = \dfrac{35}{21} = \dfrac{5}{3}$

$\cot\theta = \dfrac{\text{adjacent}}{\text{opposite}} = \dfrac{21}{28} = \dfrac{3}{4}$

9. $\cos 30° = \dfrac{\text{length of side adjacent to } 30°}{\text{length of hypotenuse}}$

$\qquad = \dfrac{\sqrt{3}}{2}$

11. $\sec 45° = \dfrac{\text{length of hypotenuse}}{\text{length of side adjacent to } 45°}$

$\qquad = \dfrac{\sqrt{2}}{1} = \sqrt{2}$

13. $\tan \dfrac{\pi}{3} = \tan 60°$

$\qquad = \dfrac{\text{length of side opposite } 60°}{\text{length of side adjacent to } 60°}$

$\qquad = \dfrac{\sqrt{3}}{1} = \sqrt{3}$

15. $\sin \dfrac{\pi}{4} - \cos \dfrac{\pi}{4} = \sin 45° - \cos 45°$

$\qquad\qquad\qquad\quad = \dfrac{1}{\sqrt{2}} - \dfrac{1}{\sqrt{2}} = 0$

17. $\tan \theta = \dfrac{\sin \theta}{\cos \theta} = \dfrac{\frac{8}{17}}{\frac{15}{17}} = \dfrac{8}{15}$

$\qquad \csc \theta = \dfrac{1}{\sin \theta} = \dfrac{1}{\frac{8}{17}} = \dfrac{17}{8}$

$\qquad \sec \theta = \dfrac{1}{\cos \theta} = \dfrac{1}{\frac{15}{17}} = \dfrac{17}{15}$

$\qquad \cot \theta = \dfrac{\cos \theta}{\sin \theta} = \dfrac{\frac{15}{17}}{\frac{8}{17}} = \dfrac{15}{8}$

19. $\tan \theta = \dfrac{\sin \theta}{\cos \theta} = \dfrac{\frac{1}{3}}{\frac{2\sqrt{2}}{3}} = \dfrac{1}{2\sqrt{2}}$

$\qquad\qquad = \dfrac{1}{2\sqrt{2}} \cdot \dfrac{\sqrt{2}}{\sqrt{2}} = \dfrac{\sqrt{2}}{4}$

$\qquad \csc \theta = \dfrac{1}{\sin \theta} = \dfrac{1}{\frac{1}{3}} = \dfrac{3}{1} = 3$

$\qquad \sec \theta = \dfrac{1}{\cos \theta} = \dfrac{1}{\frac{2\sqrt{2}}{3}} = \dfrac{3}{2\sqrt{2}}$

$\qquad\qquad = \dfrac{3}{2\sqrt{2}} \cdot \dfrac{\sqrt{2}}{\sqrt{2}} = \dfrac{3\sqrt{2}}{4}$

$\qquad \cot \theta = \dfrac{\cos \theta}{\sin \theta} = \dfrac{\frac{2\sqrt{2}}{3}}{\frac{1}{3}} = \dfrac{2\sqrt{2}}{1} = 2\sqrt{2}$

21. $\sin^2 \theta + \cos^2 \theta = 1$

$\qquad \left(\dfrac{6}{7}\right)^2 + \cos^2 \theta = 1$

$\qquad\quad \dfrac{36}{49} + \cos^2 \theta = 1$

$\qquad\qquad\quad \cos^2 \theta = 1 - \dfrac{36}{49}$

$\qquad\qquad\quad \cos^2 \theta = \dfrac{13}{49}$

$\qquad\qquad\quad \cos \theta = \sqrt{\dfrac{13}{49}} = \dfrac{\sqrt{13}}{7}$

23. $\sin^2 \theta + \cos^2 \theta = 1$

$\qquad \left(\dfrac{\sqrt{39}}{8}\right)^2 + \cos^2 \theta = 1$

$\qquad\quad \dfrac{39}{64} + \cos^2 \theta = 1$

$\qquad\qquad\quad \cos^2 \theta = 1 - \dfrac{39}{64}$

$\qquad\qquad\quad \cos^2 \theta = \dfrac{25}{64}$

$\qquad\qquad\quad \cos \theta = \sqrt{\dfrac{25}{64}} = \dfrac{5}{8}$

25. $\sin 37° \csc 37° = \sin 37° \cdot \dfrac{1}{\sin 37°} = 1$

27. $\sin^2 \theta + \cos^2 \theta = 1$

$\sin^2 \dfrac{\pi}{9} + \cos^2 \dfrac{\pi}{9} = 1$

29. $1 + \tan^2 \theta = \sec^2 \theta$

$1 + \tan^2 23° = \sec^2 23°$

$1 = \sec^2 23° - \tan^2 23°$

31. $\sin 7° = \cos(90° - 7°) = \cos 83°$

33. $\csc 25° = \sec(90° - 25°) = \sec 65°$

35. $\tan \dfrac{\pi}{9} = \cot\left(\dfrac{\pi}{2} - \dfrac{\pi}{9}\right)$

$= \cot\left(\dfrac{9\pi}{18} - \dfrac{2\pi}{18}\right)$

$= \cot \dfrac{7\pi}{18}$

37. $\cos \dfrac{2\pi}{5} = \sin\left(\dfrac{\pi}{2} - \dfrac{2\pi}{5}\right)$

$= \sin\left(\dfrac{5\pi}{10} - \dfrac{4\pi}{10}\right)$

$= \sin \dfrac{\pi}{10}$

39.

Many Scientific Calculators			
Function	**Mode**	**Keystrokes**	**Display** (rounded to four places)
sin 38°	Degree	38 SIN	.6157

Many Graphing Calculators			
Function	**Mode**	**Keystrokes**	**Display** (rounded to four places)
sin 38°	Degree	SIN 38 ENTER	.6157

41.

Many Scientific Calculators			
Function	**Mode**	**Keystrokes**	**Display** (rounded to four places)
tan 32.7°	Degree	32.7 TAN	.6420

Many Graphing Calculators			
Function	**Mode**	**Keystrokes**	**Display** (rounded to four places)
tan 32.7°	Degree	TAN 32.7 ENTER	.6420

43.

Many Scientific Calculators			
Function	**Mode**	**Keystrokes**	**Display** (rounded to four places)
csc 17°	Degree	17 SIN 1/x	3.4203

Many Graphing Calculators			
Function	**Mode**	**Keystrokes**	**Display** (rounded to four places)
csc 17°	Degree	(SIN 17) x^{-1} ENTER	3.4203

45.

Many Scientific Calculators			
Function	**Mode**	**Keystrokes**	**Display** (rounded to four places)
$\cos \dfrac{\pi}{10}$	Radian	π ÷ 10 = COS	.9511

Many Graphing Calculators			
Function	**Mode**	**Keystrokes**	**Display** (rounded to four places)
$\cos \dfrac{\pi}{10}$	Radian	COS (π ÷ 10) ENTER	.9511

47.

Many Scientific Calculators			
Function	**Mode**	**Keystrokes**	**Display** (rounded to four places)
$\cot \dfrac{\pi}{12}$	Radian	$\pi \div 12 = \boxed{\text{TAN}}\ \boxed{1/x}$	3.7321

Many Graphing Calculators			
Function	**Mode**	**Keystrokes**	**Display** (rounded to four places)
$\cot \dfrac{\pi}{12}$	Radian	$(\ \boxed{\text{TAN}}\ (\ \pi \div 12\ )\ )\ \boxed{x^{-1}}\ \boxed{\text{ENTER}}$	3.7321

49. $\tan 37° = \dfrac{a}{250}$

$a = 250 \tan 37°$

$a \approx 250(0.7536) \approx 188$ cm

51. $\cos 34° = \dfrac{b}{220}$

$b = 220 \cos 34°$

$b \approx 220(0.8290) \approx 182$ in.

53. $\sin 23° = \dfrac{16}{c}$

$c = \dfrac{16}{\sin 23°} \approx \dfrac{16}{0.3907} \approx 41$ m

55.

Scientific Calculator	Graphing Calculator	Display (rounded to the nearest degree)
$.2974\ \boxed{\text{SIN}^{-1}}$	$\boxed{\text{SIN}^{-1}}\ .2974\ \boxed{\text{ENTER}}$	17

If $\sin \theta = 0.2974$, then $\theta \approx 17°$.

57.

Scientific Calculator	Graphing Calculator	Display (rounded to the nearest degree)
$4.6252\ \boxed{\text{TAN}^{-1}}$	$\boxed{\text{TAN}^{-1}}\ 4.6252\ \boxed{\text{ENTER}}$	78

If $\tan \theta = 4.6252$, then $\theta \approx 78°$.

59.

Scientific Calculator	Graphing Calculator	Display (rounded to three places)
$.4112\ \boxed{\text{COS}^{-1}}$	$\boxed{\text{COS}^{-1}}\ .4112\ \boxed{\text{ENTER}}$	1.147

If $\cos \theta = 0.4112$, then $\theta \approx 1.147$ radians.

61.

Scientific Calculator	Graphing Calculator	Display (rounded to three places)
$.4169\ \boxed{\text{TAN}^{-1}}$	$\boxed{\text{TAN}^{-1}}\ .4169\ \boxed{\text{ENTER}}$	.395

If $\tan \theta = 0.4169$, then $\theta \approx 0.395$ radians.

63.
$$\frac{\tan\frac{\pi}{3}}{2} - \frac{1}{\sec\frac{\pi}{6}} = \frac{\sqrt{3}}{2} - \frac{1}{\frac{1}{\cos\frac{\pi}{6}}}$$
$$= \frac{\sqrt{3}}{2} - \frac{1}{\frac{1}{\frac{\sqrt{3}}{2}}}$$
$$= \frac{\sqrt{3}}{2} - \frac{\sqrt{3}}{2}$$
$$= 0$$

65. $1 + \sin^2 40° + \sin^2 50°$
$$= 1 + \sin^2(90° - 50°) + \sin^2 50°$$
$$= 1 + \cos^2 50° + \sin^2 50°$$
$$= 1 + 1$$
$$= 2$$

67. $\csc 37° \sec 53° - \tan 53° \cot 37°$
$$= \sec 53° \sec 53° - \tan 53° \tan 53°$$
$$= \sec^2 53° - \tan^2 53°$$
$$= 1$$

69. $f(\theta) = 2\cos\theta - \cos 2\theta$
$$f\left(\frac{\pi}{6}\right) = 2\cos\frac{\pi}{6} - \cos\left(2\cdot\frac{\pi}{6}\right)$$
$$= 2\left(\frac{\sqrt{3}}{2}\right) - \cos\left(\frac{\pi}{3}\right)$$
$$= \frac{2\sqrt{3}}{2} - \frac{1}{2}$$
$$= \frac{2\sqrt{3} - 1}{2}$$

71. $\tan\left(\frac{\pi}{2} - \theta\right) = \cot\theta = \frac{1}{4}$

73. $\tan 40° = \frac{a}{630}$
$a = 630\tan 40°$
$a \approx 630(0.8391) \approx 529$
The distance across the lake is approximately 529 yards.

75. $\tan\theta = \frac{125}{172}$

Use a calculator in degree mode to find θ.

Many Scientific Calculators	Many Graphing Calculators
125 ÷ 172 = TAN⁻¹	TAN⁻¹ (125 ÷ 172) ENTER

The display should show approximately 36. Thus, the angle of elevation of the sun is approximately 36°.

77. $\sin 10° = \frac{500}{c}$
$$c = \frac{500}{\sin 10°} \approx \frac{500}{0.1736} \approx 2880$$
The plane has flown approximately 2880 feet.

79. $\cos\theta = \frac{60}{75}$

Use a calculator in degree mode to find θ.

Many Scientific Calculators	Many Graphing Calculators
60 ÷ 75 = COS⁻¹	COS⁻¹ (60 ÷ 75) ENTER

The display should show approximately 37. Thus, the angle between the wire and the pole is approximately 37°.

93.

θ	0.4	0.3	0.2	0.1	0.01	0.001	0.0001	0.00001
$\cos\theta$	0.92106	0.95534	0.98007	0.99500	0.99995	0.9999995	0.999999995	1
$\dfrac{\cos\theta-1}{\theta}$	-0.19735	-0.148878	-0.099667	-0.04996	-0.005	-0.0005	-0.00005	0

$\dfrac{\cos\theta-1}{\theta}$ approaches 0 as θ approaches 0.

95. In a right triangle, the hypotenuse is greater than either other side. Therefore both $\dfrac{\text{opposite}}{\text{hypotenuse}}$ and $\dfrac{\text{adjacent}}{\text{hypotenuse}}$ must be less than 1 for an acute angle in a right triangle.

97. a. Let a = distance of the ship from the lighthouse.

$$\tan 35° = \frac{250}{a}$$

$$a = \frac{250}{\tan 35°} \approx \frac{250}{0.7002} \approx 357$$

The ship is approximately 357 feet from the lighthouse.

b. Let b = the plane's height above the lighthouse.

$$\tan 22° = \frac{b}{357}$$

$$b = 357\tan 22° \approx 357(0.4040) \approx 144$$

$$144 + 250 = 394$$

The plane is approximately 394 feet above the water.

Section 4.3

Checkpoint Exercises

1. $r = \sqrt{x^2 + y^2}$

$r = \sqrt{1^2 + (-3)^2} = \sqrt{1+9} = \sqrt{10}$

Now that we know x, y, and r, we can find the six trigonometric functions of θ.

$\sin\theta = \dfrac{y}{r} = \dfrac{-3}{\sqrt{10}} = -\dfrac{3\sqrt{10}}{10}$

$\cos\theta = \dfrac{x}{r} = \dfrac{1}{\sqrt{10}} = \dfrac{\sqrt{10}}{10}$

$\tan\theta = \dfrac{y}{x} = \dfrac{-3}{1} = -3$

$\csc\theta = \dfrac{r}{y} = \dfrac{\sqrt{10}}{-3} = -\dfrac{\sqrt{10}}{3}$

$\sec\theta = \dfrac{r}{x} = \dfrac{\sqrt{10}}{1} = \sqrt{10}$

$\cot\theta = \dfrac{x}{y} = \dfrac{1}{-3} = -\dfrac{1}{3}$

2. a. $\theta = 0° = 0$ radians

The terminal side of the angle is on the positive x-axis. Select the point $P = (1,0)$: $x = 1, y = 0, r = 1$

Apply the definitions of the cosine and cosecant functions.

$\cos 0° = \cos 0 = \dfrac{x}{r} = \dfrac{1}{1} = 1$

$\csc 0° = \csc 0 = \dfrac{r}{y} = \dfrac{1}{0}$, undefined

b. $\theta = 90° = \dfrac{\pi}{2}$ radians

The terminal side of the angle is on the positive y-axis. Select the point $P = (0,1)$: $x = 0, y = 1, r = 1$

Apply the definitions of the cosine and cosecant functions.

$\cos 90° = \cos\dfrac{\pi}{2} = \dfrac{x}{r} = \dfrac{0}{1} = 0$

$\csc 90° = \csc\dfrac{\pi}{2} = \dfrac{r}{y} = \dfrac{1}{1} = 1$

c. $\theta = 180° = \pi$ radians
The terminal side of the angle is on the negative x-axis. Select the point
$P = (-1,0)$: $x = -1, y = 0, r = 1$
Apply the definitions of the cosine and cosecant functions.
$$\cos 180° = \cos \pi = \frac{x}{r} = \frac{-1}{1} = -1$$
$$\csc 180° = \csc \pi = \frac{r}{y} = \frac{1}{0}, \text{ undefined}$$

d. $\theta = 270° = \frac{3\pi}{2}$ radians
The terminal side of the angle is on the negative y-axis. Select the point
$P = (0,-1)$: $x = 0, y = -1, r = 1$
Apply the definitions of the cosine and cosecant functions.
$$\cos 270° = \cos\frac{3\pi}{2} = \frac{x}{r} = \frac{0}{1} = 0$$
$$\csc 270° = \csc\frac{3\pi}{2} = \frac{r}{y} = \frac{1}{-1} = -1$$

3.   Because $\sin\theta < 0$, θ cannot lie in quadrant I; all the functions are positive in quadrant I. Furthermore, θ cannot lie in quadrant II; $\sin\theta$ is positive in quadrant II. Thus, with $\sin\theta < 0$, θ lies in quadrant III or quadrant IV.

We are also given that $\cos\theta < 0$. Because quadrant III is the only quadrant in which cosine is negative and the sine is negative, we conclude that θ lies in quadrant III.

4.   Because the tangent is negative and the cosine is negative, θ lies in quadrant II. In quadrant II, x is negative and y is positive. Thus,
$$\tan\theta = -\frac{1}{3} = \frac{y}{x} = \frac{1}{-3}$$
$x = -3, y = 1$
Furthermore,
$$r = \sqrt{x^2 + y^2} = \sqrt{(-3)^2 + 1^2} = \sqrt{9+1} = \sqrt{10}$$
Now that we know x, y, and r, we can find $\sin\theta$ and $\sec\theta$.
$$\sin\theta = \frac{y}{r} = \frac{1}{\sqrt{10}} = \frac{1}{\sqrt{10}} \cdot \frac{\sqrt{10}}{\sqrt{10}} = \frac{\sqrt{10}}{10}$$
$$\sec\theta = \frac{r}{x} = \frac{\sqrt{10}}{-3} = -\frac{\sqrt{10}}{3}$$

5.   **a.**   Because $210°$ lies between $180°$ and $270°$, it is in quadrant III. The reference angle is $\theta' = 210° - 180° = 30°$.

b.   Because $\frac{7\pi}{4}$ lies between $\frac{3\pi}{2} = \frac{6\pi}{4}$ and $2\pi = \frac{8\pi}{4}$, it is in quadrant IV. The reference angle is
$$\theta' = 2\pi - \frac{7\pi}{4} = \frac{8\pi}{4} - \frac{7\pi}{4} = \frac{\pi}{4}.$$

c.   Because $-240°$ lies between $-180°$ and $-270°$, it is in quadrant II. The reference angle is $\theta = 240 - 180 = 60°$.

d.   Because 3.6 lies between $\pi \approx 3.14$ and $\frac{3\pi}{2} \approx 4.71$, it is in quadrant III. The reference angle is $\theta' = 3.6 - \pi \approx 0.46$.

6.   **a.** $665° - 360° = 305°$
This angle is in quadrant IV, thus the reference angle is $\theta' = 360° - 305° = 55°$.

b. $\frac{15\pi}{4} - 2\pi = \frac{15\pi}{4} - \frac{8\pi}{4} = \frac{7\pi}{4}$
This angle is in quadrant IV, thus the reference angle is
$$\theta' = 2\pi - \frac{7\pi}{4} = \frac{8\pi}{4} - \frac{7\pi}{4} = \frac{\pi}{4}.$$

c. $-\frac{11\pi}{3} + 2 \cdot 2\pi = -\frac{11\pi}{3} + \frac{12\pi}{3} = \frac{\pi}{3}$
This angle is in quadrant I, thus the reference angle is $\theta' = \frac{\pi}{3}$.

7.   **a.** $300°$ lies in quadrant IV. The reference angle is $\theta' = 360° - 300° = 60°$.
$$\sin 60° = \frac{\sqrt{3}}{2}$$
Because the sine is negative in quadrant IV, $\sin 300° = -\sin 60° = -\frac{\sqrt{3}}{2}$.

b. $\frac{5\pi}{4}$ lies in quadrant III. The reference angle is $\theta' = \frac{5\pi}{4} - \pi = \frac{5\pi}{4} - \frac{4\pi}{4} = \frac{\pi}{4}$.
$$\tan\frac{\pi}{4} = 1$$

262

Because the tangent is positive in quadrant III, $\tan\dfrac{5\pi}{4} = +\tan\dfrac{\pi}{4} = 1$.

c. $-\dfrac{\pi}{6}$ lies in quadrant IV. The reference angle is $\theta' = \dfrac{\pi}{6}$.

$\sec\dfrac{\pi}{6} = \dfrac{2\sqrt{3}}{3}$

Because the secant is positive in quadrant IV, $\sec\left(-\dfrac{\pi}{6}\right) = +\sec\dfrac{\pi}{6} = \dfrac{2\sqrt{3}}{3}$.

8. a. $\dfrac{17\pi}{6} - 2\pi = \dfrac{17\pi}{6} - \dfrac{12\pi}{6} = \dfrac{5\pi}{6}$ lies in quadrant II. The reference angle is

$\theta' = \pi - \dfrac{5\pi}{6} = \dfrac{\pi}{6}$.

The function value for the reference angle is $\cos\dfrac{\pi}{6} = \dfrac{\sqrt{3}}{2}$.

Because the cosine is negative in quadrant II, $\cos\dfrac{17\pi}{6} = \cos\dfrac{5\pi}{6} = -\cos\dfrac{\pi}{6} = -\dfrac{\sqrt{3}}{2}$.

b. $\dfrac{-22\pi}{3} + 8\pi = \dfrac{-22\pi}{3} + \dfrac{24\pi}{3} = \dfrac{2\pi}{3}$ lies in quadrant II. The reference angle is

$\theta' = \pi - \dfrac{2\pi}{3} = \dfrac{\pi}{3}$.

The function value for the reference angle is $\sin\dfrac{\pi}{3} = \dfrac{\sqrt{3}}{2}$.

Because the sine is positive in quadrant II,

$\sin\dfrac{-22\pi}{3} = \sin\dfrac{2\pi}{3} = \sin\dfrac{\pi}{3} = \dfrac{\sqrt{3}}{2}$.

Exercise Set 4.3

1.   We need values for x, y, and r. Because $P = (-4, 3)$ is a point on the terminal side of θ, $x = -4$ and $y = 3$. Furthermore,

$r = \sqrt{x^2 + y^2} = \sqrt{(-4)^2 + 3^2} = \sqrt{16 + 9} = \sqrt{25} = 5$

Now that we know x, y, and r, we can find the six trigonometric functions of θ.

$\sin\theta = \dfrac{y}{r} = \dfrac{3}{5}$

$\cos\theta = \dfrac{x}{r} = \dfrac{-4}{5} = -\dfrac{4}{5}$

$\tan\theta = \dfrac{y}{x} = \dfrac{3}{-4} = -\dfrac{3}{4}$

$\csc\theta = \dfrac{r}{y} = \dfrac{5}{3}$

$\sec\theta = \dfrac{r}{x} = \dfrac{5}{-4} = -\dfrac{5}{4}$

$\cot\theta = \dfrac{x}{y} = \dfrac{-4}{3} = -\dfrac{4}{3}$

3.   We need values for x, y, and r. Because $P = (2, 3)$ is a point on the terminal side of θ, $x = 2$ and $y = 3$. Furthermore,

$r = \sqrt{x^2 + y^2} = \sqrt{2^2 + 3^2} = \sqrt{4 + 9} = \sqrt{13}$

Now that we know x, y, and r, we can find the six trigonometric functions of θ.

$\sin\theta = \dfrac{y}{r} = \dfrac{3}{\sqrt{13}} = \dfrac{3}{\sqrt{13}} \cdot \dfrac{\sqrt{13}}{\sqrt{13}} = \dfrac{3\sqrt{13}}{13}$

$\cos\theta = \dfrac{x}{r} = \dfrac{2}{\sqrt{13}} = \dfrac{2}{\sqrt{13}} \cdot \dfrac{\sqrt{13}}{\sqrt{13}} = \dfrac{2\sqrt{13}}{13}$

$\tan\theta = \dfrac{y}{x} = \dfrac{3}{2}$

$\csc\theta = \dfrac{r}{y} = \dfrac{\sqrt{13}}{3}$

$\sec\theta = \dfrac{r}{x} = \dfrac{\sqrt{13}}{2}$

$\cot\theta = \dfrac{x}{y} = \dfrac{2}{3}$

5. We need values for *x*, *y*, and *r*. Because
$P = (3, -3)$ is a point on the terminal side of
θ, $x = 3$ and $y = -3$. Furthermore,

$$r = \sqrt{x^2 + y^2} = \sqrt{3^2 + (-3)^2} = \sqrt{9+9}$$
$$= \sqrt{18} = 3\sqrt{2}$$

Now that we know *x*, *y*, and *r*, we can find the
six trigonometric functions of θ.

$$\sin\theta = \frac{y}{r} = \frac{-3}{3\sqrt{2}} = \frac{-1}{\sqrt{2}} \cdot \frac{\sqrt{2}}{\sqrt{2}} = -\frac{\sqrt{2}}{2}$$

$$\cos\theta = \frac{x}{r} = \frac{3}{3\sqrt{2}} = \frac{1}{\sqrt{2}} \cdot \frac{\sqrt{2}}{\sqrt{2}} = \frac{\sqrt{2}}{2}$$

$$\tan\theta = \frac{y}{x} = \frac{-3}{3} = -1$$

$$\csc\theta = \frac{r}{y} = \frac{3\sqrt{2}}{-3} = -\sqrt{2}$$

$$\sec\theta = \frac{r}{x} = \frac{3\sqrt{2}}{3} = \sqrt{2}$$

$$\cot\theta = \frac{x}{y} = \frac{3}{-3} = -1$$

7. We need values for *x*, *y*, and *r*. Because
$P = (-2, -5)$ is a point on the terminal side of
θ, $x = -2$ and $y = -5$. Furthermore,

$$r = \sqrt{x^2 + y^2} = \sqrt{(-2)^2 + (-5)^2} = \sqrt{4+25} = \sqrt{29}$$

Now that we know *x*, *y*, and *r*, we can find the
six trigonometric functions of θ.

$$\sin\theta = \frac{y}{r} = \frac{-5}{\sqrt{29}} = \frac{-5}{\sqrt{29}} \cdot \frac{\sqrt{29}}{\sqrt{29}} = -\frac{5\sqrt{29}}{29}$$

$$\cos\theta = \frac{x}{r} = \frac{-2}{\sqrt{29}} = \frac{-2}{\sqrt{29}} \cdot \frac{\sqrt{29}}{\sqrt{29}} = -\frac{2\sqrt{29}}{29}$$

$$\tan\theta = \frac{y}{x} = \frac{-5}{-2} = \frac{5}{2}$$

$$\csc\theta = \frac{r}{y} = \frac{\sqrt{29}}{-5} = -\frac{\sqrt{29}}{5}$$

$$\sec\theta = \frac{r}{x} = \frac{\sqrt{29}}{-2} = -\frac{\sqrt{29}}{2}$$

$$\cot\theta = \frac{x}{y} = \frac{-2}{-5} = \frac{2}{5}$$

9. $\theta = \pi$ radians
The terminal side of the angle is on the negative
x-axis. Select the point $P = (-1, 0)$:
$x = -1$, $y = 0$, $r = 1$ Apply the definition of the
cosine function.

$$\cos\pi = \frac{x}{r} = \frac{-1}{1} = -1$$

11. $\theta = \pi$ radians
The terminal side of the angle is on the negative
x-axis. Select the point $P = (-1, 0)$:
$x = -1$, $y = 0$, $r = 1$ Apply the definition of the
secant function.

$$\sec\pi = \frac{r}{x} = \frac{1}{-1} = -1$$

13. $\theta = \dfrac{3\pi}{2}$ radians

The terminal side of the angle is on the negative
y-axis. Select the point $P = (0, -1)$:
$x = 0$, $y = -1$, $r = 1$ Apply the definition of the

tangent function. $\tan\dfrac{3\pi}{2} = \dfrac{y}{x} = \dfrac{-1}{0}$, undefined

15. $\theta = \dfrac{\pi}{2}$ radians

The terminal side of the angle is on the positive
y-axis. Select the point $P = (0, 1)$:
$x = 0$, $y = 1$, $r = 1$ Apply the definition of the

cotangent function. $\cot\dfrac{\pi}{2} = \dfrac{x}{y} = \dfrac{0}{1} = 0$

17. Because $\sin\theta > 0$, θ cannot lie in quadrant III
or quadrant IV; the sine function is negative in
those quadrants. Thus, with $\sin\theta > 0$, θ lies in
quadrant I or quadrant II. We are also given that
$\cos\theta > 0$. Because quadrant I is the only
quadrant in which the cosine is positive and
sine is positive, we conclude that θ lies in
quadrant I.

19. Because $\sin\theta < 0$, θ cannot lie in quadrant I or
quadrant II; the sine function is positive in those
two quadrants. Thus, with $\sin\theta < 0$, θ lies in
quadrant III or quadrant IV. We are also given
that $\cos\theta < 0$. Because quadrant III is the only
quadrant in which the cosine is positive and the
sine is negative, we conclude that θ lies in
quadrant III.

21. Because $\tan\theta < 0$, θ cannot lie in quadrant I or
quadrant III; the tangent function is positive in
those quadrants. Thus, with $\tan\theta < 0$, θ lies in
quadrant II or quadrant IV. We are also given
that $\cos\theta < 0$. Because quadrant II is the only
quadrant in which the cosine is negative and the
tangent is negative, we conclude that θ lies in
quadrant II.

23. In quadrant III x is negative and y is negative.

Thus, $\cos\theta = -\dfrac{3}{5} = \dfrac{x}{r} = \dfrac{-3}{5}$, $x = -3$, $r = 5$.

Furthermore,

$r^2 = x^2 + y^2$

$5^2 = (-3)^2 + y^2$

$y^2 = 25 - 9 = 16$

$y = -\sqrt{16} = -4$

Now that we know x, y, and r, we can find the remaining trigonometric functions of θ.

$\sin\theta = \dfrac{y}{r} = \dfrac{-4}{5} = -\dfrac{4}{5}$

$\tan\theta = \dfrac{y}{x} = \dfrac{-4}{-3} = \dfrac{4}{3}$

$\csc\theta = \dfrac{r}{y} = \dfrac{5}{-4} = -\dfrac{5}{4}$

$\sec\theta = \dfrac{r}{x} = \dfrac{5}{-3} = -\dfrac{5}{3}$

$\cot\theta = \dfrac{x}{y} = \dfrac{-3}{-4} = \dfrac{3}{4}$

25. In quadrant II x is negative and y is positive.

Thus, $\sin\theta = \dfrac{5}{13} = \dfrac{y}{r}$, $y = 5$, $r = 13$.

Furthermore,

$x^2 + y^2 = r^2$

$x^2 + 5^2 = 13^2$

$x^2 = 169 - 25 = 144$

$x = -\sqrt{144} = -12$

Now that we know x, y, and r, we can find the remaining trigonometric functions of θ.

$\cos\theta = \dfrac{x}{r} = \dfrac{-12}{13} = -\dfrac{12}{13}$

$\tan\theta = \dfrac{y}{x} = \dfrac{5}{-12} = -\dfrac{5}{12}$

$\csc\theta = \dfrac{r}{y} = \dfrac{13}{5}$

$\sec\theta = \dfrac{r}{x} = \dfrac{13}{-12} = -\dfrac{13}{12}$

$\cot\theta = \dfrac{x}{y} = \dfrac{-12}{5} = -\dfrac{12}{5}$

27. Because $270° < \theta < 360°$, θ is in quadrant IV. In quadrant IV x is positive and y is negative.

Thus, $\cos\theta = \dfrac{8}{17} = \dfrac{x}{r}$, $x = 8$, $r = 17$. Furthermore

$x^2 + y^2 = r^2$

$8^2 + y^2 = 17^2$

$y^2 = 289 - 64 = 225$

$y = -\sqrt{225} = -15$

Now that we know x, y, and r, we can find the remaining trigonometric functions of θ.

$\sin\theta = \dfrac{y}{r} = \dfrac{-15}{17} = -\dfrac{15}{17}$

$\tan\theta = \dfrac{y}{x} = \dfrac{-15}{8} = -\dfrac{15}{8}$

$\csc\theta = \dfrac{r}{y} = \dfrac{17}{-15} = -\dfrac{17}{15}$

$\sec\theta = \dfrac{r}{x} = \dfrac{17}{8}$

$\cot\theta = \dfrac{x}{y} = \dfrac{8}{-15} = -\dfrac{8}{15}$

29. Because the tangent is negative and the sine is positive, θ lies in quadrant II. In quadrant II, x is negative and y is positive. Thus,

$\tan\theta = -\dfrac{2}{3} = \dfrac{y}{x} = \dfrac{2}{-3}$, $x = -3$, $y = 2$.

Furthermore,

$r = \sqrt{x^2 + y^2} = \sqrt{(-3)^2 + 2^2} = \sqrt{9+4} = \sqrt{13}$

Now that we know x, y, and r, we can find the remaining trigonometric functions of θ.

$\sin\theta = \dfrac{y}{r} = \dfrac{2}{\sqrt{13}} = \dfrac{2}{\sqrt{13}} \cdot \dfrac{\sqrt{13}}{\sqrt{13}} = \dfrac{2\sqrt{13}}{13}$

$\cos\theta = \dfrac{x}{r} = \dfrac{-3}{\sqrt{13}} = \dfrac{-3}{\sqrt{13}} \cdot \dfrac{\sqrt{13}}{\sqrt{13}} = -\dfrac{3\sqrt{13}}{13}$

$\csc\theta = \dfrac{r}{y} = \dfrac{\sqrt{13}}{2}$

$\sec\theta = \dfrac{r}{x} = \dfrac{\sqrt{13}}{-3} = -\dfrac{\sqrt{13}}{3}$

$\cot\theta = \dfrac{x}{y} = \dfrac{-3}{2} = -\dfrac{3}{2}$

31. Because the tangent is positive and the cosine is negative, θ lies in quadrant III. In quadrant III, x is negative and y is negative. Thus,

$$\tan\theta = \frac{4}{3} = \frac{y}{x} = \frac{-4}{-3}, x = -3, y = -4.$$

Furthermore,

$$r = \sqrt{x^2 + y^2} = \sqrt{(-3)^2 + (-4)^2} = \sqrt{9+16}$$
$$= \sqrt{25} = 5$$

Now that we know x, y, and r, we can find the remaining trigonometric functions of θ.

$$\sin\theta = \frac{y}{r} = \frac{-4}{5} = -\frac{4}{5}$$

$$\cos\theta = \frac{x}{r} = \frac{-3}{5} = -\frac{3}{5}$$

$$\csc\theta = \frac{r}{y} = \frac{5}{-4} = -\frac{5}{4}$$

$$\sec\theta = \frac{r}{x} = \frac{5}{-3} = -\frac{5}{3}$$

$$\cot\theta = \frac{x}{y} = \frac{-3}{-4} = \frac{3}{4}$$

33. Because the secant is negative and the tangent is positive, θ lies in quadrant III. In quadrant III, x is negative and y is negative. Thus,

$$\sec\theta = -3 = \frac{r}{x} = \frac{3}{-1}, \ x = -1, r = 3.$$

Furthermore,

$$x^2 + y^2 = r^2$$
$$(-1)^2 + y^2 = 3^2$$
$$y^2 = 9 - 1 = 8$$
$$y = -\sqrt{8} = -2\sqrt{2}$$

Now that we know x, y, and r, we can find the remaining trigonometric functions of θ.

$$\sin\theta = \frac{y}{r} = \frac{-2\sqrt{2}}{3} = -\frac{2\sqrt{2}}{3}$$

$$\cos\theta = \frac{x}{r} = \frac{-1}{3} = -\frac{1}{3}$$

$$\tan\theta = \frac{y}{x} = \frac{-2\sqrt{2}}{-1} = 2\sqrt{2}$$

$$\csc\theta = \frac{r}{y} = \frac{3}{-2\sqrt{2}} = \frac{3}{-2\sqrt{2}} \cdot \frac{\sqrt{2}}{\sqrt{2}} = -\frac{3\sqrt{2}}{4}$$

$$\cot\theta = \frac{x}{y} = \frac{-1}{-2\sqrt{2}} = \frac{1}{2\sqrt{2}} \cdot \frac{\sqrt{2}}{\sqrt{2}} = \frac{\sqrt{2}}{4}$$

35. Because $160°$ lies between $90°$ and $180°$, it is in quadrant II. The reference angle is $\theta' = 180° - 160° = 20°$.

37. Because $205°$ lies between $180°$ and $270°$, it is in quadrant III. The reference angle is $\theta' = 205° - 180° = 25°$.

39. Because $355°$ lies between $270°$ and $360°$, it is in quadrant IV. The reference angle is $\theta' = 360° - 355° = 5°$.

41. Because $\frac{7\pi}{4}$ lies between $\frac{3\pi}{2} = \frac{6\pi}{4}$ and $2\pi = \frac{8\pi}{4}$, it is in quadrant IV. The reference angle is $\theta' = 2\pi - \frac{7\pi}{4} = \frac{8\pi}{4} - \frac{7\pi}{4} = \frac{\pi}{4}$.

43. Because $\frac{5\pi}{6}$ lies between $\frac{\pi}{2} = \frac{3\pi}{6}$ and $\pi = \frac{6\pi}{6}$, it is in quadrant II. The reference angle is $\theta' = \pi - \frac{5\pi}{6} = \frac{6\pi}{6} - \frac{5\pi}{6} = \frac{\pi}{6}$.

45. $-150° + 360° = 210°$
Because the angle is in quadrant III, the reference angle is $\theta' = 210° - 180° = 30°$.

47. $-335° + 360° = 25°$
Because the angle is in quadrant I, the reference angle is $\theta' = 25°$.

49. Because 4.7 lies between $\pi \approx 3.14$ and $\frac{3\pi}{2} \approx 4.71$, it is in quadrant III. The reference angle is $\theta' = 4.7 - \pi \approx 1.56$.

51. $565° - 360° = 205°$
Because the angle is in quadrant III, the reference angle is $\theta' = 205° - 180° = 25°$.

53. $\frac{17\pi}{6} - 2\pi = \frac{17\pi}{6} - \frac{12\pi}{6} = \frac{5\pi}{6}$
Because the angle is in quadrant II, the reference angle is $\theta' = \pi - \frac{5\pi}{6} = \frac{\pi}{6}$.

55. $\frac{23\pi}{4} - 4\pi = \frac{23\pi}{4} - \frac{16\pi}{4} = \frac{7\pi}{4}$
Because the angle is in quadrant IV, the reference angle is $\theta' = 2\pi - \frac{7\pi}{4} = \frac{\pi}{4}$.

57. $-\dfrac{11\pi}{4}+4\pi=-\dfrac{11\pi}{4}+\dfrac{16\pi}{4}=\dfrac{5\pi}{4}$

Because the angle is in quadrant III, the

reference angle is $\theta'=\dfrac{5\pi}{4}-\pi=\dfrac{\pi}{4}$.

59. $-\dfrac{25\pi}{6}+6\pi=-\dfrac{25\pi}{6}+\dfrac{36\pi}{6}=\dfrac{11\pi}{6}$

Because the angle is in quadrant IV, the

reference angle is $\theta'=2\pi-\dfrac{11\pi}{6}=\dfrac{\pi}{6}$.

61. $225°$ lies in quadrant III. The reference angle is
$\theta'=225°-180°=45°$.

$\cos 45°=\dfrac{\sqrt{2}}{2}$

Because the cosine is negative in quadrant III,

$\cos 225°=-\cos 45°=-\dfrac{\sqrt{2}}{2}$.

63. $210°$ lies in quadrant III. The reference angle is
$\theta'=210°-180°=30°$.

$\tan 30°=\dfrac{\sqrt{3}}{3}$

Because the tangent is positive in quadrant III,

$\tan 210°=\tan 30°=\dfrac{\sqrt{3}}{3}$.

65. $420°$ lies in quadrant I. The reference angle is
$\theta'=420°-360°=60°$.

$\tan 60°=\sqrt{3}$

Because the tangent is positive in quadrant I,
$\tan 420°=\tan 60°=\sqrt{3}$.

67. $\dfrac{2\pi}{3}$ lies in quadrant II. The reference angle is

$\theta'=\pi-\dfrac{2\pi}{3}=\dfrac{3\pi}{3}-\dfrac{2\pi}{3}=\dfrac{\pi}{3}$.

$\sin\dfrac{\pi}{3}=\dfrac{\sqrt{3}}{2}$

Because the sine is positive in quadrant II,

$\sin\dfrac{2\pi}{3}=\sin\dfrac{\pi}{3}=\dfrac{\sqrt{3}}{2}$.

69. $\dfrac{7\pi}{6}$ lies in quadrant III. The reference angle is

$\theta'=\dfrac{7\pi}{6}-\pi=\dfrac{7\pi}{6}-\dfrac{6\pi}{6}=\dfrac{\pi}{6}$.

$\csc\dfrac{\pi}{6}=2$

Because the cosecant is negative in quadrant III,

$\csc\dfrac{7\pi}{6}=-\csc\dfrac{\pi}{6}=-2$.

71. $\dfrac{9\pi}{4}$ lies in quadrant I. The reference angle is

$\theta'=\dfrac{9\pi}{4}-2\pi=\dfrac{9\pi}{4}-\dfrac{8\pi}{4}=\dfrac{\pi}{4}$.

$\tan\dfrac{\pi}{4}=1$

Because the tangent is positive in quadrant I,

$\tan\dfrac{9\pi}{4}=\tan\dfrac{\pi}{4}=1$

73. $-240°$ lies in quadrant II. The reference angle is
$\theta'=240°-180°=60°$.

$\sin 60°=\dfrac{\sqrt{3}}{2}$

Because the sine is positive in quadrant II,

$\sin(-240°)=\sin 60°=\dfrac{\sqrt{3}}{2}$.

75. $-\dfrac{\pi}{4}$ lies in quadrant IV. The reference angle is

$\theta'=\dfrac{\pi}{4}$.

$\tan\dfrac{\pi}{4}=1$

Because the tangent is negative in quadrant IV,

$\tan\left(-\dfrac{\pi}{4}\right)=-\tan\dfrac{\pi}{4}=-1$

77. $\sec 495°=\sec 135°=-\sqrt{2}$

79. $\cot\dfrac{19\pi}{6}=\cot\dfrac{7\pi}{6}=\sqrt{3}$

81. $\cos\dfrac{23\pi}{4}=\cos\dfrac{7\pi}{4}=\dfrac{\sqrt{2}}{2}$

83. $\tan\left(-\dfrac{17\pi}{6}\right)=\tan\dfrac{7\pi}{6}=\dfrac{\sqrt{3}}{3}$

85. $\sin\left(-\dfrac{17\pi}{3}\right) = \sin\dfrac{\pi}{3} = \dfrac{\sqrt{3}}{2}$

87. $\sin\dfrac{\pi}{3}\cos\pi - \cos\dfrac{\pi}{3}\sin\dfrac{3\pi}{2}$

$= \left(\dfrac{\sqrt{3}}{2}\right)(-1) - \left(\dfrac{1}{2}\right)(-1)$

$= -\dfrac{\sqrt{3}}{2} + \dfrac{1}{2}$

$= \dfrac{1-\sqrt{3}}{2}$

89. $\sin\dfrac{11\pi}{4}\cos\dfrac{5\pi}{6} + \cos\dfrac{11\pi}{4}\sin\dfrac{5\pi}{6}$

$= \left(\dfrac{\sqrt{2}}{2}\right)\left(-\dfrac{\sqrt{3}}{2}\right) + \left(-\dfrac{\sqrt{2}}{2}\right)\left(\dfrac{1}{2}\right)$

$= -\dfrac{\sqrt{6}}{4} - \dfrac{\sqrt{2}}{4}$

$= -\dfrac{\sqrt{6}+\sqrt{2}}{4}$

91. $\sin\dfrac{3\pi}{2}\tan\left(-\dfrac{15\pi}{4}\right) - \cos\left(-\dfrac{5\pi}{3}\right)$

$= (-1)(1) - \left(\dfrac{1}{2}\right)$

$= -1 - \dfrac{1}{2}$

$= -\dfrac{2}{2} - \dfrac{1}{2}$

$= -\dfrac{3}{2}$

93. $f\left(\dfrac{4\pi}{3} + \dfrac{\pi}{6}\right) + f\left(\dfrac{4\pi}{3}\right) + f\left(\dfrac{\pi}{6}\right)$

$= \sin\left(\dfrac{4\pi}{3} + \dfrac{\pi}{6}\right) + \sin\dfrac{4\pi}{3} + \sin\dfrac{\pi}{6}$

$= \sin\dfrac{3\pi}{2} + \sin\dfrac{4\pi}{3} + \sin\dfrac{\pi}{6}$

$= (-1) + \left(-\dfrac{\sqrt{3}}{2}\right) + \left(\dfrac{1}{2}\right)$

$= -\dfrac{\sqrt{3}+1}{2}$

95. $(h \circ g)\left(\dfrac{17\pi}{3}\right) = h\left(g\left(\dfrac{17\pi}{3}\right)\right)$

$= 2\left(\cos\left(\dfrac{17\pi}{3}\right)\right)$

$= 2\left(\dfrac{1}{2}\right)$

$= 1$

97. The average rate of change is the slope of the line through the points $(x_1, f(x_1))$ and $(x_2, f(x_2))$

$m = \dfrac{f(x_2) - f(x_1)}{x_2 - x_1}$

$= \dfrac{\sin\left(\dfrac{3\pi}{2}\right) - \sin\left(\dfrac{5\pi}{4}\right)}{\dfrac{3\pi}{2} - \dfrac{5\pi}{4}}$

$= \dfrac{-1 - \left(-\dfrac{\sqrt{2}}{2}\right)}{\dfrac{\pi}{4}}$

$= \dfrac{-1 + \dfrac{\sqrt{2}}{2}}{\dfrac{\pi}{4}}$

$= \dfrac{4\left(-1 + \dfrac{\sqrt{2}}{2}\right)}{4\left(\dfrac{\pi}{4}\right)}$

$= \dfrac{2\sqrt{2} - 4}{\pi}$

99. $\sin\theta = \dfrac{\sqrt{2}}{2}$ when the reference angle is $\dfrac{\pi}{4}$ and θ is in quadrants I or II.

QI	QII
$\theta = \dfrac{\pi}{4}$	$\theta = \pi - \dfrac{\pi}{4}$
	$= \dfrac{3\pi}{4}$

$\theta = \dfrac{\pi}{4}, \dfrac{3\pi}{4}$

101. $\sin\theta = -\dfrac{\sqrt{2}}{2}$ when the reference angle is $\dfrac{\pi 1}{4}$

and θ is in quadrants III or IV.

     <u>QIII</u>   <u>QIV</u>

$\theta = \pi + \dfrac{\pi}{4}$ $\theta = 2\pi - \dfrac{\pi}{4}$

$= \dfrac{5\pi}{4}$ $= \dfrac{7\pi}{4}$

$\theta = \dfrac{5\pi}{4}, \dfrac{7\pi}{4}$

103. $\tan\theta = -\sqrt{3}$ when the reference angle is $\dfrac{\pi}{3}$ and

θ is in quadrants II or IV.

     <u>QII</u>   <u>QIV</u>

$\theta = \pi - \dfrac{\pi}{3}$ $\theta = 2\pi - \dfrac{\pi}{3}$

$= \dfrac{2\pi}{3}$ $= \dfrac{5\pi}{3}$

$\theta = \dfrac{2\pi}{3}, \dfrac{5\pi}{3}$

Section 4.4

Check Point Exercises

1. $P\left(\dfrac{\sqrt{3}}{2}, \dfrac{1}{2}\right)$

$\sin t = y = \dfrac{1}{2}$

$\cos t = x = \dfrac{\sqrt{3}}{2}$

$\tan t = \dfrac{y}{x} = \dfrac{\frac{1}{2}}{\frac{\sqrt{3}}{2}} = \dfrac{\sqrt{3}}{3}$

$\csc t = \dfrac{1}{y} = 2$

$\sec t = \dfrac{1}{x} = \dfrac{2\sqrt{3}}{3}$

$\cot t = \dfrac{x}{y} = \sqrt{3}$

2.   The point P on the unit circle that corresponds to $t = \pi$ has coordinates $(-1, 0)$. Use $x = -1$ and $y = 0$ to find the values of the trigonometric functions.

$\sin\pi = y = 0$

$\cos\pi = x = -1$

$\tan\pi = \dfrac{y}{x} = \dfrac{0}{-1} = 0$

$\sec\pi = \dfrac{1}{x} = \dfrac{1}{-1} = -1$

$\cot\pi = \dfrac{x}{y} = \dfrac{-1}{0} = \text{undefined}$

$\csc\pi = \dfrac{1}{y} = \dfrac{1}{0} = \text{undefined}$

3.   **a.** $\cos(-60^0) = \cos 60^0 = \dfrac{1}{2}$

     b. $\tan\left(-\dfrac{\pi}{6}\right) = -\tan\left(\dfrac{\pi}{6}\right) = -\dfrac{\sqrt{3}}{3}$

4.   **a.** $\cos 405^0 = \cos(360^0 + 45^0)$

            $= \cos 45^0 = \dfrac{\sqrt{2}}{2}$

     b. $\sin\dfrac{7\pi}{3} = \sin\left(\dfrac{\pi}{3} + 2\pi\right) = \sin\dfrac{\pi}{3} = \dfrac{\sqrt{3}}{2}$

Exercise Set 4.4

1.   The point P on the unit circle has coordinates $\left(-\dfrac{15}{17}, \dfrac{8}{17}\right)$. Use $x = -\dfrac{15}{17}$ and $y = \dfrac{8}{17}$ to find the values of the trigonometric functions.

$\sin t = y = \dfrac{8}{17}$

$\cos t = x = -\dfrac{15}{17}$

$\tan t = \dfrac{y}{x} = \dfrac{\frac{8}{17}}{-\frac{15}{17}} = -\dfrac{8}{15}$

$\csc t = \dfrac{1}{y} = \dfrac{17}{8}$

$\sec t = \dfrac{1}{x} = -\dfrac{17}{15}$

$\cot t = \dfrac{x}{y} = -\dfrac{15}{8}$

3. The point P on the unit circle that corresponds to $t = -\dfrac{\pi}{4}$ has coordinates $\left(\dfrac{\sqrt{2}}{2}, -\dfrac{\sqrt{2}}{2} \right)$. Use $x = \dfrac{\sqrt{2}}{2}$ and $y = -\dfrac{\sqrt{2}}{2}$ to find the values of the trigonometric functions.

$$\sin t = y = -\frac{\sqrt{2}}{2}$$

$$\cos t = x = \frac{\sqrt{2}}{2}$$

$$\tan t = \frac{y}{x} = \frac{-\frac{\sqrt{2}}{2}}{\frac{\sqrt{2}}{2}} = -1$$

$$\csc t = \frac{1}{y} = -\sqrt{2}$$

$$\sec t = \frac{1}{x} = \sqrt{2}$$

$$\cot t = \frac{x}{y} = -1$$

5. $\sin \dfrac{\pi}{6} = \dfrac{1}{2}$

7. $\cos \dfrac{5\pi}{6} = -\dfrac{\sqrt{3}}{2}$

9. $\tan \pi = \dfrac{0}{-1} = 0$

11. $\csc \dfrac{7\pi}{6} = \dfrac{1}{-\frac{1}{2}} = -2$

13. $\sec \dfrac{11\pi}{6} = \dfrac{1}{\frac{\sqrt{3}}{2}} = \dfrac{2\sqrt{3}}{3}$

15. $\sin \dfrac{3\pi}{2} = -1$

17. $\sec \dfrac{3\pi}{2} = \text{undefined}$

19. a. $\cos \dfrac{\pi}{6} = \dfrac{\sqrt{3}}{2}$

   b. $\cos \left(-\dfrac{\pi}{6} \right) = \cos \dfrac{\pi}{6} = \dfrac{\sqrt{3}}{2}$

21. a. $\sin \dfrac{5\pi}{6} = \dfrac{1}{2}$

   b. $\sin \left(-\dfrac{5\pi}{6} \right) = -\sin \dfrac{5\pi}{6} = -\dfrac{1}{2}$

23. a. $\tan \dfrac{5\pi}{3} = \dfrac{-\frac{\sqrt{3}}{2}}{\frac{1}{2}} = -\sqrt{3}$

   b. $\tan \left(-\dfrac{5\pi}{3} \right) = -\tan \dfrac{5\pi}{3} = \sqrt{3}$

25. a. $\sin \dfrac{3\pi}{4} = \dfrac{\sqrt{2}}{2}$

   b. $\sin \dfrac{11\pi}{4} = \sin \left(\dfrac{3\pi}{4} + 2\pi \right) = \sin \dfrac{3\pi}{4} = \dfrac{\sqrt{2}}{2}$

27. a. $\cos \dfrac{\pi}{2} = 0$

   b.
$$\cos \dfrac{9\pi}{2} = \cos \left(\dfrac{\pi}{2} + 4\pi \right)$$
$$= \cos \left[\dfrac{\pi}{2} + 2(2\pi) \right]$$
$$= \cos \dfrac{\pi}{2}$$
$$= 0$$

29. a. $\tan \pi = \dfrac{0}{-1} = 0$

   b.
$$\tan 17\pi = \tan(\pi + 16\pi)$$
$$= \tan[\pi + 8(2\pi)]$$
$$= \tan \pi$$
$$= 0$$

31. a. $\sin\dfrac{7\pi}{4} = -\dfrac{\sqrt{2}}{2}$

    b.

$$\sin\dfrac{47\pi}{4} = \sin\left(\dfrac{7\pi}{4} + 10\pi\right)$$

$$= \sin\left[\dfrac{7\pi}{4} + 5(2\pi)\right]$$

$$= \sin\dfrac{7\pi}{4}$$

$$= -\dfrac{\sqrt{2}}{2}$$

33. $\sin(-t) - \sin t = -\sin t - \sin t = -2\sin t = -2a$

35. $4\cos(-t) - \cos t = 4\cos t - \cos t = 3\cos t = 3b$

37. $\sin(t + 2\pi) - \cos(t + 4\pi) + \tan(t + \pi)$

$$= \sin(t) - \cos(t) + \tan(t)$$

$$= a - b + c$$

39. $\sin(-t - 2\pi) - \cos(-t - 4\pi) - \tan(-t - \pi)$

$$= -\sin(t + 2\pi) - \cos(t + 4\pi) + \tan(t + \pi)$$

$$= -\sin(t) - \cos(t) + \tan(t)$$

$$= -a - b + c$$

41. $\cos t + \cos(t + 1000\pi) - \tan t - \tan(t + 999\pi)$

$$\qquad\qquad\qquad\qquad - \sin t + 4\sin(t - 1000\pi)$$

$$= \cos t + \cos t - \tan t - \tan t - \sin t + 4\sin t$$

$$= 2\cos t - 2\tan t + 3\sin t$$

$$= 3a + 2b - 2c$$

43. a. $H = 12 + 8.3\sin\left[\dfrac{2\pi}{365}(80 - 80)\right]$

$$= 12 + 8.3\sin 0 = 12 + 8.3(0)$$

$$= 12$$

There are 12 hours of daylight in Fairbanks on March 21.

    b. $H = 12 + 8.3\sin\left[\dfrac{2\pi}{365}(172 - 80)\right]$

$$\approx 12 + 8.3\sin 1.5837$$

$$\approx 20.3$$

There are about 20.3 hours of daylight in Fairbanks on June 21.

    c. $H = 12 + 8.3\sin\left[\dfrac{2\pi}{365}(355 - 80)\right]$

$$\approx 12 + 8.3\sin 4.7339$$

$$\approx 3.7$$

There are about 3.7 hours of daylight in Fairbanks on December 21.

45. a.   For $t = 7$,

$$E = \sin\dfrac{\pi}{14} \cdot 7 = \sin\dfrac{\pi}{2} = 1$$

For $t = 14$,

$$E = \sin\dfrac{\pi}{14} \cdot 14 = \sin\pi = 0$$

For $t = 21$,

$$E = \sin\dfrac{\pi}{14} \cdot 21 = \sin\dfrac{3\pi}{2} = -1$$

For $t = 28$,

$$E = \sin\dfrac{\pi}{14} \cdot 28 = \sin 2\pi = \sin 0 = 0$$

For $t = 35$,

$$E = \sin\dfrac{\pi}{14} \cdot 35 = \sin\dfrac{5\pi}{2} = \sin\dfrac{\pi}{2} = 1$$

Observations may vary.

    b.   Because $E(35) = E(7) = 1$, the period is $35 - 7 = 28$ or 28 days.

53.   91° lies in quadrant II. The reference angle is $\theta' = 180° - 91° = 89°$.
Because the cosine is negative in quadrant II, $\cos 91° = -\cos 89°$.
Likewise, 92°, 93°, . . . , 178°, and 179° all lie in quadrant II. Their reference angles are
$\theta' = 180° - 92° = 88°$
$\theta' = 180° - 93° = 87°$
...
$\theta' = 180° - 178° = 2°$
$\theta' = 180 - 179° = 1°$
Because the cosine is negative in quadrant II,
$\cos 92° = -\cos 88°$
$\cos 93° = -\cos 87°$
...
$\cos 178° = -\cos 2°$
$\cos 178 = -\cos 1°$
Also, $\cos 180° = -1 = -\cos 0°$

Thus,
$$\cos 0° + \cos 1° + ... + \cos 88° + \cos 89°$$
$$+ \cos 90° + \cos 91° + \cos 92° + ...$$
$$+ \cos 179° + \cos 180°$$
$$= \cos 0° + \cos 1° + ... + \cos 88° + \cos 89°$$
$$+ \cos 90° - \cos 89° - \cos 88° - ...$$
$$- \cos 1° - \cos 0°$$
$$= \cos 90° = 0$$

55. Because $f(x) = \sin x$, $f(x)$ is an odd function. Thus, $f(-a) = -f(a)$. Therefore,

55. Because $f(x) = \sin x$, $f(x)$ is an odd function. Thus, $f(-a) = -f(a)$. Therefore,•
$$f(a) + 2f(-a) = f(a) - 2f(a)$$
$$= \frac{1}{4} - 2 \cdot \frac{1}{4}$$
$$= -\frac{1}{4}$$

Chapter 4 Check Point

1. $10° = 10° \cdot \dfrac{\pi \text{ radians}}{180°} = \dfrac{10\pi}{180}$ radians
$$= \frac{\pi}{18} \text{ radians}$$

2. $-105° = -105° \cdot \dfrac{\pi \text{ radians}}{180°} = -\dfrac{105\pi}{180}$ radians
$$= -\frac{7\pi}{12} \text{ radians}$$

3. $\dfrac{5\pi}{12}$ radians $= \dfrac{5\pi \text{ radians}}{12} \cdot \dfrac{180°}{\pi \text{ radians}} = 75°$

4. $-\dfrac{13\pi}{20}$ radians $= -\dfrac{13\pi \text{ radians}}{20} \cdot \dfrac{180°}{\pi \text{ radians}}$
$$= -117°$$

5. a. $\dfrac{11\pi}{3} - 2\pi = \dfrac{11\pi}{3} - \dfrac{6\pi}{3} = \dfrac{5\pi}{3}$

b.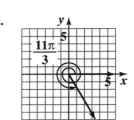

c. Since $\dfrac{5\pi}{3}$ is in quadrant IV, the reference angle is $2\pi - \dfrac{5\pi}{3} = \dfrac{6\pi}{3} - \dfrac{5\pi}{3} = \dfrac{\pi}{3}$

6. a. $-\dfrac{19\pi}{4} + 6\pi = -\dfrac{19\pi}{4} + \dfrac{24\pi}{4} = \dfrac{5\pi}{4}$

b.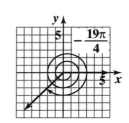

c. Since $\dfrac{5\pi}{4}$ is in quadrant III, the reference angle is $\dfrac{5\pi}{4} - \pi = \dfrac{5\pi}{4} - \dfrac{4\pi}{4} = \dfrac{\pi}{4}$

7. a. $510° - 360° = 150°$

b.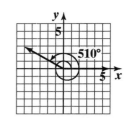

c. Since $150°$ is in quadrant II, the reference angle is $180° - 150° = 30°$

8. Use the Pythagorean theorem to find b.

$$a^2 + b^2 = c^2$$
$$5^2 + b^2 = 6^2$$
$$25 + b^2 = 36$$
$$b^2 = 11$$
$$b = \sqrt{11}$$

$$\sin\theta = \frac{\text{opposite}}{\text{hypotenuse}} = \frac{5}{6}$$

$$\cos\theta = \frac{\text{adjacent}}{\text{hypotenuse}} = \frac{\sqrt{11}}{6}$$

$$\tan\theta = \frac{\text{opposite}}{\text{adjacent}} = \frac{5\sqrt{11}}{11}$$

$$\csc\theta = \frac{\text{hypotenuse}}{\text{opposite}} = \frac{6}{5}$$

$$\sec\theta = \frac{\text{hypotenuse}}{\text{adjacent}} = \frac{6}{\sqrt{11}} = \frac{6\sqrt{11}}{11}$$

$$\cot\theta = \frac{\text{adjacent}}{\text{opposite}} = \frac{\sqrt{11}}{5}$$

9. $r = \sqrt{x^2 + y^2}$

$$r = \sqrt{3^2 + (-2)^2} = \sqrt{9+4} = \sqrt{13}$$

Now that we know *x, y,* and *r,* we can find the six trigonometric functions of θ.

$$\sin\theta = \frac{y}{r} = \frac{-2}{\sqrt{13}} = -\frac{2\sqrt{13}}{13}$$

$$\cos\theta = \frac{x}{r} = \frac{3}{\sqrt{13}} = \frac{3\sqrt{13}}{13}$$

$$\tan\theta = \frac{y}{x} = \frac{-2}{3} = -\frac{2}{3}$$

$$\csc\theta = \frac{r}{y} = \frac{\sqrt{13}}{-2} = -\frac{\sqrt{13}}{2}$$

$$\sec\theta = \frac{r}{x} = \frac{\sqrt{13}}{3}$$

$$\cot\theta = \frac{x}{y} = \frac{3}{-2} = -\frac{3}{2}$$

10. $r = \sqrt{x^2 + y^2}$

$$r = \sqrt{\left(-\frac{3}{5}\right)^2 + \left(-\frac{4}{5}\right)^2} = \sqrt{\frac{9}{25} + \frac{16}{25}} = \sqrt{\frac{25}{25}} = 1$$

Now that we know *x, y,* and *r,* we can find the six trigonometric functions of θ.

$$\sin\theta = \frac{y}{r} = \frac{-\frac{4}{5}}{1} = -\frac{4}{5}$$

$$\cos\theta = \frac{x}{r} = \frac{-\frac{3}{5}}{1} = -\frac{3}{5}$$

$$\tan\theta = \frac{y}{x} = \frac{-\frac{4}{5}}{-\frac{3}{5}} = \frac{4}{3}$$

$$\csc\theta = \frac{r}{y} = \frac{1}{-\frac{4}{5}} = -\frac{5}{4}$$

$$\sec\theta = \frac{r}{x} = \frac{1}{-\frac{3}{5}} = -\frac{5}{3}$$

$$\cot\theta = \frac{x}{y} = \frac{-\frac{3}{5}}{-\frac{4}{5}} = \frac{3}{4}$$

11. Because the tangent is negative and the cosine is negative, θ is in quadrant II. In quadrant II, *x* is negative and *y* is positive. Thus,

$$\tan\theta = -\frac{3}{4} = \frac{x}{y}, \quad x = -4,\ y = 3.\ \text{Furthermore,}$$

$$r^2 = x^2 + y^2$$
$$r^2 = (-3)^2 + 4^2$$
$$r^2 = 9 + 16 = 25$$
$$r = 5$$

Now that we know *x, y,* and *r,* we can find the remaining trigonometric functions of θ.

$$\sin\theta = \frac{y}{r} = \frac{3}{5}$$

$$\cos\theta = \frac{x}{r} = \frac{-4}{5} = -\frac{4}{5}$$

$$\csc\theta = \frac{r}{y} = \frac{5}{3}$$

$$\sec\theta = \frac{r}{x} = \frac{5}{-3} = -\frac{5}{4}$$

$$\cot\theta = \frac{x}{y} = \frac{-3}{4} = -\frac{4}{3}$$

12. Since $\cos\theta = \dfrac{3}{7} = \dfrac{x}{r}$, $x = 3$, $r = 7$. Furthermore,

$$x^2 + y^2 = r^2$$
$$3^2 + y^2 = 7^2$$
$$9 + y^2 = 49$$
$$y^2 = 40$$
$$y = \pm\sqrt{40} = \pm 2\sqrt{10}$$

Because the cosine is positive and the sine is negative, θ is in quadrant IV. In quadrant IV, x is positive and y is negative.

Therefore $y = -2\sqrt{10}$

Use x, y, and r to find the remaining trigonometric functions of θ.

$$\sin\theta = \frac{y}{r} = \frac{-2\sqrt{10}}{7} = -\frac{2\sqrt{10}}{7}$$

$$\tan\theta = \frac{y}{x} = \frac{-2\sqrt{10}}{3} = -\frac{2\sqrt{10}}{3}$$

$$\csc\theta = \frac{r}{y} = \frac{7}{-2\sqrt{10}} = -\frac{7\sqrt{10}}{20}$$

$$\sec\theta = \frac{r}{x} = \frac{7}{3}$$

$$\cot\theta = \frac{x}{y} = \frac{3}{-2\sqrt{10}} = -\frac{3\sqrt{10}}{20}$$

13. $\tan\theta = \dfrac{\text{side opposite } \theta}{\text{side adjacent } \theta}$

$$\tan 41° = \frac{a}{60}$$
$$a = 60\tan 41°$$
$$a \approx 52 \text{ cm}$$

14. $\cos\theta = \dfrac{\text{side adjacent } \theta}{\text{hypotenuse}}$

$$\cos 72° = \frac{250}{c}$$
$$c = \frac{250}{\cos 72°}$$
$$c \approx 809 \text{ m}$$

15. Since $\cos\theta = \dfrac{1}{6} = \dfrac{x}{r}$, $x = 1$, $r = 6$. Furthermore,

$$x^2 + y^2 = r^2$$
$$1^2 + y^2 = 6^2$$
$$1 + y^2 = 36$$
$$y^2 = 35$$
$$y = \pm\sqrt{35}$$

Since θ is acute, $y = +\sqrt{35} = \sqrt{35}$

$$\cot\left(\frac{\pi}{2} - \theta\right) = \tan\theta = \frac{y}{x} = \frac{\sqrt{35}}{1} = \sqrt{35}$$

16. $\tan 30° = \dfrac{\sqrt{3}}{3}$

17. $\cot 120° = \dfrac{1}{\tan 120°} = \dfrac{1}{-\tan 60°} = \dfrac{1}{-\sqrt{3}} = -\dfrac{\sqrt{3}}{3}$

18. $\cos 240° = -\cos 60° = -\dfrac{1}{2}$

19. $\sec\dfrac{11\pi}{6} = \dfrac{1}{\cos\dfrac{11\pi}{6}} = \dfrac{1}{\cos\dfrac{\pi}{6}} = \dfrac{1}{\dfrac{\sqrt{3}}{2}} = \dfrac{2}{\sqrt{3}} = \dfrac{2\sqrt{3}}{3}$

20. $\sin^2\dfrac{\pi}{7} + \cos^2\dfrac{\pi}{7} = 1$

21. $\sin\left(-\dfrac{2\pi}{3}\right) = \sin\left(-\dfrac{2\pi}{3} + 2\pi\right)$

$$= \sin\frac{4\pi}{3} = -\sin\frac{\pi}{3}$$
$$= -\frac{\sqrt{3}}{2}$$

22. $\csc\left(\dfrac{22\pi}{3}\right) = \csc\left(\dfrac{22\pi}{3} - 6\pi\right) = \csc\dfrac{4\pi}{3}$

$$= \frac{1}{\sin\dfrac{4\pi}{3}} = \frac{1}{-\sin\dfrac{\pi}{3}} = \frac{1}{-\dfrac{\sqrt{3}}{2}}$$
$$= -\frac{2}{\sqrt{3}} = -\frac{2\sqrt{3}}{3}$$

23. $\cos 495° = \cos(495° - 360°) = \cos 135°$

$$= -\cos 45° = -\frac{\sqrt{2}}{2}$$

24. $\tan\left(-\dfrac{17\pi}{6}\right) = \tan\left(-\dfrac{17\pi}{6}+4\pi\right) = \tan\dfrac{7\pi}{6}$

$\qquad = \tan\dfrac{\pi}{6} = \dfrac{\sqrt{3}}{3}$

25. $\sin^2\dfrac{\pi}{2} - \cos\pi = (1)^2 - (-1) = 1+1 = 2$

26. $\cos\left(\dfrac{5\pi}{6}+2\pi n\right) + \tan\left(\dfrac{5\pi}{6}+n\pi\right)$

$\qquad = \cos\dfrac{5\pi}{6} + \tan\dfrac{5\pi}{6} = -\cos\dfrac{\pi}{6} - \tan\dfrac{\pi}{6}$

$\qquad = -\dfrac{\sqrt{3}}{2} - \dfrac{\sqrt{3}}{3} = -\dfrac{3\sqrt{3}}{6} - \dfrac{2\sqrt{3}}{6}$

$\qquad = -\dfrac{5\sqrt{3}}{6}$

27. Begin by converting from degrees to radians.

$36° = 36° \cdot \dfrac{\pi \text{ radians}}{180°} = \dfrac{\pi}{5} \text{ radians}$

$s = r\theta = 40 \cdot \dfrac{\pi}{5} = 8\pi \approx 25.13 \text{ cm}$

28. Linear speed is given by $\nu = r\omega$. It is given that $r = 10$ feet and the merry-go-round rotates at 8 revolutions per minute. Convert 8 revolutions per minute to radians per minute.
8 revolutions per minute

$= 8 \text{ revolutions per minute} \cdot \dfrac{2\pi \text{ radians}}{1 \text{ revolution}}$

$= 16\pi \text{ radians per minute}$

$\nu = r\omega = (10)(16\pi) = 160\pi \approx 502.7 \text{ feet per minute}$

The linear speed of the horse is about 502.7 feet per minute.

29. $\sin\theta = \dfrac{\text{side opposite }\theta}{\text{hypotenuse}}$

$\sin 6° = \dfrac{h}{5280}$

$h = 5280\sin 6°$

$h \approx 551.9 \text{ feet}$

30. $\tan\theta = \dfrac{\text{side opposite }\theta}{\text{side adjacent }\theta}$

$\tan\theta = \dfrac{50}{60}$

$\theta = \tan^{-1}\left(\dfrac{50}{60}\right)$

$\theta \approx 40°$

Chapter 4 Review Exercises

1. The radian measure of a central angle is the length of the intercepted arc divided by the circle's radius.

$\theta = \dfrac{27}{6} = 4.5 \text{ radians}$

2. $15° = 15° \cdot \dfrac{\pi \text{ radians}}{180°} = \dfrac{15\pi}{180} \text{ radian}$

$\qquad = \dfrac{\pi}{12} \text{ radian}$

3. $120° = 120° \cdot \dfrac{\pi \text{ radians}}{180°} = \dfrac{120\pi}{180} \text{ radians}$

$\qquad = \dfrac{2\pi}{3} \text{ radians}$

4. $315° = 315° \cdot \dfrac{\pi \text{ radians}}{180°} = \dfrac{315\pi}{180} \text{ radians}$

$\qquad = \dfrac{7\pi}{4} \text{ radians}$

5. $\dfrac{5\pi}{3} \text{ radians} = \dfrac{5\pi}{3} \text{ radians} \cdot \dfrac{180°}{\pi \text{ radians}}$

$\qquad = \dfrac{5 \cdot 180°}{3} = 300°$

6. $\dfrac{7\pi}{5} \text{ radians} = \dfrac{7\pi}{5} \text{ radians} \cdot \dfrac{180°}{\pi \text{ radians}}$

$\qquad = \dfrac{7 \cdot 180°}{5} = 252°$

7. $-\dfrac{5\pi}{6} \text{ radians} = -\dfrac{5\pi}{6} \text{ radians} \cdot \dfrac{180°}{\pi \text{ radians}}$

$\qquad = -\dfrac{5 \cdot 180°}{6} = -150°$

8.

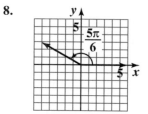

9.

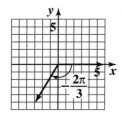

10.

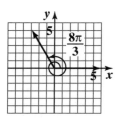

11.

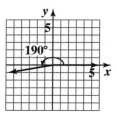

12.

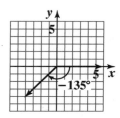

13. $400° - 360° = 40°$

14. $-445° + (2)360° = 275°$

15. $\dfrac{13\pi}{4} - 2\pi = \dfrac{13\pi}{4} - \dfrac{8\pi}{4} = \dfrac{5\pi}{4}$

16. $\dfrac{31\pi}{6} - (2)2\pi = \dfrac{31\pi}{6} - \dfrac{24\pi}{6} = \dfrac{7\pi}{6}$

17. $-\dfrac{8\pi}{3} + (2)2\pi = -\dfrac{8\pi}{3} + \dfrac{12\pi}{3} = \dfrac{4\pi}{3}$

18. $135° = 135° \cdot \dfrac{\pi \text{ radians}}{180°} = \dfrac{135 \cdot \pi}{180}$ radians

$= \dfrac{3\pi}{4}$ radians

$s = r\theta$

$s = (10 \text{ ft})\left(\dfrac{3\pi}{4}\right) = \dfrac{15\pi}{2}$ ft ≈ 23.56 ft

19. $\dfrac{10.3 \text{ revolutions}}{1 \text{ minute}} \cdot \dfrac{2\pi \text{ radians}}{1 \text{ revolution}}$

$= \dfrac{20.6\pi \text{ radians}}{1 \text{ minute}} = 20.6\pi$ radians per minute

20. Use $\nu = r\omega$ where ν is the linear speed and ω is the angular speed in radians per minute.

$\omega = \dfrac{2250 \text{ revolutions}}{1 \text{ minute}} \cdot \dfrac{2\pi \text{ radians}}{1 \text{ revolution}}$

$= 4500\pi$ radians per minute

$\nu = 3 \text{ feet } \dfrac{4500\pi}{\text{minute}} = \dfrac{13,500\pi \text{ feet}}{\text{min}}$

$\approx 42,412$ ft per min

21. Use the Pythagorean Theorem to find the hypotenuse, c.

$c^2 = a^2 + b^2$

$c = \sqrt{8^2 + 5^2} = \sqrt{64 + 25} = \sqrt{89}$

$\sin\theta = \dfrac{5}{\sqrt{89}} = \dfrac{5\sqrt{89}}{\sqrt{89}}$

$\cos\theta = \dfrac{8}{\sqrt{89}} = \dfrac{8\sqrt{89}}{\sqrt{89}}$

$\tan\theta = \dfrac{5}{8}$

$\csc\theta = \dfrac{\sqrt{89}}{5}$

$\sec\theta = \dfrac{\sqrt{89}}{8}$

$\cot\theta = \dfrac{3}{5}$

22. $\sin\dfrac{\pi}{6} + \tan^2\dfrac{\pi}{3} = \dfrac{1}{2} - \left(\sqrt{3}\right)^2$

$= \dfrac{1}{2} - 3$

$= -\dfrac{5}{2}$

qwertyDan-Answer file varies from this solution

23. $\cos^2\dfrac{\pi}{4} + \tan^2\dfrac{\pi}{4} = \left(\dfrac{\sqrt{2}}{2}\right)^2 - (1)^2$

$= \dfrac{1}{2} - 1$

$= -\dfrac{1}{2}$

24. $\sec^2\dfrac{\pi}{5} - \tan^2\dfrac{\pi}{5} = 1$

25. $\cos\dfrac{2\pi}{9}\sec\dfrac{2\pi}{9} = 1$

26. We can find the value of $\cos\theta$ by using the Pythagorean identity.

$$\sin^2\theta + \cos^2\theta = 1$$

$$\left(\dfrac{2\sqrt{7}}{7}\right)^2 + \cos^2\theta = 1$$

$$\dfrac{4}{7} + \cos^2\theta = 1$$

$$\cos^2\theta = 1 - \dfrac{4}{7}$$

$$\cos^2\theta = \dfrac{3}{7}$$

$$\cos\theta = \dfrac{\sqrt{3}}{\sqrt{7}} = \dfrac{\sqrt{3}}{\sqrt{7}}\cdot\dfrac{\sqrt{7}}{\sqrt{7}} = \dfrac{\sqrt{21}}{7}$$

Thus, $\cos\theta = \dfrac{\sqrt{21}}{7}$.

27. $\sin 70° = \cos(90° - 70°) = \cos 20°$

28. $\cos\dfrac{\pi}{2} = \sin\left(\dfrac{\pi}{2} - \dfrac{\pi}{2}\right) = \sin 0$

29. $\tan 23° = \dfrac{a}{100}$

$$a = 100\tan 23°$$

$$a \approx 100(0.4245) \approx 42\,\text{mm}$$

30. $\sin 61° = \dfrac{20}{c}$

$$c = \dfrac{20}{\sin 61°}$$

$$c \approx \dfrac{20}{0.8746} \approx 23\,\text{cm}$$

31. $\sin 48° = \dfrac{a}{50}$

$$a = 50\sin 48°$$

$$a \approx 50(0.7431) \approx 37\,\text{in.}$$

32. $\sin\theta = \dfrac{y}{r} = \dfrac{1}{4}$

$$x^2 + y^2 = r^2$$

$$x^2 + 1^2 = 4^2$$

$$x^2 = 15$$

$$x = \sqrt{15}$$

$$\tan\left(\dfrac{\pi}{2} - \theta\right) = \cot\theta = \dfrac{x}{y} = \dfrac{\sqrt{15}}{1} = \sqrt{15}$$

33. $\dfrac{1}{2}\,\text{mi.} = \dfrac{1}{2}\cdot 5280\,\text{ft} = 2640\,\text{ft}$

$$\sin 17° = \dfrac{a}{2640}$$

$$a = 2640\cdot\sin 17°$$

$$a \approx 2640(0.2924) \approx 772$$

The hiker gains 772 feet of altitude.

34. $\tan 32° = \dfrac{d}{50}$

$$d = 50\tan 32°$$

$$d \approx 50(0.6249) \approx 31$$

The distance across the lake is about 31 meters.

35. $\tan\theta = \dfrac{6}{4}$

Use a calculator in degree mode to find θ.

Scientific Calculator
6 ÷ 4 = TAN⁻¹

Graphing Calculator
TAN⁻¹ (6 ÷ 4) ENTER

The display should show approximately 56. Thus, the angle of elevation of the sun is approximately 56°.

36. We need values for x, y, and r. Because $P = (-1, -5)$ is a point on the terminal side of θ, $x = -1$ and $y = -5$. Furthermore,

$$r = \sqrt{(-1)^2 + (-5)^2}$$
$$= \sqrt{1 + 25} = \sqrt{26}$$

Now that we know x, y, and r, we can find the six trigonometric functions of θ.

$$\sin\theta = \frac{y}{r} = \frac{-5}{\sqrt{26}} = \frac{-5\sqrt{26}}{\sqrt{26} \cdot \sqrt{26}} = -\frac{5\sqrt{26}}{26}$$

$$\cos\theta = \frac{x}{r} = \frac{-1}{\sqrt{26}} = \frac{-1\sqrt{26}}{\sqrt{26} \cdot \sqrt{26}} = -\frac{\sqrt{26}}{26}$$

$$\tan\theta = \frac{y}{x} = \frac{-5}{-1} = 5$$

$$\csc\theta = \frac{r}{y} = \frac{\sqrt{26}}{-5} = -\frac{\sqrt{26}}{5}$$

$$\sec\theta = \frac{r}{x} = \frac{\sqrt{26}}{-1} = -\sqrt{26}$$

$$\cot\theta = \frac{x}{y} = \frac{-1}{-5} = \frac{1}{5}$$

37. We need values for x, y, and r. Because $P = (0, -1)$ is a point on the terminal side of θ, $x = 0$ and $y = -1$. Furthermore,

$$r = \sqrt{x^2 + y^2} = \sqrt{0^2 + (-1)^2}$$
$$= \sqrt{0 + 1} = \sqrt{1} = 1$$

Now that we know x, y, and r, we can find the six trigonometric functions of θ.

$$\sin\theta = \frac{y}{r} = \frac{-1}{1} = -1$$

$$\cos\theta = \frac{x}{r} = \frac{0}{1} = 0$$

$$\tan\theta = \frac{y}{x} = \frac{-1}{0}, \text{ undefined}$$

$$\csc\theta = \frac{r}{y} = \frac{1}{-1} = -1$$

$$\sec\theta = \frac{r}{x} = \frac{1}{0}, \text{ undefined}$$

$$\cot\theta = \frac{x}{y} = \frac{0}{-1} = 0$$

38. Because $\tan\theta > 0$, θ cannot lie in quadrant II and quadrant IV; the tangent function is negative in those two quadrants. Thus, with $\tan\theta > 0$, θ lies in quadrant I or quadrant III. We are also given that $\sec\theta > 0$. Because quadrant I is the only quadrant in which the tangent is positive and the secant is positive, we conclude that θ lies in quadrant I.

39. Because $\tan\theta > 0$, θ cannot lie in quadrant II and quadrant IV; the tangent function is negative in those two quadrants. Thus, with $\tan\theta > 0$, θ lies in quadrant I or quadrant III. We are also given that $\cos\theta < 0$. Because quadrant III is the only quadrant in which the tangent is positive and the cosine is negative, we conclude that θ lies in quadrant III.

40. Because the cosine is positive and the sine is negative, θ lies in quadrant IV. In quadrant IV, x is positive and y is negative. Thus,

$$\cos\theta = \frac{2}{5} = \frac{x}{r}, \; x = 2, r = 5. \text{ Furthermore,}$$

$$x^2 + y^2 = r^2$$
$$2^2 + y^2 = 5^2$$
$$y^2 = 25 - 4 = 21$$
$$y = -\sqrt{21}$$

Now that we know x, y, and r, we can find the six trigonometric functions of θ.

$$\sin\theta = \frac{y}{r} = \frac{-\sqrt{21}}{5} = -\frac{\sqrt{21}}{5}$$

$$\tan\theta = \frac{y}{x} = \frac{-\sqrt{21}}{2} = -\frac{\sqrt{21}}{2}$$

$$\csc\theta = \frac{r}{y} = \frac{5}{-\sqrt{21}} = -\frac{5 \cdot \sqrt{21}}{\sqrt{21} \cdot \sqrt{21}} = -\frac{5\sqrt{21}}{21}$$

$$\sec\theta = \frac{r}{x} = \frac{5}{2}$$

$$\cot\theta = \frac{x}{y} = \frac{2}{-\sqrt{21}} = -\frac{2\sqrt{21}}{\sqrt{21} \cdot \sqrt{21}} = -\frac{2\sqrt{21}}{21}$$

41. Because the tangent is negative and the sine is positive, θ lies in quadrant II. In quadrant II x is negative and y is positive. Thus,

$$\tan\theta = -\frac{1}{3} = \frac{y}{x} = \frac{1}{-3}, \; x = -3, y = 1.$$

Furthermore,

$$r = \sqrt{x^2 + y^2} = \sqrt{(-3)^2 + 1^2} = \sqrt{9 + 1} = \sqrt{10}$$

Now that we know x, y, and r, we can find the six trigonometric functions of θ.

$$\sin\theta = \frac{y}{r} = \frac{1}{\sqrt{10}} = \frac{1\cdot\sqrt{10}}{\sqrt{10}\cdot\sqrt{10}} = \frac{\sqrt{10}}{10}$$

$$\cos\theta = \frac{x}{r} = \frac{-3}{\sqrt{10}} = -\frac{3\sqrt{10}}{\sqrt{10}\cdot\sqrt{10}} = -\frac{3\sqrt{10}}{10}$$

$$\csc\theta = \frac{r}{y} = \frac{\sqrt{10}}{1} = \sqrt{10}$$

$$\sec\theta = \frac{r}{x} = \frac{\sqrt{10}}{-3} = -\frac{\sqrt{10}}{3}$$

$$\cot\theta = \frac{x}{y} = \frac{-3}{1} = -3$$

42. Because the cotangent is positive and the cosine is negative, θ lies in quadrant III. In quadrant III x and y are both negative. Thus,

$$\cot\theta = \frac{3}{1} = \frac{x}{y} = \frac{-3}{-1},\ x = -3,\ y = -1.$$

Furthermore,

$$r = \sqrt{x^2 + y^2} = \sqrt{(-3)^2 + (-1)^2} = \sqrt{9+1} = \sqrt{10}$$

Now that we know x, y, and r, we can find the six trigonometric functions of θ.

$$\sin\theta = \frac{y}{r} = \frac{-1}{\sqrt{10}} = -\frac{\sqrt{10}}{10}$$

$$\cos\theta = \frac{x}{r} = \frac{-3}{\sqrt{10}} = -\frac{3\sqrt{10}}{10}$$

$$\tan\theta = \frac{y}{x} = \frac{-1}{-3} = \frac{1}{3}$$

$$\csc\theta = \frac{r}{y} = \frac{\sqrt{10}}{-1} = -\sqrt{10}$$

$$\sec\theta = \frac{r}{x} = \frac{\sqrt{10}}{-3} = -\frac{\sqrt{10}}{3}$$

43. Because $265°$ lies between $180°$ and $270°$, it is in quadrant III.
The reference angle is $\theta' = 265° - 180° = 85°$.

44. Because $\dfrac{5\pi}{8}$ lies between $\dfrac{\pi}{2} = \dfrac{4\pi}{8}$ and

$\pi = \dfrac{8\pi}{8}$, it is in quadrant II.
The reference angle is

$$\theta' = \pi - \frac{5\pi}{8} = \frac{8\pi}{8} - \frac{5\pi}{8} = \frac{3\pi}{8}.$$

45. Find the coterminal angle:
$-410° + (2)360° = 310°$
Find the reference angle: $360° - 310° = 50°$

46. Find the coterminal angle: $\dfrac{17\pi}{6} - 2\pi = \dfrac{5\pi}{6}$

Find the reference angle: $2\pi - \dfrac{5\pi}{6} = \dfrac{\pi}{6}$

47. Find the coterminal angle: $-\dfrac{11\pi}{3} + 4\pi = \dfrac{\pi}{3}$

Find the reference angle: $\dfrac{\pi}{3}$

48. $240°$ lies in quadrant III.
The reference angle is
$\theta' = 240° - 180° = 60°$.

$$\sin 60° = \frac{\sqrt{3}}{2}$$

In quadrant III, $\sin\theta < 0$, so

$$\sin 240° = -\sin 60° = -\frac{\sqrt{3}}{2}.$$

49. $120°$ lies in quadrant II.
The reference angle is
$\theta' = 180° - 120° = 60°$.

$$\tan 60° = \sqrt{3}$$

In quadrant II, $\tan\theta < 0$, so
$\tan 120° = -\tan 60° = -\sqrt{3}$.

50. $\dfrac{7\pi}{4}$ lies in quadrant IV.
The reference angle is

$$\theta' = 2\pi - \frac{7\pi}{4} = \frac{8\pi}{4} - \frac{7\pi}{4} = \frac{\pi}{4}.$$

$$\sec\frac{\pi}{4} = \sqrt{2}$$

In quadrant IV, $\sec\theta > 0$, so

$$\sec\frac{7\pi}{4} = \sec\frac{\pi}{4} = \sqrt{2}.$$

51. $\dfrac{11\pi}{6}$ lies in quadrant IV.
The reference angle is

$$\theta' = 2\pi - \frac{11\pi}{6} = \frac{12\pi}{6} - \frac{11\pi}{6} = \frac{\pi}{6}.$$

$$\cos\frac{\pi}{6} = \frac{\sqrt{3}}{2}$$

In quadrant IV, $\cos\theta > 0$, so

$$\cos\frac{11\pi}{6} = \cos\frac{\pi}{6} = \frac{\sqrt{3}}{2}.$$

52. $-210°$ lies in quadrant II.
The reference angle is
$\theta' = 210° - 180° = 30°$.

$\cot 30° = \sqrt{3}$
In quadrant II, $\cot\theta < 0$, so
$\cot(-210°) = -\cot 30° = -\sqrt{3}$.

53. $-\dfrac{2\pi}{3}$ lies in quadrant III.
The reference angle is
$\theta' = \pi + \dfrac{-2\pi}{3} = \dfrac{3\pi}{3} - \dfrac{2\pi}{3} = \dfrac{\pi}{3}$.

$\csc\left(\dfrac{\pi}{3}\right) = \dfrac{2\sqrt{3}}{3}$
In quadrant III, $\csc\theta < 0$, so
$\csc\left(-\dfrac{2\pi}{3}\right) = -\csc\left(\dfrac{\pi}{3}\right) = -\dfrac{2\sqrt{3}}{3}$.

54. $-\dfrac{\pi}{3}$ lies in quadrant IV.
The reference angle is
$\theta' = \dfrac{\pi}{3}$.

$\sin\left(\dfrac{\pi}{3}\right) = \dfrac{\sqrt{3}}{2}$
In quadrant IV, $\sin\theta < 0$, so
$\sin\left(-\dfrac{\pi}{3}\right) = -\sin\left(\dfrac{\pi}{3}\right) = -\dfrac{\sqrt{3}}{2}$.

55. $495°$ lies in quadrant II.
$495° - 360° = 135°$
The reference angle is
$\theta' = 180° - 135° = 45°$.

$\sin 45° = \dfrac{\sqrt{2}}{2}$
In quadrant II, $\sin\theta > 0$, so
$\sin 495° = \sin 45° = \dfrac{\sqrt{2}}{2}$.

56. $\dfrac{13\pi}{4}$ lies in quadrant III.

$\dfrac{13\pi}{4} - 2\pi = \dfrac{13\pi}{4} - \dfrac{8\pi}{4} = \dfrac{5\pi}{4}$
The reference angle is
$\theta' = \dfrac{5\pi}{4} - \pi = \dfrac{5\pi}{4} - \dfrac{4\pi}{4} = \dfrac{\pi}{4}$.

$\tan\dfrac{\pi}{4} = 1$

In quadrant III, $\tan\theta > 0$, so $\tan\dfrac{13\pi}{4} = \tan\dfrac{\pi}{4} = 1$.

57. $\sin\dfrac{22\pi}{3} = \sin\left(\dfrac{22\pi}{3} - 6\pi\right)$

$= \sin\dfrac{4\pi}{3}$

$= -\sin\dfrac{\pi}{3}$

$= -\dfrac{\sqrt{3}}{2}$

58. $\cos\left(-\dfrac{35\pi}{6}\right) = \cos\left(-\dfrac{35\pi}{6} + 6\pi\right)$

$= \cos\dfrac{\pi}{6}$

$= \dfrac{\sqrt{3}}{2}$

Chapter 4 Test

1. $135° = 135° \cdot \dfrac{\pi \text{ radians}}{180°}$

$= \dfrac{135\pi}{180}$ radians

$= \dfrac{3\pi}{4}$ radians

2. $75° = 75° \cdot \dfrac{\pi \text{ radians}}{180°} = \dfrac{75\pi}{180}$ radians

$= \dfrac{5\pi}{12}$ radians

$s = r\theta$

$s = 20\left(\dfrac{5\pi}{12}\right) = \dfrac{25\pi}{3}$ ft ≈ 26.18 ft

3. **a.** $\dfrac{16\pi}{3} - 4\pi = \dfrac{16\pi}{3} - \dfrac{12\pi}{3} = \dfrac{4\pi}{3}$

b. $\dfrac{16\pi}{3}$ is coterminal with $\dfrac{4\pi}{3}$.

$\dfrac{4\pi}{3} - \pi = \dfrac{4\pi}{3} - \dfrac{3\pi}{3} = \dfrac{\pi}{3}$

4. P = (–2, 5) is a point on the terminal side of θ, $x = -2$ and $y = 5$. Furthermore,

$r = \sqrt{x^2 + y^2} = \sqrt{(-2)^2 + (5)^2}$

$= \sqrt{4 + 25} = \sqrt{29}$

Use x, y, and r, to find the six trigonometric functions of θ.

280

$$\sin\theta = \frac{y}{r} = \frac{5}{\sqrt{29}} = \frac{5\sqrt{29}}{\sqrt{29}\sqrt{29}} = \frac{5\sqrt{29}}{29}$$

$$\cos\theta = \frac{x}{r} = \frac{-2}{\sqrt{29}} = -\frac{2\sqrt{29}}{\sqrt{29}\sqrt{29}} = -\frac{2\sqrt{29}}{29}$$

$$\tan\theta = \frac{y}{x} = \frac{5}{-2} = -\frac{5}{2}$$

$$\csc\theta = \frac{r}{y} = \frac{\sqrt{29}}{5}$$

$$\sec\theta = \frac{r}{x} = \frac{\sqrt{29}}{-2} = -\frac{\sqrt{29}}{2}$$

$$\cot\theta = \frac{x}{y} = \frac{-2}{5} = -\frac{2}{5}$$

5. Because $\cos\theta < 0$, θ cannot lie in quadrant I and quadrant IV; the cosine function is positive in those two quadrants. Thus, with $\cos\theta < 0$, θ lies in quadrant II or quadrant III. We are also given that $\cot\theta > 0$. Because quadrant III is the only quadrant in which the cosine is negative and the cotangent is positive, θ lies in quadrant III.

6. Because the cosine is positive and the tangent is negative, θ lies in quadrant IV. In quadrant IV x is positive and y is negative. Thus,

$$\cos\theta = \frac{1}{3} = \frac{x}{r},\ x = 1,\ r = 3.\ \text{Furthermore,}$$

$$x^2 + y^2 = r^2$$

$$1^2 + y^2 = 3^2$$

$$y^2 = 9 - 1 = 8$$

$$y = -\sqrt{8} = -2\sqrt{2}$$

Use x, y, and r, to find the six trigonometric functions of θ.

$$\sin\theta = \frac{y}{r} = \frac{-2\sqrt{2}}{3} = -\frac{2\sqrt{2}}{3}$$

$$\tan\theta = \frac{y}{x} = \frac{-2\sqrt{2}}{1} = -2\sqrt{2}$$

$$\csc\theta = \frac{r}{y} = \frac{3}{-2\sqrt{2}} = -\frac{3\sqrt{2}}{2\sqrt{2}\cdot\sqrt{2}} = -\frac{3\sqrt{2}}{4}$$

$$\sec\theta = \frac{r}{x} = \frac{3}{1} = 3$$

$$\cot\theta = \frac{x}{y} = \frac{1}{-2\sqrt{2}} = -\frac{1\cdot\sqrt{2}}{2\sqrt{2}\sqrt{2}} = -\frac{\sqrt{2}}{4}$$

7. $\tan\dfrac{\pi}{6}\cos\dfrac{\pi}{3} - \cos\dfrac{\pi}{2} = \dfrac{\sqrt{3}}{3}\cdot\dfrac{1}{2} - 0 = \dfrac{\sqrt{3}}{6}$

8. $300°$ lies in quadrant IV. The reference angle is
$$\theta' = 360° - 300° = 60°$$
$$\tan 60° = \sqrt{3}$$
In quadrant IV, $\tan\theta < 0$, so
$$\tan 300° = -\tan 60 = -\sqrt{3}.$$

9. $\dfrac{7\pi}{4}$ lies in quadrant IV.
The reference angle is
$$\theta' = 2\pi - \frac{7\pi}{4} = \frac{8\pi}{4} - \frac{7\pi}{4} = \frac{\pi}{4}$$
$$\sin\frac{\pi}{4} = \frac{\sqrt{2}}{2}$$
In quadrant IV, $\sin\theta < 0$, so
$$\sin\frac{7\pi}{4} = -\sin\frac{\pi}{4} = -\frac{\sqrt{2}}{2}.$$

10. $\sec\dfrac{22\pi}{3} = \sec\dfrac{4\pi}{3} = -\sec\dfrac{\pi}{3}$
$$= \frac{1}{-\cos\dfrac{\pi}{3}} = \frac{1}{-\dfrac{1}{2}} = -2$$

11. $\cot\left(-\dfrac{8\pi}{3}\right) = \cot\left(\dfrac{4\pi}{3}\right) = \cot\dfrac{\pi}{3}$
$$= \frac{1}{\tan\dfrac{\pi}{3}} = \frac{1}{\sqrt{3}} = \frac{\sqrt{3}}{3}$$

12. $\tan\left(\dfrac{7\pi}{3} + n\pi\right) = \tan\dfrac{7\pi}{3} = \tan\dfrac{\pi}{3} = \sqrt{3}$

13. a. $\sin(-\theta) + \cos(-\theta) = -\sin(\theta) + \cos(\theta)$
$$= -a + b$$

    b. $\tan\theta - \sec\theta = \dfrac{\sin\theta}{\cos\theta} - \dfrac{1}{\cos\theta}$
$$= \frac{a}{b} - \frac{1}{b}$$
$$= \frac{a-1}{b}$$

Cumulative Review Exercises (Chapters 1-4)

1. $x^2 = 18 + 3x$

      $x^2 - 3x - 18 = 0$

      $(x - 6)(x + 3) = 0$

      $x - 6 = 0$ or $x + 3 = 0$

        $x = 6$ $x = -3$

      The solution set is $\{-3, 6\}$.

2. $x^3 + 5x^2 - 4x - 20 = 0$

      $x^2(x + 5) - 4(x + 5) = 0$

         $(x^2 - 4)(x + 5) = 0$

    $(x - 2)(x + 2)(x + 5) = 0$

    $x - 2 = 0$ or $x + 2 = 0$ or $x + 5 = 0$

      $x = 2$ $x = -2$ $x = -5$

      The solution set is $\{-5, -2, 2\}$.

3. $\sqrt{x - 3} + 5 = x$

      $\sqrt{x - 3} = x - 5$

      $\left(\sqrt{x - 3}\right)^2 = (x - 5)^2$

      $x - 3 = x^2 - 10x + 25$

      $x^2 - 11x + 28 = 0$

      $(x - 4)(x - 7) = 0$

      $x - 4 = 0$ or $x - 7 = 0$

        $x = 4$ $x = 7$

      $\sqrt{4 - 3} + 5 = 4$

         $\sqrt{1} + 5 = 4$

           $1 + 5 = 4$ false

    $x = 4$ is not a solution

      $\sqrt{7 - 3} + 5 = 7$

         $\sqrt{4} + 5 = 7$

           $2 + 5 = 7$ true

      The solution set is $\{7\}$.

4. $|2x - 5| \le 11$

      $-11 \le 2x - 5 \le 11$

      $-6 \le 2x \le 16$

      $-3 \le x \le 8$

      The solution set is $\{x \mid -3 \le x \le 8\}$

5. $\dfrac{14\pi}{9}$ radians $= \dfrac{14\pi}{9}$ radians $\cdot \dfrac{180°}{\pi \text{ radians}}$

                   $= \dfrac{14 \cdot 180°}{9} = 280°$

6. $(x - 2)^2 + y^2 = 1$

      The graph is a circle with center $(2, 0)$ and $r = 1$.

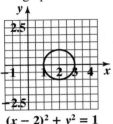

$(x - 2)^2 + y^2 = 1$

7. $C(p) = 30,000 + 2500p$

      $R(p) = 3125p$

      $30,000 + 2500p = 3125p$

           $30,000 = 625p$

                $p = 48$

      48 performances must be played for you to break even.